Natural History

of

New York City's Parks
And Great Gull Island

Transactions
of the
Linnaean Society of New York
Volume X

New York City
September 2007

Natural History of New York City's Parks and Great Gull Island.
Transactions of the Linnaean Society of New York, Volume X

Linnaean Society of New York
15 West 77th Street
New York NY 10024

Book Design by DonnaClaireDesign, Seattle WA

Printed by Edwards Brothers, Inc., Ann Arbor MI

Front cover photograph of an American Kestrel at Floyd Bennett Field, 2006, by Ardith Bondi.
Back cover photograph of Monarch butterfly on Goldenrod, Gateway National Recreation Area by Alexander R. Brash.

ISSN: 0075-9708
ISBN: 978-0-9799679-0-0

New York City
September 2007

In a collaboration aimed at highlighting the natural history of New York City area parks at the turn of this century, these *Transactions* were a joint endeavor of the Linnaean Society of New York, the National Parks Conservation Association, and City of New York Department of Parks & Recreation.

Linnaean Society of New York

National Parks Conservation Association®
Protecting Our National Parks for Future Generations®

City of New York
Parks & Recreation

The Linnaean Society of New York

The Linnaean Society of New York, organized in 1878, is the second oldest American ornithological society. Regular meetings of the Society are held on the second and fourth Tuesdays of each month from September to May, inclusive. Informal meetings are held once a month during June, July, and August. All meetings are open to the public and are usually held at the American Museum of Natural History.

Persons interested in natural history are eligible for election to membership in the Society.

The Society conducts field trips. It also maintains a website at linnaeannewyork.org. It distributes free to all members a monthly *News-Letter*, and every few years an issue of *Proceedings* containing longer articles and notes of ornithological interest. At irregular intervals the Society publishes longer papers and monographs called *Transactions*, which members receive free or at a substantial discount.

Communications should be addressed to:
> Secretary
> Linnaean Society of New York
> 15 West 77th Street
> New York NY 10024

Editorial Committee
> Alice Deutsch, Editor
> Terence Clarke, Past Editor
> Joseph DiCostanzo
> Helen Hays
> Mary LeCroy

Contents

Forward

CONCEIVED IN ORDER TO SIMULTANEOUSLY CELEBRATE the 125thAnniversary of the Linnaean Society of New York, the 20th Anniversary of the Department of Park's Natural Resource Group, and the opening of a new office of the National Park Conservation Association, this volume reflects recent research regarding the area's natural history. Inside, you will find an array of papers covering countless facets of the area's natural history; papers written by an array of scholars, students and native naturalists. There is also a series of splendid maps depicting some of the city's finest parks, drawn by Society members James R. Nolan and noted cartographer, Richard Edes Harrison, nearly 40 years ago. We hope this volume will feed your interest, spark your enthusiasm and strengthen your commitment to the beauty and wonder inherent to New York City's natural history.

Founded in 1878 and celebrating its 125th Anniversary in 2003, the Linnaean Society's mandate was that it be "composed primarily of persons living in the New York City area who are interested in the natural sciences." In keeping with this mandate, the Society originally fostered a strong relationship with the American Museum of Natural History (AMNH), and broadened its relations to include other institutions such as the New York City Department of Parks & Recreation. The Society has always sought to build a membership encompassing people from all walks of life who share an interest in the natural world.

Throughout its existence, the Society has been a venue for New Yorkers to share their insights into nature or provide an opportunity for those with research experience abroad to bring their knowledge to New York City's natural areas. As a Bronx birder, Roger Tory Peterson introduced field guides to a ready audience. Joe Hickey's passion for peregrines led to an understanding of the awful toll DDT was taking on avian populations; with Rachel Carson then conveying Hickey's findings to the world with her inspired *Silent Spring*. Margaret Morse Nice published her treatise on the life history of the Song Sparrow as a Linnaean Society Transaction and it is still considered a classic in population biology. Past society member and scientific assistant at AMNH, John Bull, wrote the *Birds of New York State*, one of the most comprehensive species account of the area. Celebrated members such as Dean Amadon, John Burroughs, Frank Chapman, Guy Coheleach, Allan Cruickshank, William T. Davis, Jean Delacour, Don Eckleberry, Eugene Eisenmann, Ludlow Griscom, G. Stuart Keith, John Kieran, Thomas Lovejoy, Ernst Mayr, C. Hart Merriam, Richard Pough, Theodore Roosevelt, Arthur Singer, Edwin Way Teale, Niko Tinbergen, Guy Tudor, Alexander Wetmore and Leroy Wilcox all made significant contributions to science, public education and conservation. Through the Society, they have shared their artistic and intellectual gifts, their profound love of nature, and their desire to impart knowledge to the people of New York City and the world. Indeed, in one case such work has even led to a new national park. Between his trips to the southern oceans, the renowned Robert Cushman Murphy, who was both Chair of the AMNH Department of Ornithology and a Society member, published in 1943 a small article on a place he found unique: Fire Island's maritime forest. As he continued to relentlessly advocate for Fire Island he remarked that he found the article's ensuing popularity "quite astonishing", and noted that it demonstrated "that the homely and familiar is likely to have wider appeal than something from the ends of the earth." His efforts culminated with the creation of Fire Island National Seashore in the 1960s.

We believe his words still hold true today, and we hope that the ongoing efforts of our organizations, including this volume, will continue to inspire interest and support for both local and global conservation initiatives. It may be hard to imagine, but when the Society was founded, much of New York City was still pastures, fields and forest tracts. Van Cortlandt mansion was surrounded by wheat fields, and little boys and girls were still rolling wooden hoops down dirt roads. Draft horses transported nearly everything, Alexander Graham Bell had only just invented the telegraph, and Central Park was brand new. But the remnants of rural New York City were quickly fading, and in 1878, construction began on the Brooklyn Bridge, two buildings had risen to over ten stories tall, and the infamous Boss

Tweed was spending his final days behind bars. Two years later, streetlights first illuminated Madison Square, and soon thereafter, the city's population surpassed one and a half million.

Since that time, the area's natural history has undergone a great number of changes. Development reached its zenith and then slowed as by the early twentieth century most of the city's natural areas were paved and the remnant fragments were captured in parks. With the post-war Baby Boom and the advent of new technologies, buildings started growing ever taller in the confined spaces. Both *Silent Spring* and the burning rivers of Cleveland loosened society's blinders and the resulting environmental reformation of the 1960s inspired aggressive legislation aimed at cleaner air, waters and landscapes.

Arising amidst civil rights issues and urban burdens, in 1972 the City's greatest park was launched. Twenty-six thousand acres of salt marsh, old airfields and abandoned forts were cobbled together to create Gateway National Recreation Area. Sadly though, this park has not become the iconic national park called for. By the 1990s, the city's air, once gray with soot, and the Hudson, Bronx and Hutchinson Rivers, once turbid with industrial pollution, had all slowly regained much of their clarity. Herons and egrets, nearly obliterated by the millinery trade before being granted federal protection in 1913, subsequently returned to the city as common breeders. Peregrine Falcons, Bald Eagles and other raptors that were pursued by hunters and egg collectors through the 1940s and adversely affected by DDT and habitat loss, then returned to the region after a host of intricate re-introduction programs. Peregrines were brought back by Tom Cade and his cadre at Cornell during the 1970s, and Bald Eagles were re-introduced to upper Manhattan by the City's Park Rangers in the 1990s. Finally, as a capstone to all these efforts, in 2001 the remaining natural areas in the city's parks were officially designated as nature preserves in the Forever Wild Program.

In the past three decades the New York City Department of Parks & Recreation expanded its mission to encompass the preservation and restoration of remnant natural areas. The Urban Park Rangers were launched in 1979 and empowered as the uniformed stewards of city parkland. In 1984, the Natural Resources Group (NRG) was formed and given the mission to acquire and restore such natural areas. Since then, more than 1642 acres were acquired by Parks and another 950 acres were substantially restored. NRG was also the guiding force behind the *Forever Wild Nature Preserves*. Along with Gateway's great marshes, these preserves now officially delineate the wildest gems of the City's emerald necklace of parks. Seton Falls, Pelham Bay,

Inwood, Alley Pond, Forest Park, Prall's Island, Wolfe's Pond, and others hold the last fragments of New York City's original salt marshes, upland meadows and forest primeval.

In opening an office in New York City in 2004, the National Parks Conservation Association (NPCA) joined with these and many other partners in order to protect Jamaica Bay and Gateway National Park. Working with Columbia University's School of Architecture, Planning and Preservation and the Van Alen Institute, NPCA is now initiating a public process that will culminate in a new vision for Gateway, much as Olmsted created one for Central Park. In early 2007 there was an international landscape design contest focused on Gateway with the hope that the winning design(s) will engage the public and chart a new path for Gateway. As an adjunct effort, NPCA is also working with groups such as the EPA's Harbor Estuary Program and The Harbor Roundtable in order to clean-up and restore New York Harbor (including Jamaica Bay) so that they might be "swimmable and fishable" in the 21st century. In addition, NPCA brings national issues to New Yorkers, and recently partnered with Yellowstone to Yukon and the AMNH's Center for Biodiversity to bring a beautiful photographic exhibit about the Rockies to the AMNH. Highlighting ecological corridors, the exhibit's eight month run was estimated to have seven hundred and fifty thousand visitors. Finally, NPCA works on projects like this volume with the Linnaean Society, which aim to build the public appreciation and the support necessary to protect and enhance all parks far into the future.

For over one hundred and twenty-five years, the Linnaean Society has a solid trajectory facilitating research and disseminating knowledge. The Society has consistently produced publications, field trips and lectures, all aimed at inculcating an appreciation and understanding of natural history. The Society has always worked closely with other organizations, and in recent years has worked to continually broaden its collaborative efforts. Several years ago the Society collaboratively offered field trips with NYC Parks & Recreation, and these *Transactions* are another example of this broader view. Produced with NYC Parks & Recreation, and NPCA, these *Transactions* reflect our organizations' shared purpose: to continue to introduce generations of interested New Yorkers to the region's ecology and conservation issues, especially as they are reflected in the City's great parks.

Therefore, in concluding, we are delighted to present this collection of papers in celebration of the Society's 125th Anniversary, NRG's 20th Anniversary, and the opening of NPCA's office in New York. Hopefully, not only will these *Transactions* stand as a record of the state of nature in New York

City at the beginning of the 21st century, but will also stand as a testament to fruitful relationships among partners, and to our shared commitment to impart knowledge of the natural world to future generations.

Alan Messer
President
Linnaean Society
of New York
2005-2007

Adrian Benepe
Commissioner
City of New York
Parks & Recreation

Thomas Kiernan
President
National Parks
Conservation
Association

Acknowledgements

THE PRODUCTION OF THIS PUBLICATION has been a long process involving many people. The Editorial Committee thanks all the authors for their contributions and patience while the work proceeded. We thank Alexander Brash under whose leadership the project was initiated, and who also both collected and contributed papers; Bob DeCandido who helped early on; Terry Clarke who was the first Editor for the project; and Peggy Cooper who then undertook the beginning of the editorial work. In addition, personnel from both the New York City Department of Parks & Recreation and the National Parks Conservation Association gave much of their time in helping to bring these *Transactions* to fruition. Lastly, we want to thank all of the National Park and New York City Park Rangers for protecting the natural treasures of our city.

Alice Deutsch, Editor

Classic Maps of New York City Area Parks

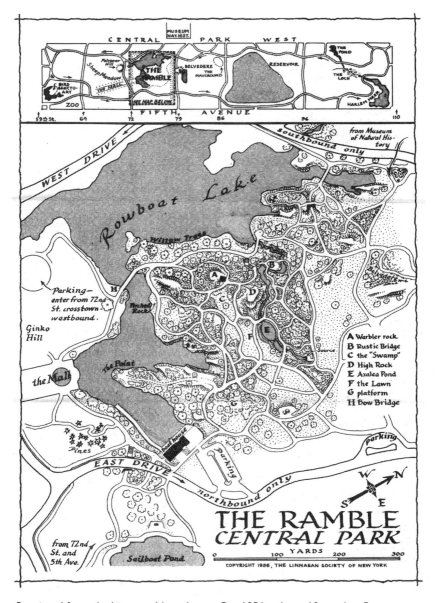

THE RAMBLE
CENTRAL PARK

YARDS

A Warbler rock
B Rustic Bridge
C the "Swamp"
D High Rock
E Azalea Pond
F the Lawn
G platform
H Bow Bridge

COPYRIGHT 1956, THE LINNAEAN SOCIETY OF NEW YORK

Reprinted from the Linnaean News-Letter, Oct 1956, volume 10, number 5.

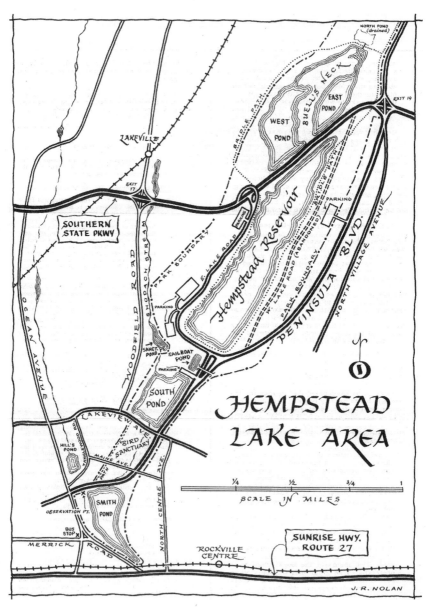

Reprinted from the Linnaean News-Letter, April 1957, volume 11, number 2.

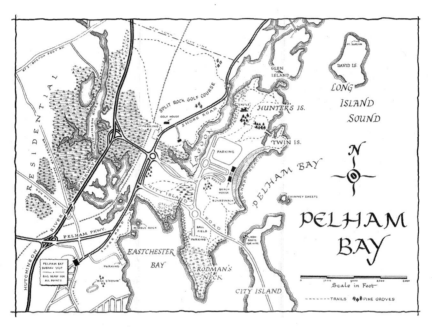

Reprinted from the Linnaean News-Letter, Jan 1957, volume 10, number 8.

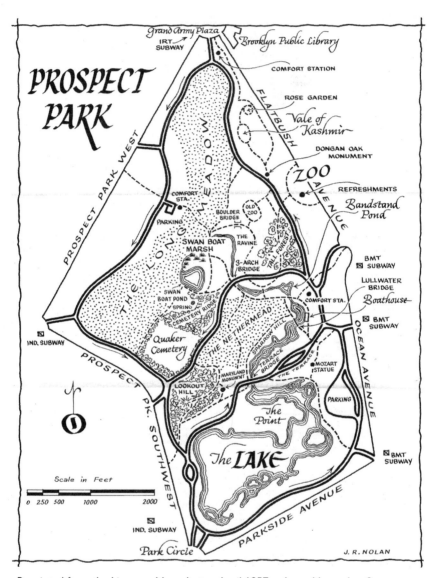

Reprinted from the Linnaean News-Letter, April 1957, volume 11, number 2.

Inwood Hill and Isham Parks: Geology, Geography and History

Sidney Horenstein
American Museum of Natural History
Central Park West at 79th Street
New York NY 10024
horenst@amnh.org
and
The Bronx County Historical Society
3309 Bainbridge Avenue
The Bronx NY 10467

MOST CITIES HAVE A SPECIAL PLACE that exhibits unique features not found elsewhere. In New York City, Inwood Hill Park, located at the northwestern corner of Manhattan Island (Map 1), is one of those special places. As Manhattan's last forest with stands of Red Oak (*Quercus rubra*) and Tulip Trees (*Liriodendron tulipifera*) and clusters of Black Locust (*Robinia pseudo-acacia*) and Hackberry (*Celtis occidentalis*) (Anderson 1994), it is one of the few areas on Manhattan Island where you can be completely sheltered from the "city" environment, walk in deep woods and from its hilltop enjoy fine vistas up and down the Hudson Valley as well as across northern Manhattan and parts of The Bronx.

Its topography, varied geological components and history of land use make Inwood Hill Park an intriguing locality for students, professionals and the public interested to study many aspects of the city's natural history and also maintain a connection with our Native American past. People familiar with the park today have the same positive feelings toward it that advocates for its creation had at the beginning of the 20th century: "It is the most beautiful hill on Manhattan Island" (American Scenic and Historic Preservation Society 1912).

Adjacent Isham Park, once part of the Isham family estate, was given to the city in 1912 by the daughter and sister of William B. Isham, a wealthy leather merchant, to memorialize him and preserve the view, especially westward to Inwood Hill, Spuyten Duyvil Hill, the Hudson River and the

Map 1. Location of Inwood Hill and Isham Parks on Manhattan
Island. (Used with permission.)

Palisades beyond. This park is especially included here because it contains
some of the best exposures of Inwood Marble, an extensively distributed
marble named for Inwood.

Recognizing that landforms and even the landscape in the urban
environment have undergone changes, in some cases substantial, this report
contains a discussion of land use history of Inwood Hill and Isham Parks.
It is particularly important because reports occasionally not only describe
Inwood Hill as containing the last woodlands on Manhattan Island but
identify them as "primeval," suggesting that what is seen today is what Henry
Hudson saw when he traveled up the Hudson in 1609. Of course, visitors see
paths, storm-water drains, and stonewalls, and recognize that the Daffodils

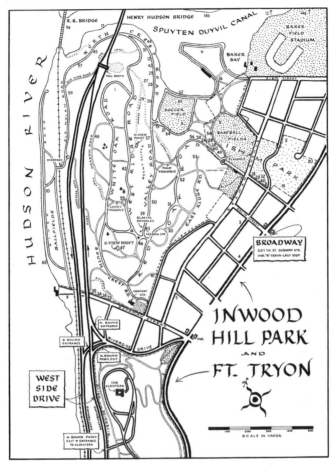

Map 2. Localities and named paths. The dashed line shows Inwood Hill and Isham Parks' actual boundary.

(*Narcissus pseudo-narcissus*) and exotic trees are not native but placed in the environment by people. This is stated not to minimize the importance of the parks but to recognize that they have a history and that history impacts on the way the landscape is interpreted, how geological processes change and on the distribution and relationships of resident plants and animals.

Localities and place names in the text refer to Map 2, originally drawn by James Nolan (Linnaean News-Letter 1956). This map is used here because it clearly shows the paths, which have been named, making it easier to locate the features discussed in the text. Numbered locations (loc.) referred to in the text are on Map 2.

Location and Size

Inwood Hill and Isham Parks lie at the northwest corner of Manhattan Island, the Borough of Manhattan (and New York County) centering at 40°52'15"N, 74°55'45"W (U.S. Geological Survey Central Park and Yonkers Topographic Quadrangles (1: 24,000).

Inwood Hill Park is bounded by Dyckman Street on the south, the Harlem River on the north and the Hudson River along its western edge. City streets (notably Payson Avenue) and Isham Park abut its irregular eastern margin (Map 3).

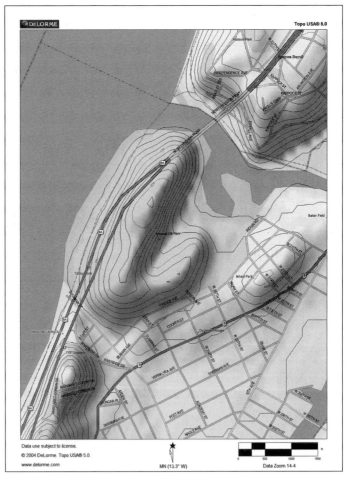

Map 3. Local Streets surrounding Inwood and Isham Parks and simple topographic map. (Used with permission.)

Isham Park's eastern boundary is Broadway; its southern boundary is, in part, Isham Street and its northern boundary lies just south of 215th Street. As Map 2 illustrates, an irregular boundary separates Isham Park and Inwood Hill Park. Although their common boundary is popularly believed to be Seaman Avenue, it is actually more complex as a result of original property lines, landfill, and the history of additions to the parks.

Inwood Hill Park contains 196.4 acres [79.5 hectares] (City of New York, Parks & Recreation 1999a), less than one-quarter the area of Central Park, and Isham Park contains 20.1 acres [8.1 hectares] (City of New York, Parks & Recreation 1999b).

Topography

Two metamorphic rock types—marble and schist—dominate the parks, each controlling their topographic configuration. Schist forms the higher elevations of Inwood Hill Park (elev. 70.7 m, Map 2, loc. 1) in a Y-shaped configuration, with the open area between the arms of the Y facing north. The eastern arm is shorter than the western arm, and Inwood Marble underlies the low area between them, the Clove Valley, and the surrounding lowlands.

The low ridge at Isham Park (elev. 32 m, loc. 2) held up, in part, by resistant layers of marble, formerly extended southward toward Dyckman Street (Gratacap 1909, New York Sunday News 1967) and northward to Marble Hill, north of the present-day bed of the Harlem River. Today, there are a few outposts of this hill south of Isham Park, one located at the west side of Cooper Street, south of 207th Street (loc. 3). A complementary hill on the east side of the street was removed several years ago to accommodate construction for two-story brick housing. Marble also underlies the rise where Dyckman House stands (Broadway at 204th Street) (loc. 4). An outcrop of the marble is exposed in the cellar of this historic building, and marble still crops out at the intersection of Cumming Street and Seaman Avenue (loc. 5). Broadway, when it was called Kingsbridge Road, was at nearly the same level as the Dyckman House porch, but the roadway was subsequently lowered to reduce its grade.

The ridges of Inwood Hill Park slope precipitously downward to the surrounding lowlands. At its southern end, the Dyckman Street valley separates Inwood Hill Park from Fort Tryon Park. Its northern end drops off to the Harlem River, the northern shore of which forms the boundary between Manhattan and the Spuyten Duyvil neighborhood of The Bronx. Here the Henry Hudson Bridge, opened for traffic in 1936, spans the Harlem River, connecting these sections. Spuyten Duyvil begins the high elevation of the

Photo: S. Horenstein

Fig. 1. Debris from the construction of the "A" line subway filled in the Hudson creating Dyckman Fields.

Riverdale Ridge that extends northward to Yonkers.

Although the ridge top of Inwood Hill Park still retains its overall topographic configuration, the surrounding lowlands have been, in many places, substantially altered, almost all changes resulting from landfills raising the surface. An embayment at the western end of Dyckman Street (Tubby Hook) was filled in by the Hudson River Railroad (now Amtrak), while the flat field extending nearly the length of the park west of the railroad track and north of Tubby Hook was created by filling in the Hudson River with construction debris from the excavation of the Eighth (IND) Avenue subway (Fig. 1).

The flat ball fields and a substantial portion of the "soccer field" (Gaelic Field) (loc. 6) on the east side of the park, once partly the original bed of Spuyten Duyvil Creek, were created during the 1930s with landfill from the IND subway construction, debris obtained from local apartment house construction, dredge material and rocks blasted away during construction of the U. S. Shipping Canal (Harlem River Canal). Other changes include the substantial retaining wall supporting the raised surface of Seaman Avenue, elevation 15-18 meters, laid out in 1908 and extended in 1912 (Bolton 1914) (loc. 7).

An excellent place to see the local relationships between rocks and topography is at the northwest corner of Park Terrace West and Isham Street (loc. 8). At their intersection, Inwood Marble, generally the weak rock of the area, underlies the low terrain of this location. Facing westward toward Inwood Hill, the resistant schist ridge rises abruptly from the tennis courts and ball fields, while to the south in the direction of the Good Shepherd School and Park Terrace East (and Cooper Street), Fort Tryon Park's hill, dominated by the Cloisters, is the continuation of the schist ridge of Inwood Hill. A 90-degree turn to the east will bring your view across the Harlem River valley to distant University Heights, supported by resistant Fordham Gneiss. There, on the ridge is Bronx Community College and domed Gould Memorial Library with the Hall of Fame at its base. Another 90-degree turn to the left takes you north to the low ridge of marble held up, in part, by some resistant layers and their upward northern tilt that continues, except for the break by the Harlem River, to Marble Hill, once the northernmost section of Manhattan Island.

Land Use

When the last glacial advance reached our area about 21,600 years ago (Boothroyd et al. 1998), bedrock was scoured by rock debris embedded in the base of the ice mass, estimated to be 300 meters thick. Later, about 19,000 years ago, as the glacier began its retreat by melting and evaporation, it left behind a veneer of glacial till of variable thickness blanketing the area. With time and climatic warming, the glacial till and exposed bedrock were subjected to weathering and erosion under different climatic regimes, and vegetation cover developed ranging from tundra to pine and ultimately deciduous forest about 6500 years ago.

Shell middens, predominantly composed of the Common Oyster (*Crassostrea virginica*), left behind in heaps by Native Americans at many localities within and adjacent to the parks, are the telltale signs of the earliest inhabitants known in the area. Carbon-14 analyses of shell material have yielded dates of 1500 carbon-14 years B.P. (Walter Newman, pers. comm.). No one knows when the first Native Americans arrived at Inwood, but other sites in New York City and nearby in the Hudson Valley extend back to the Early Archaic (8000-10,000 years B.P.). For additional information on Native Americans in the park see Bolton (1909, 1920), Skinner (1909, 1947), and Cantwell and Wall (2001).

At the end of the 19th and beginning of the 20th centuries, a group of dedicated amateur archeologists and historians scoured and dug up the area searching for Native American artifacts and also for materials left by

British and Hessian occupiers during the American Revolution. Some of this material is on view at the Dyckman House, and many of the collections are housed at the American Museum of Natural History.

Dutch colonial farmers moved into the area rather quickly after the establishment of New Amsterdam in 1624, rapidly displacing Native Americans. The Nagels and Dyckmans, now commemorated by neighborhood street names, were the dominant families in the area. They cleared land for orchards, and each owned marshland and forested uplands for woodlots (Bolton 1924). Wolves were exterminated in an organized hunt in 1686, and Native Americans had departed from northern Manhattan by 1715, the remnant population induced to leave by cash payments (Bolton 1934).

At the very beginning of the Revolutionary War, American troops constructed Fort Cock Hill at the summit of Inwood Hill (70.7 m, loc 1), built to defend the junction of Spuyten Duyvil Creek with the Hudson River. The British essentially bypassed it in their assault on Fort Washington (184th Street and Fort Washington Avenue). As a result, the fort did not enter much into the fighting and was occupied by the British after Fort Washington fell.

A landscape painting by Thomas Davies, a British officer, illustrating the attack on Fort Washington in 1776 (color reproduction in Fleming 1997) depicts the low terrain of Inwood as open land planted with what appears to be orchards and occasional trees, the wooded slopes of Fort George and Fort Washington hills, Dyckman Street valley and the southern edge of Inwood Hill. This remarkable illustration by an artist with a reputation for great accuracy was created on the spot, during his participation in the fighting. His illustration shows mostly wooded ridges, but large bare patches are an indication of what was to come.

British and Hessian soldiers occupied the area for the duration of the Revolutionary War. The need for wood for fortifications, housing and fuel (see Calver and Bolton 1950) during typically much colder winters than occur at the present time resulted in the wholesale cutting down of the woodlands, most likely causing significant loss of soil from the steeper slopes. Loss of the woodlands did not occur only in Inwood; eventually all of Manhattan was stripped bare of its trees.

After the troops evacuated the area in 1783, farming returned to the lowlands, the abandoned hill slopes slowly rejuvenated, and by the 1830's the thick woods returned, dense enough to create a compelling landscape for people seeking properties for summer homes and estates in a rural setting.

In 1814, Curtis and John Bolton, operators of a nearby marble quarry, acquired a major portion of Inwood Hill. They planned a residential development for their picturesque property and partially constructed a system of roads. After 1830, the land was sold as parcels for small homes and estates, mostly on the western ridge of Inwood Hill (Loeb 1986). Gale (1839) mentions in his geological survey of Manhattan that "a considerable part" of the northern section "is still covered with its native forests.

In 1844, a stage ran from the Battery to Harlem (Knight 1932), and people wishing to reach Tubby Hook (on the Hudson River at what is now Dyckman Street) had to walk from Harlem or provide their own transportation. A visitor to the 10-acre [4 h] estate of Samuel Thompson on Mount Washington described his trip: "As we entered this gate at the road, we seemed to have left the world behind us, as it was one-half mile [0.8 km] through the primeval forest to his residence" (Knight 1932). It was one of the early homes on the hill, described as a "rustic gothic pavilion or summer house" (Kouwenhoven 1953).

Although the name Mount Washington initially referred to the area surrounding the location of Fort Washington, it was extended to cover areas north and south along the ridge. It remained in use until the 1850s, when the name Tubby Hook replaced it for the part that would become known as Inwood Hill.

However, as with many of the older names in New York City, there is not complete agreement about the derivation of place names. "Tubby Hook was a point of land which juts out into the Hudson just below Spuyten Duyvil…. The curious name was given to the point because…to one passing on the Hudson River the little bay in the creek resembled a tub, the high hills forming it sides" (Knight 1932) (loc. 9). On the other hand, Richards (1861) states that "Tubby Hook is little more than a name borrowed, it is said, from a whilom ferryman of the neighborhood." Wade (1846) published a notable panorama along the Hudson River, and although he depicted many houses both to the north and south, there seem to be only three illustrated for Tubby Hook (Inwood Hill). With the arrival of the Hudson River Railroad, people now could work in the city and commute to the woods at Tubby Hook. The railroad bridge over Spuyten Duyvil Creek (loc. 9a) was completed in 1848, and the railroad line to Poughkeepsie opened for business on December 31, 1849 (Fig. 2).

A publication of the Hudson River Railroad (1851) describes Tubby Hook as "a romantic and secluded spot…though at present there are very few buildings in the neighborhood," a description reinforced by the 1851 Dripps Map, which shows eight structures.

Photo: S. Horenstein

Fig. 2. Railroad Bridge over the Harlem River at it junction with the Hudson.

Richards (1861) indicates that "the upper portion of our island yet presents…very much of its primitive forest look…the shore is as yet little disturbed by the city encroachments…. The lofty table ridge which overlooks the Spuyten Duyvil continues unbroken for the distance of a mile [1.6 km], when it drops nearly to the river level at the railway station of Tubby Hook. The whole way is closely occupied by quiet country retreats, with woods, and lawns, extending back to Kingsbridge Road."

In 1871, train service was drastically reduced when the passenger railroad was rerouted along the northern shore of Spuyten Duyvil Creek, then down the Harlem River, eventually to terminate at newly constructed Grand Central Depot. As a result, for the next few decades, population growth slowed in northern Manhattan (Payson 1914). By 1874, the woods and streams of this lovely rus in urbe were as attractive as one could imagine. Calver (1948) recounts in his recollections written in 1932 that in the early 1880s one could still meet farmers who allegedly had not been down to New York for the past 25 years. He relates that the name Inwood was "bestowed upon it" in the 1860s "by a venerable clerk of one of our courts—so he told us himself—to encourage its settlement by nature-lovers." Confirming the date at least, are the lines from Butler (1868):

Down there, on old Manhattan,
Where land-sharks breed and fatten,
They've wiped out Tubby Hook,
That famous promontory,
Renowned in song and story,
which time nor tempest shook,
whose name for aye had been good,
Stand newly-christened 'Inwood,'
And branded with the shame
Of some old rogue who passes
By dint of aliases
afraid of his own name!

Herds of cattle browsed in the pastures east and west of what is now Broadway. Even as late as 1900, children late for school often had the excuse that they had to take the cows out to pasture (Tieck 1971).

On March 31, 1880, the United States Senate passed a bill authorizing the formation of a corporation to develop a world's fair in New York in 1883. Inwood was selected as a possible site for the proposed fair after considerable pressure eliminated Central Park, the favorite location. At the time, Inwood still remained rural, much further uptown and more out of the way than another choice, the west side of Manhattan between 110th-125th Streets. Of the latter site, it was said that it is "almost as little known to New Yorkers as to the residents of Illinois." One can only imagine what was known of Inwood (Stern et al. 1999).

The 1885 Robinson Map shows three brick and 27 wood buildings and 11 wood stables. Many of these buildings had dirt roads leading to them, surrounding lawns, and steeper slopes terraced with stonewall. The U.S. Geological Survey 1897 Harlem Quadrangle (scale 1:62500) shows approximately the same number of main buildings (Map 4).

But by the late 1880s, "many of these beautiful homes, one by one, began to be deserted" and the area "in a few years became a veritable wilderness. The splendid residences were occupied solely, if at all, by caretakers" (Knight 1932).

The idea for an Inwood Park was suggested in 1895 by Andrew Haswell Green, an important late 19th century figure, the "father of the City of Greater New York," and a significant participant in the development of Central Park. He proposed to create a park of 20-30 hectares on the western ridge in conjunction with a proposed bridge over Spuyten Duyvil Creek to

Map 4. U.S.G.S. Topographic Map, 1897 (1:62,500). Black squares are buildings.

the Bronx. The proposal was immediately turned down by New York City because Inwood Hill was zoned for housing, a plan attributed to Frederick Law Olmsted and J. James Croes (Gody 1939). Actually their proposal related to a similar hilly site in Spuyten Duyvil and Riverdale (Olmsted and Croes 1874) where they envisioned a terraced residential area with gardens, grassy open spaces and fern and alpine gardens between the crescent-shaped tracts of housing. Perhaps they transmitted these ideas for Inwood Hill as well.

Green was interested in preserving the area, not only for its archeological finds but also for its geological features and historical associations, its original wooded character, the vast views of the Hudson River and because it was just a beautiful place (American Scenic and Historic Preservation Society 1904b). This attention for local park creation was occurring within the context of a simultaneous national movement.

Discovery of Native American artifacts and the connection with the original inhabitants of Inwood Hill deserves fuller attention because of the role these artifacts and, by extension, the Native Americans played in the park's creation. There was great interest in creating a link with the past and preserving that connection by establishing the park. One of the first to explore this area was Alexander Chenoweth, a well-known civil engineer who already had experience in archeology when he worked in Panama. He joined the engineering staff of the Croton Aqueduct as an assistant engineer in 1885 and as resident engineer of the aqueduct from 1889 to 1895 and moved to Inwood in 1890. Prior to that time, Captain Cortwright, a New York City police officer, called Chenoweth's attention to the shell deposits and Revolutionary War remains in 1886 and 1887. When Chenoweth moved to Inwood, he devoted his spare time to the systematic excavation of the deposits under the direction of Prof. F.W. Putnam, curator of the Peabody Museum at Harvard University (American Scenic and Historic Preservation Society 1904a). As he extended his studies throughout Inwood, he was joined by other kindred spirits, including Reginald P. Bolton and William L. Calver who together published descriptions of many of their finds (Calver and Bolton 1950).

It was in the 1890s that the residents of Inwood were hoping that some day soon electric cars (trolleys) and—a vague possibility—rapid transit would connect them with the city. Inwood had no telegraph station, telephone or even a stage, and only a "few lonely trains on the tail end" of the Hudson River Railroad dragged their uncomfortable passengers back and forth from Inwood (Tubby Hook) to the 30th Street station.

However, in a few years Inwood would change rapidly from a separate village to becoming part of the metropolis. The Broadway trolley line was laid through Inwood to Kingsbridge in 1900, and the IRT subway line reached Dyckman Street in 1905 and a few years later Van Cortlandt Park at 242nd Street. These events transformed Inwood and brought large numbers of people to live in new apartment houses. Not only was there much vacant land to build on but additional new land was created by filling in the Sherman Creek wetlands that extended almost to Broadway between Dyckman Street and Nagel Avenue. As a result Inwood Hill was simply bypassed.

In 1898, Andrew Haswell Green described the northern summit of the hill as being difficult to access, almost impassable "in a carriage ride rendered perilous by the dangerous conditions of the rude roadway" (American Scenic and Historic Preservation Society 1916). A description of Inwood Hill in

1907 still identified it as thickly wooded, little altered by modern improvements and in "practically the same condition as that in which Henry Hudson saw it 300 years ago" (American Scenic and Historic Preservation 1907).

Beginning in 1904, interest in developing the park began to peak as several opportunities arose for promoting its creation: the upcoming Hudson Fulton celebration of 1909 and the planned Hudson Memorial Bridge over Spuyten Duyvil, the discovery of numerous artifacts, and later the donation of land to create Isham Park in 1912. Representing the American Scenic and Historic Preservation Society and the Local Board of Improvements of the Washington Heights District, at a public hearing on May 24, 1904, Reginald P. Bolton presented a proposition to initiate proceedings for the creation of a public park at the northern end of Inwood Heights. (American Scenic and Historic Preservation Society 1904a).

In 1912, Mrs. Henry Osborn Taylor (née Julia Isham) donated six acres [2.4 h] of land for a street and a public park to be known as Isham Park, land her father Samuel Isham had purchased in 1864 and used for his residence until his death in 1908. At the time the hill commanded beautiful western views of the Hudson across Spuyten Duyvil Creek and eastern views of the Harlem River valley, University Heights, and Fort George Hill. In order that the charming vista toward Spuyten Duyvil Creek might not be cut off by the erection of buildings, she purchased additional property and gave it to the city. Her aunt, Flora E. Isham, donated additional parcels. The properties contained the original mansion and a greenhouse, among other structures. The mansion was renovated for public use and the greenhouse was kept up as a source of plants for the parks. Unfortunately, the cost of maintaining these facilities became prohibitive and they were demolished in the 1940s.

As far as Inwood Hill was concerned, the City was still considering development and approved the sale of its northern tip to a private dock company that announced, "work clearing the hill of timber will soon be underway and the ground will be broken for the construction of docks and warehouses." The company intended to construct a basin for the accommodation of canal barges along the Hudson between Dyckman Street and Spuyten Duyvil Creek, from 91 meters north of Dyckman Street for a distance of 670 m, within the largest possible area enclosed by a breakwater. Fortunately, nothing happened and the land was sold to a speculator who hoped to profit by the sale of lots when Riverside Drive was extended north to Dyckman Street (Barlow 1971).

The City finally relented and formally decided to create Inwood Hill

Park in 1915. On May 21, "the Board of Estimate adopted a resolution to change the map or plan of the City so as to lay out a public park" (American Scenic and Historic Preservation 1916) on the westerly slope of Inwood Hill about 550 meters north of Dyckman Street and began purchasing land beginning in 1916.

Although the park was officially created in name, the land was essentially left in its original state, allowing it to retain its "primitive nature," but was encumbered by the presence of very old and dilapidated buildings (City of New York, Department of Parks 1927). Some of the former owners stayed on while others moved out and squatters looking for rent-free quarters took their places. The squatters planted gardens and raised chickens and pigs (New York Times 1938).

However, it would be a long decade as Inwood Hill Park began to be altered. First, extending the park along the Hudson River by dumping fill taken from the excavation of the IND subway created 3.9 hectares, saving the city millions of dollars that it would have cost to dispose of the material (loc. 10) (Fig. 1). Plans were made to landscape the new addition and "harmonize it with the surrounding park land…. This work when completed as planned will tend to enhance the aesthetic beauty of The Greatest of All Rivers…the Hudson" (City of New York, Department Parks, 1927, p. 89). Work began in the park by removing all dead and dangerous trees, resulting in the removal of 789 trees, and 1117 stumps, which included numerous dead chestnut trees (City of New York, Parks Department 1927).

Preparation for additional improvements included laying out paths, drainage system and landscaping, and the removal of 97 buildings, but not their foundations, from the park (City of New York, Parks Department 1931). Map 5 (Bolton, 1932) locates some of the structures that were demolished as well as those still in existence in 1932. By 1934, Depression relief forces were put to work "improving" the park, installing water and lights, macadamizing new and old paths, installing a drainage system to "save hillsides from erosion" and evicting the squatters.

Final development and reconfiguration of the park began in 1936, as work on the Harlem Ship Canal and the Henry Hudson Parkway and Bridge progressed, when Crescent Island and the land under Spuyten Duyvil Creek (now partially filled in), land under the boat basin, the peninsula, and a small parcel at the westernmost corner on the Hudson River, were added to complete the park by 1941.

By the end of the 1930s, driveways, a few walls and foundations, unusual plants and trees such as the Ginkgo (*Ginkgo biloba*), the "avenue

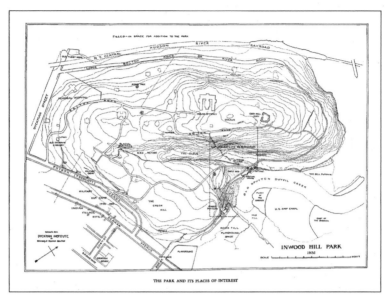

Map 5. Bolton (1932) map, showing location of some former and current (1932) structures.

of the Rose-of-Sharon [*Hibiscus syriacus*] bushes" and fruit trees were the only remaining evidence of the residential period (U.S. Works Progress Administration 1939).

Caro (1974) describes the political and economic intrigue that accompanied building the Henry Hudson Parkway and Bridge. Robert Moses rejected alternate routes, not because they were inappropriate but because building the roadway in the park made funding available from state and federal sources. Considerable opposition to placing the highway in the park arose because of the removal of a portion of the park for highway use, destruction of trees, undercutting the cliffs facing the Hudson River, splitting the park, and the intrusion of highway noise into the park area. Moses (1970) dismissed these and other complaints.

As to the specific criticism related to Inwood Hill Park, he states, "In the path of the Henry Hudson Bridge approach to Inwood park there was a huge, old, decayed tulip tree…. There were other trees, many decrepit. In the middle was a kiln where an Indian princess taught ceramics under dubious auspices. She had a son who didn't work. Both were on relief, and the relief check was delivered to the princess in a mailbox fastened to a tree. The hullabaloo about disturbing the princess, the kiln, the old tulip tree, and other flora and fauna was terrific. Among the protestants were parlor conservationists who manifestly had never climbed Inwood Hill Park who regarded stopping the parkway and bridge as a holy cause and a romantic escape from boredom" (Moses 1970). His words reveal his philosophy of urban planning, and it should be pointed out that the tulip tree as well as the kiln were not near the highway right-of-way and not a factor in the objection to building the highway.

The view of the park from an automobile is certainly a pleasant sight, but the view of the highway from the park is not.

The Henry Hudson Bridge was needed to complete Moses's network of bridges and expressways, and he received his required funds by classifying the six-lane highway as a park access road. By sacrificing the original Inwood Hill he showed consistency in his belief that these benefits deserved priority over those of the environment (Pollara 1997).

In the early 1970s, lighting was added to the woods and subsequently removed—and a small geological display near the caves was completely vandalized. The last building demolished was a comfort station along the West Ridge Road, but its concrete floor and drains still remain, now covered with a thin layer of soil and plant litter and overgrown with shrubs and trees. In 1992, New York City Councilman Stanley Michaels designated the natural parts of the park as the Shorakapok Natural Area. Today, the Parks Department is proceeding with a major restoration program for the park that includes planting native vegetation, removing inappropriate exotic trees and shrubs, and repairing paths.

Recently, the Triborough Bridge and Tunnel Authority enlarged its parking area at the expense of the park and cut down a number of trees during remedial work on the highway. People who live in our quintessential urban setting feel the loss of parkland acutely, because it is they who probably appreciate most the beauty of nature and the parks that preserve it. It is the parks that make living in the city tolerable and add an immeasurable dimension to city life. Without green spaces a city can be an oppressive and degrading place. An important facility, the Inwood Hill Park Urban Ecology Center, was opened in 1995, providing public lectures, field trips, and information to park visitors.

Harlem River Ship Canal (United States Ship Canal) and Spuyten Duyvil Creek

No longer the waterway it once was, the Harlem River is an integral part of Inwood Hill Park. From benches on the peninsula (loc.11) to the overlooks along paths there is both a joy and fascination viewing its constantly changing

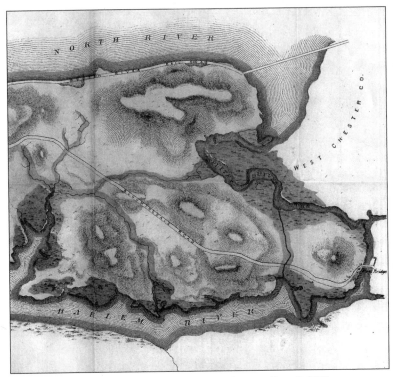

Map 6. Viele Map of Northern Manhattan and Spuyten Duyvil, 1865.

appearance. Part of the complex system of waterways that make up the Hudson-Raritan estuary, the Harlem River today is a 12.2 km tidal strait connecting the East River with the Hudson, forming the boundary between Manhattan Island and The Bronx.

In the past, prior to 1895, the Harlem River was considered a separate body connected to the Hudson River by Spuyten Duyvil Creek an S-shaped stream that looped around Manhattan Island (Map 6). Today, Spuyten Duyvil Creek no longer exists, cut through its center to create the United States Ship Canal in two operations, one in 1895 and the other in 1937, leaving the loops above and below abandoned and later filled in with rock debris (Map 4). Beyond these changes, the entire Harlem River channel from its beginning (end) at the East River to the Hudson River has been altered by dredging and the straightening of its shoreline.

One of the consequences of the 1895 project was the reduction of the length of Manhattan Island. The canal's cut severed the Marble Hill section of the island, leaving it isolated and surrounded by water until filling attached it to The Bronx and the mainland. Although still part of the Borough of Manhattan, Marble Hill is no longer physically part of it.

Several explanations for the origin of the name Spuyten Duyvil have been suggested, but in reality its genesis remains somewhat obscure. "Spitting Devil" may refer to one of the voluminous springs entering the creek or probably the vigorous tide (McNamara 1991). The combination of its shallow depth and the tidal flow up the East River that did not coincide with the Hudson's resulted in the creek exhibiting a double tide, an abnormality which the Dutch felt was surely the work of the devil.

Washington Irving, who describes Anthony Corlear's attempt to cross Spuyten Duyvil Creek during a storm, created the explanation "In Spite of the Devil." "It was dark and stormy night when the good Anthony arrived.... The wind was high, and the elements were in an uproar, and no Charon could be found to ferry the adventurous sounder of brass across the water.... Bethinking himself of the urgency of his errand, he took a hearty embrace of his stone bottle, swore most valorously, that he would swim across, "en spijt den Duyvel" (in spite of the Devil!)" (Irving 1880).

The Harlem was altered to deepen its channel and remove its curves to provide a second access to the port of New York and Long Island Sound. After the Erie Canal was completed, Governor Dewitt Clinton, in 1827, formulated legislation for a canal that would provide a proper outlet for commerce to Long Island Sound by linking the Hudson River with the Harlem River, the East River and Long Island Sound. Making the Harlem navigable would also give the port of New York a second entry. Thus vessels coming or going to Albany would not have to go around the southern tip of Manhattan but would be able to take a short cut by way of the Harlem (Hermalyn 1983).

A company was incorporated in 1827 to dig a canal, but little was done and the company abandoned the project. As a result, the canal project lay dormant for many years until the need to provide New York with modern port facilities became a major goal. As the idea of the canal again progressed in the 1850s, there were several false starts, political and legal obstacles, property disputes and lack of funding, all contributing to the delayed construction of the waterway. For example, when finally contracts were given to private companies, it was realized that it was inappropriate to put an "arm of the sea," public access, into the controlling hands of a private company. Finally, the federal government turned over the project to the U. S. Army Corp of Engineers who began digging the canal in January 1888. But as the project got underway, poor construction techniques and the famous March blizzard

Photo: S. Horenstein

Fig. 3. The embankment at Columbia University's Baker Field was created with Inwood Marble from the 1895 section of the Harlem Ship Canal. It is covered with fresh marble from a nearby construction site.

of 1888 retarded its completion. Finally, the first section of this major endeavor by the Army Corp of Engineers to alter the course of the Harlem and make it navigable was finished in 1895 (Hermalyn 1983), the same year that Inwood Hill Park was proposed. Eventually, some of the abandoned loop of the waterway, located beneath the Marble Hill Houses, 230th Street and the valley between Marble Hill and Spuyten Duyvil Hill (location of J. F. Kennedy High School) (loc.13), was partly filled in with the debris from the construction of Grand Central Terminal (Tieck 1968).

However, a major curve in the river still remained, as did the debate on how and where to eliminate it. The peninsula responsible for the curve contained the Johnson Iron Foundry, which was dealt with by condemnation in 1923 and the land ceded to the federal government, allowing construction to begin, but it did not commence until 1936. At its completion in 1938, the canal cut included a vertical wall now containing the graffito "C" (Fig. 3).

The resulting channel as well as the entire Harlem River was maintained

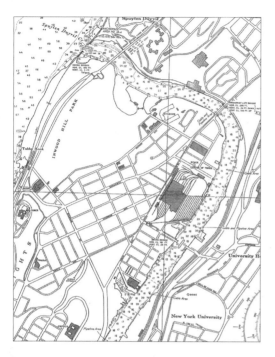

Map 7. Nautical chart (1996) of northern part of Harlem River.

Map 8. Stages in the conversion of Spuyten Duyvil Creek to Harlem Ship Canal (from Hermalyn, 1983)

at a depth of 4.5 meters, and for the most part, 120 meters wide (Map 7). Map 8 shows some of the stages and dates for the conversion of Spuyten Duyvil Creek to the Harlem River Shipping Canal (Hermalyn 1983). Good views, from the peninsula (loc.11) as well as the North Crest Road (loc.12), of the first cut adjacent to and under the Broadway/225th Street Bridge (loc. 14a), and of the second cut containing the letter "C," reveal the entire extent of the canal (loc. 14b). Originally, the railroad ran along Spuyten Duyvil Creek around the north end of Marble Hill. After the first cut was made, the railroad was moved so that it could follow the new waterway, which necessitated creating a "bench," or terrace, cut into the north side of the canal wall to accommodate the rail bed.

The final reconfiguration of Spuyten Duyvil Creek left behind an embayment (lagoon) partially enclosed by a peninsula, originally an island, after the second cut was completed. Filling the abandoned section of Spuyten Duyvil Creek between the island and 218th Street formed the peninsula. It is interesting to note that when you stand on the peninsula near the Environmental Center (loc. 11), you are on land that was once part of Westchester County. In 1874, Westchester ceded it to New York City. Designated as the Annexed Territory, it eventually became part of The Bronx and, after the completion of the canal, the Borough of Manhattan (Fig. 4).

Fig. 4. View of completed Ship Canal, 1895 cut adjacent to the bridge and 1938 cut is located at the "C"

Photo: S. Horenstein

Photo: S. Horenstein

Fig. 5. Lagoon mudflats

A yacht basin was planned, but not completed, for the lagoon to accommodate more than 100 vessels. On the peninsula, a parking lot (now covered with sod), launching ramps and a building were constructed, now the home of the excellent Inwood Hill Park Environmental Center.

Construction of the ship canal altered the tidal flow of the Harlem. No longer are there eight changes of tide. Today, high tide fluctuations are between about 1.0 and 1.5 meters and minus tides are small. An excellent place to watch the changing character of the Harlem River and the lagoon is from the peninsula (loc. 11) adjacent to the river and opposite the "C."

Understanding the dynamics of the river, its flow and sediments is essential to the understanding of the flora and fauna occupying the lagoon's marsh and shoreline. Because construction of the boat basin never proceeded, the depth of the lagoon was not maintained. In 1938, depth of water in the deeper parts of the basin ranged between 5.5 and 6.0 meters. Since that time, it has diminished with accumulating sediment derived from erosion from the surrounding hills, along the shoreline, from sediment brought up by the Harlem from the East River, outflow from storm sewers prior to their interception and, most importantly, sediment from the Hudson River. For the few hours that the currents turn into the Harlem, a portion of the Hudson River's sediment load travels into the Harlem and is partly trapped in the lagoon. Over the years, this variable supply of material has caused the lagoon to fill substantially, becoming especially apparent in recent years during low tide when vast mudflats are exposed, broken only by a few tidal streams (Fig. 5).

Knowledge of the tidal flows and input of fresh water from rain and runoff makes understandable why the salinity of the Harlem and its embayment vary enormously, ranging from nearly fresh to marine water.

Tulip Tree

A tablet on a painted glacial erratic of Palisades Diabase (loc. 15) marks the position of a large tulip tree that received its final blow during the major hurricane of 1938. Loeb (1986) reports that many large trees were killed in Inwood Park among the thousands felled in the city during the storm on September 21. This particular tulip tree is, in many ways, iconic, referred to often, and its former location is the northern starting point for walkers and joggers leading to the trails rising into the wooded hills of the park. It was listed as one of the notable trees of New York City (Britton 1913).

Surrounded by an area much frequented by picnic parties, the tulip tree was discovered "officially" in 1912 and was thought to be the largest and oldest tree on Manhattan Island. Located near the Harlem River (Spuyten Duyvil Creek) partly on a knoll of oyster shells, its roots were damaged where erosion washed soil away. On October 30, 1912, a celebration commemo-

Photo: S. Horenstein

Fig. 6. Tulip tree 1909

rated the tree's longevity. In preparation for the ceremony, even though it stood on private land, the Parks Department had "all the dead wood cut out of the tree, filled the cavities with cement according to modern methods of surgery, and erected around it an iron picket fence, in the hope that this tree may stand for centuries to come." The upper cement filling received the following inscription enhanced with gold letters: "Tulip Tree. *Liriodendron tulipifera*. Circumference, 19 feet [5.8 m], Age, 225 years. Hendrick Hudson entered this inlet in 1609, and may have met the Indians here, who used the place for a camp, as shown by the quantity of old broken oyster shells around the tree and near by. The tree was thoroughly repaired, and the fence erected around it, October, 1912" (City of New York, Department of Parks 1913). Dr. Nathaniel L. Britton, director of the New York Botanical Garden, determined the age of the tree by comparing its 1.9 m diameter (or a radius of 0.94 m) with known growth rates of this species elsewhere. By assuming that there are six yearly rings per 2.5 cm, he indicated "an approximate age of 222 years" (Britton 1913) (Fig. 6).

In 1927, to improve its health "1000 pounds" [454 kg] of bone meal and sheep manure were fed into its roots. "A mulch of ten cubic yards [7.6 m3] of well decomposed cow manure was spread over a large area at the base of this tree" (City of New York, Parks Department 1927).

When Graves (1930) examined the tree on July 8, 1930, the inscribed dimensions were little changed, but "with the aid of a boy scout I measured the tree" with the following results: "circumference 4 feet [1.2 m] from the ground—17 feet, 9¼ inches [5.43 m]; one foot [0.3 m] from the ground—23 feet, 6½ inches [7.17 m]."

After the tree's destruction, a 1.2 m high stump remained (Gody, 1939), which was eventually removed and later replaced by a glacial erratic of Palisades diabase at the tree's location. An installed plaque on the boulder states:

SHORAKKOPOCH

ACCORDING TO LEGEND, ON THIS SITE OF THE
PRINCIPAL MANHATTAN INDIAN VILLAGE, PETER MINUIT
IN 1626 PURCHASED MANHATTAN ISLAND FOR TRINKETS
AND BEADS THEN WORTH ABOUT 60 GUILDERS.

THIS BOULDER ALSO MARKS THE SPOT WHERE
A TREE (LIRIODENDRON TULIPIFERA) GREW TO A HEIGHT

OF 165 FEET [50 M] AND A GIRTH OF 20 FEET [6.1 M]. IT WAS UNTIL
ITS DEATH IN 1938 AT THE AGE OF 280 YEARS, THE
LAST LIVING LINK WITH THE RECHGAWANANC INDIANS
WHO LIVED HERE.

DEDICATED AS PART OF
NEW YORK CITY'S 300TH ANNIVERSARY CELEBRATION BY
THE PETER MINUIT POST 1247, AMERICAN LEGION
JANUARY 1, 1954.

The phrase "according to legend" perhaps pardons several historical
inaccuracies.

Regional Geology

Inwood Hill and Isham Parks lie within the Manhattan Prong of the New
England geomorphic or physiographic province (Schuberth 1968). Provinces
are regions characterized by similar topography, geology and landforms. The
New England Province is described as a complex of mountains that contains
for the most part Proterozoic to Paleozoic metamorphic (gneiss, slate, schist,
marble) and igneous (granite) rocks that formed deep in the Earth's crust and
through a process of uplift and intense stream erosion (and recent glacial
erosion) become exposed at the surface (Fenneman 1938, Thornbury 1965).
Near its southern margin this province divides into two southwesterly
oriented "prongs," one extending through the Hudson Highlands and
Ramapo Mountains of New Jersey and terminating at Reading, Pennsylvania.
The other, the Manhattan Prong, continues through Westchester into The
Bronx, Manhattan, westernmost Queens, Hoboken and terminates in
northern Staten Island.

The topography of the Manhattan Prong is controlled by rock type:
schists and gneisses form ridges, and marble underlies valleys that trend
northeast to southwest. Intersecting this grain are cross-valleys developed along
faults, among which the 125th Street and Dyckman Street faults in Manhattan
and the Moshulu Fault in The Bronx are most notable. The highest elevation on
Manhattan Island (84 m) is in Bennett Park, 184th Street and Fort Washington
Avenue. Occasional hills underlain by serpentinite produce local high elevations,
such as 58th Street and Amsterdam Avenue, and Castle Point, in Hoboken.
Todt Hill on Staten Island, (elev. 125 m), is not only the highest natural place
in New York City but also the highest East Coast hill south of central Maine.

The prongs of the New England Province are separated by the Piedmont Province, which extends from Rockland County in southern New York State, where it is narrowest, to Alabama. Traditionally, the province is divided into upland and lowland sections. In our area only the lowland section, the Newark Basin, is present, containing Upper Triassic and Lower Jurassic reddish sandstones and shales, interlayered with lava flows and sills. Across the Hudson River, the dramatic Palisades cliffs, composed of the igneous rock diabase, is a sill forming the eastern edge of the Newark Basin.

To the south, the younger Atlantic Coastal Plain surrounds and covers the subsurface extension of the Manhattan Prong and part of the Newark Basin with a thick deposit of gently sloping marine, deltaic and terrestrial clay, silt and sand. Within most of New York City, these materials are covered by a veneer of glacial debris of variable thickness.

Composed of an assortment of unsorted and unconsolidated material, from clay particles to huge boulders, glacial till is found nearly everywhere underfoot. The southern edge of the till is marked by a ridge-like deposit, the end or terminal moraine, approximately 1.5-3.0 km in width and extending through central Queens and Brooklyn, to the southern tip of Staten Island.

While most cities extend over one or two provinces, New York City is the only urban center that spreads across three (New England Upland, Piedmont and Coastal Plain) and, in addition, has been glaciated, providing it with the most complex geology of any large city in the United States (Baskerville 1982).

Bedrock Geology—Introduction

The foundation rocks of Inwood Hill and Isham Parks are highly metamorphosed and intensely deformed rocks of Precambrian to Ordovician ages (1.1 billion to 435 million years ago) (Map 9). These rocks generally dip down southwestward, resulting in the appearance at the surface of older rocks northeastward, across the Harlem River in The Bronx. They form part of the New York City sequence of rocks that contain the records of an extremely complicated and dynamic history. Typically, two basic sequences of rocks occur; one that formed in shallow seas on the continental shelf of ancestral North America and the other at various depths in the adjacent Iapetus Ocean. (In Greek myth, Iapetus was the father of Atlas from whose name Atlantic is derived.) As a result of convergent plates resulting in the collision of a volcanic island belt during Ordovician Period (Taconic Orogeny), the oceanic sequence was transported onto the continental margins along a major low-angle thrust fault named Cameron's Line. Parallel to and above Cameron's

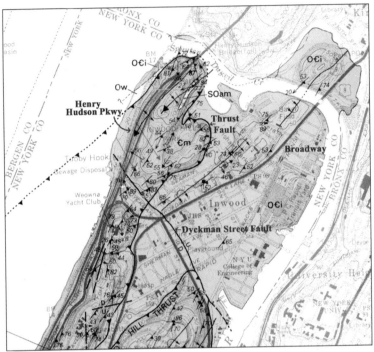

Map 9. Geologic map of the Inwood area and Marble Hill. Modified from Baskerville (1994). The bulk of Inwood Hill Park is underlain by Cm (Manhattan schist) with small amounts of Ow (Walloomsac Formation and SOam (Amphibolite). OCi (Inwood Marble) underlies the rest of the area. The lines with triangular tick marks are thrust faults. Other symbols indicate the structure of the rocks. Refer to Baskerville (1994) for a full explanation.

Line are subparallel faults that further displaced segments of the rock series. During collision and transport, all the rocks were metamorphosed and deformed, including the faults, not only by this initial movement but also by subsequent movements (especially, the Acadian Orogeny, 380 million years ago). Thus, deformation and subsequent erosion have produced an irregular distribution of these rocks and fault lines, making interpretation difficult and sometimes contradictory. Collision during the middle and late Ordovician (the Taconic Orogeny) raised these rocks high into substantial mountains, and subsequent collisions rejuvenated them until the Mesozoic Era, when erosion dominated the area and wore the mountains down.

Cameron's Line is also a major tectonic boundary of eastern New England, marking the position between North American rocks and rocks formed elsewhere but which are now part of the continent. In our area, these exotic oceanic volcanic rocks belong to the "Hartland" Terrain whose distribution, as well as the location of Cameron's Line, is subject to ongoing discussion. For example, Cameron's Line in the Bronx has been mapped just east of Webster Avenue, in the central Bronx, or adjacent to Pelham Bay Park, its location dependent on interpretation of neighboring rocks (Baskerville 1992, Isachsen et al. 1991, Merguerian 1994, Brock and Brock 2001).

Many detailed rock descriptions and the interpretations that flow from them have been obtained by examining very thin slices of rocks under a petrographic microscope, microprobe chemical analysis, radiometric dating and other instrumentation. Many features crucial to interpretation are not seen even with a hand lens.

Metamorphic rocks derive from previously formed rocks (protolith) and are classified, for the most part, by the kinds of minerals they contain, their texture and bulk chemical composition. As a result, for example, the name of a common metamorphic rock is biotite-garnet schist. Schist has a foliated texture, one that contains platy minerals (e.g., mica), which are arranged parallel or subparallel to one another. Gneiss consists of alternating layers of different minerals that give it its distinctive banding. When a rock has been subjected to high-grade metamorphism (high temperature and pressure), it may be difficult to determine the original protolith, while in low-grade metamorphic rocks, where the prototlith is still recognizable, the prefix "meta" often appers in their description—such as "metabasalt." Where minerals are much larger than those surrounding them, the term "porphyroblast" is used to describe these minerals that grew later in the rock at the expense of others. Most of the garnets in the Inwood Hill Park schists are porphyroblastic.

Minerals subjected to heat and pressure undergo chemical reactions and changes that produce new minerals which are stable under the new conditions. Increasing heat and pressure is called progressive metamorphism, but if a metamorphic rock undergoes heat and pressure at a lower temperature and pressure than formed it previously, the resulting new minerals are a product of retrograde metamorphism. This process often makes interpretation difficult because later intense metamorphism often obscures the earlier event. Minerals are geologic thermometers, the product of temperature and pressure conditions under which they formed. For example, the mineral kyanite converts to sillimanite as temperature and pressure increases and changes back during further metamorphism at lower temperature and pressure. Added to the temperature/pressure control of mineral formation is the introduction of fluids and new elements during the collisional processes.

Because an individual mineral's stability range may be large, associations of minerals give the best indication of the conditions under which a rock has formed.

This brief discussion of the kinds of processes that rocks in the parks have been subjected to can be considerably enhanced by consulting a modern text on petrology. The following descriptions refer to formations located in the Inwood/Isham Parks area. It is beyond the scope of this report to discuss many of the other aspects of New York's bedrock geology, but further information can be obtained by consulting the list of references.

Autochthonous Formations (Autochthonous rocks are those that formed in the place where they are found.)

FORDHAM GNEISS: The Fordham Gneiss has been divided into four members based on overall appearance of the rock (Baskerville 1992, 1994). Named for its occurrence at Fordham Heights, it has a distinctive alternation of light and dark gray to black bands. The bands vary in thickness, from less than 2.5 to several centimeters, and even in a small exposure may thicken and thin considerably, sometimes disappearing completely, as displayed on the boulder (loc. 16). Another characteristic of this rock is its intensely distorted nature, exhibiting folds and faults, also apparent in the rock mentioned above. The light bands are composed of quartz and orthoclase feldspar, while dark bands contain abundant black biotite and some hornblende. Minor amounts of other minerals that include garnet and muscovite can be seen with a hand lens.

Fordham Gneiss is the oldest formation in New York City (Precambrian, Proterozoic, 1.1 billion years old). Originally volcanic rock, it was laid down and then metamorphosed during the Grenville Orogeny at the time the supercontinent Rodinia was assembling. Although not naturally exposed in Inwood Hill/Isham Parks, it forms the prominent slopes and cliff on the north side of the Harlem River in the Spuyten Duyvil section of The Bronx. The steep undercut slope with its officially sanctioned graffito, the letter "C," contains excellent exposures that dip below the younger rocks of Inwood Hill Park. As a result, it is included here and fortunately two large boulders, perhaps pieces of glacially transported erratics, are used for part of a low retaining wall in a cutout for benches created for viewing pleasure along North Crest Road (loc. 12). The other specimen, part of the riprap, can be seen at the end of the drainage canal cutting through the peninsula (loc. 16).

Photo: S. Horenstein

Fig. 7. Inwood marble and quartzite boudin.

INWOOD MARBLE: The Inwood Marble (Lower Cambrian to Lower Ordovician, 540-485 million years old) was originally deposited as calcitic and dolomitic mud and sand in a shallow tropical sea on the eroded surface of the Fordham Gneiss. It has been divided into four members (Hall 1968) in Westchester but cannot be separately mapped in New York City due to inadequate exposures (Baskerville 1994). The Inwood Marble is named for the exposures found in this part of Manhattan. Several varieties of marble are exposed in Isham Park along Isham Street (loc. 18), the slope adjacent to the park path (former carriage road to the Isham mansion) (loc. 19), the northeast corner of the park above Broadway (loc. 20) and Inwood Hill Park (loc. 21). This foliated calc-schist, fine-grained calcitic marble, and coarse-grained dolomitic marble, contain the silicate minerals, diopside, the light brown mica phlogopite, quartz and tremolite, easily recognized as white nodules protruding above the rock surface, probably formed as a result of retrogressive metamorphism occurring during the Acadian Orogeny 380 million years ago (Brock and Brock, 2001).

Randomly distributed are beds of quartzite, metamorphosed quartz sand or chert, that snapped during deformation and broke into distinct pods and slabs termed boudins (French for "blood sausage") (loc. 22). A close look reveals how the marble flowed into the provided spaces as the quartzite beds broke apart (Fig. 7).

Gale (1839) mentions "a line of abandoned quarries, which many years ago were extensively wrought for burning into lime," traces of which, can still be seen behind some buildings along Broadway. On the west side of Broadway at 217th Street, a marble arch, the former entrance of the Seaman-Drake estate, today located behind a group of auto repair shops, is built of Inwood Marble quarried north of 218th Street, west of Broadway.

WALLOOMSAC FORMATION: The Walloomsac Formation (Middle Ordovician, 465 million years old) originally deposited as marine mud and silt on the eroded surface of the Inwood Marble, is a gray, fissile, fine- to medium-grained plagioclase-garnet-muscovite-biotite-quartz schist that usually weathers to various shades of tan (Baskerville 1994). Locally much of the rock consists of muscovite and garnet porphyroblasts of up to 1.3 cm diameter that stand out in relief. While Walloomsac sediments were originally metamorphosed at a high temperature and a depth of 40 km, later metamorphism occurring at lower temperatures and 20 km depth accounts for the occurrence of the muscovite (Brock and Brock 2001).

Near the base of the Walloomsac Formation lie continuous layers of fine- to medium-grained bluish white and white dolomitic and siliceous marble with diopside, phlogopite, and discontinuous tan- and rusty-weathering lenses of mica schist (Baskerville 1994). The marble can be seen along the Harlem River shoreline at low tide, accessed along a dangerously steep dirt path that begins beneath the Henry Hudson Bridge and leads to the river just west of the bridge (loc. 17). However, although the marble beds are usually considered part of the Walloomsac (Baskerville 1994), some investigators suggest that they may be Inwood Marble (Schuberth 1968, Merguerian and Sanders 1991).

Allochthonous Formations (Allochthonous rocks were pushed from the site where they were formed to a new location.)

MANHATTAN SCHIST: Manhattan Schist (Precambrian, Neoproterozoic, 570 million years old) is a gray, medium to coarse-grained, layered sillimanite-muscovite-biotite-kyanite schist and gneiss interlayered with tourmaline-garnet-plagioclase-biotite-quartz schist and gneiss. It frequently contains deformed lenses and nodules of kyanite and sillimanite and streaks of leucosomes, a mixture of quartz and feldspar (loc. 24) (Baskerville 1994, Brock and Brock 1999). Leucosomes form from the partial melting of the rocks under high temperature and pressure. Generally, where garnet occurs, they are abundant and may reach 2.5 cm in diameter. Manhattan Schist is the most widespread formation in the park (Map 9). Manhattan Schist weathers gray, tan, rusty and maroon (Baskerville 1992). Rusty weathered outcrops are micaceous, resulting from the weathering of iron-bearing minerals (loc. 25). Manhattan Schist is in fault contact, the Inwood Hill Park Thrust Fault, everywhere with the underlying rock formations.

Along many path edges and retaining walls broken pieces of bright micaceous Manhattan Schist (loc. 26) stand out in contrast to the otherwise

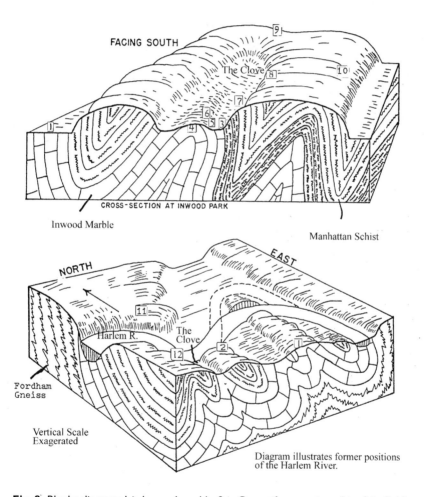

Fig. 8. Blocks diagram: 1 is Inwood marble, 2 is Garnetiferous mica schist, 3 is Cold Spring, 4 is Inwood marble, 5 is historical marker for Tulip Tree, 6 is Indian shell middens, 7 is Indian Caves. 8 is pot holes, 9 is Dyckman Street fault overlook, 10 is Hudson River overlook, 11 is Fordham gneiss. 12 is Hornblende schist. Modified handout from City College of New York

Fig. 9. Fold in Manhattan schist.

dull outcrops (loc. 27). Very few outcrops in the park exhibit this silvery, lustrous schist, the apparent result of the difference between weathered outcrops and freshly broken slabs.

Associated with Manhattan Schist are sills and dikes of amphibolite (hornblende schist), and Inwood Park contains an excellent example of this rock whose protolith was the igneous rock basalt. The outcrop, 18.3 m high, forms a prominent exposure along North Crest Road (loc. 28) and the trail above it (loc. 29). A close look at the amphibolite reveals the parallel arrangement of its black hornblende crystals. Intruding the amphibolite are dikes of light-colored granitic rock up to 30 cm thick. Both the granitic rock and the muscovite in the schist result from retrograde metamorphism that occurred during the Acadian Orogeny, 380 million years ago (Merguerian and Sanders 1987).

FAULTS AND FOLDS: Inwood Hill and Isham Parks also contain excellent examples of the types of folds and faults that occur within the Manhattan Prong. The block diagram (Fig. 8) depicts the series of folds mapped in the parks, and although it does not represent the relationships between the formations correctly, it is still useful because it does show how the rocks are folded and how the folds relate to topography. The wiggly symbol within the Manhattan Schist indicates a folding event during the

Taconic Orogeny. Later, gentler deformation folded the rocks into the broad loops depicted in the cross-section. Unraveling the successive folding events points to at least five periods of deformation (loc. 30) (Brock and Brock 2001). Weaker beds within the layers are buckled to a greater degree than the surrounding layers, forming kink bands and other internal wrinkles (loc. 31) (Fig. 9).

Deformation of the bedrock (folding and faulting) occurred during the middle and late Ordovician (Taconic Orogeny) in several phases, over 440 million years ago and again during the Devonian (Acadian Orogeny) and, although much less intense, at the end of the Pennsylvanian (Alleghanian Orogeny), and again during Upper Triassic-Lower Jurassic some 200 million years ago. These periods are associated with major tectonic events which involved major mountain building, the closing of Iapetus Ocean and then later, during the Upper Triassic-Lower Jurassic, with the formation of Newark Basin, the beginning stages of the opening of the Atlantic Ocean.

The terms "syncline" and "anticline" are used to describe folds in sedimentary rocks, while "synform" and "antiform" describe folded metamorphic rocks. At Inwood Hill Park, the Clove Valley is developed along the axis of a large antiform structure pitching southwestward. Because the crest of schist has been eroded away, the underlying Inwood Marble core (loc. 21) is exposed. Its greater susceptibility to weathering and erosion than the adjacent schist resulted in the formation of the Clove Valley.

Several minor folds (drag folds) can also be seen in the Inwood Marble (loc. 32). In the middle of the outcrop, the marble beds no longer dip steeply but are nearly horizontal, because the beds of the fold have flopped over, forming an overturned fold. During folding some marble layers also slipped past each other along a small fault, which can be seen where the beds meet at a sharp angle.

The Inwood Hill Park Thrust fault, a low-angle thrust fault formed during the Taconic Orogeny, is not seen, but its location can be inferred by the juxtaposition of the Manhattan Schist and the Walloomsac Formation (Map 7) (Baskerville 1992).

Although the Dyckman Street fault (loc. 33) is not deformed and cuts across the bedrock structure, indicating that it formed after the major deformation phases, its age is uncertain. By comparing it to the 125th Street fault, to which it is subparallel, we may get some help. Traditionally, the 125th Street fault is drawn continuously across the Hudson River to just north of Edgewater, 1.5 km south of the George Washington Bridge, where it offsets the Palisades and the underlying sedimentary rocks. Assuming they

Photo: S. Horenstein

Fig. 10. Joints in Manhattan Schist

are connected beneath the river, then it is probable that the 125th Street fault developed after formation of the Palisades. By analogy, if we assume that the Dyckman Street fault is the same age as the 125th Street fault then this scenario will also hold true for the Dyckman Street fault, even though that fault does not extend to the Palisades. However, it is also possible that the 125th Street fault and the Palisades fault are separate and not related or that the 125th Street fault is older but was reactivated and extended soon after the Palisades formed or even later, when this region was uplifted some six million years ago.

Although the Dyckman Street Fault itself is not exposed, the Dyckman Street valley is the result of weathering and erosion along the crushed and broken rocks produced by faulting. Its position is mapped as lying above the outcrop on the north side of the street where the flat surface ends and the slope begins (Baskerville 1994) (Map 9). At the Dyckman Street outcrop (loc. 34), the rocks are broken and fractured to a greater degree than elsewhere in the park, the result of its location near the fault zone. Many of the vertical fractures show signs of movement (loc. 35). Baskerville (1994) mentions that he did not indicate on his map the numerous subparallel shallow arcuate thrust faults that occur in the formation because they did not break the surface and therefore are not mappable. This type of fault can be seen in the road cut just east of the wet area as low-angle open curving cracks (loc. 36).

JOINTS: Cracks or fractures that have not moved are called joints, the result of stresses applied to the rock. As with most materials that crack, the joints have regular patterns or sets. In Inwood Hill Park, one joint direction in the schist is parallel to the layers, and on steep cliffs joints are responsible for setting in place the mechanism that created some of the notable landslides (loc. 37). The other directions are at right angles, generally vertical, and impart rectangular, hummocky topography while providing a foothold for tree roots (loc. 38) (Fig. 10).

Within the hornblende schist (amphibolite), the joint system is at 56 and 124 degrees, mimicking the cleavage directions of the hornblende and forming an easily recognizable rhombic pattern, because some joints are filled with thin white veins. Other joints are "open," allowing water to move through them. Fluids weather the minerals to a tan color at the joint surfaces, making them easy to see. The larger joint set gives the rock a blocky pattern, helping to distinguish amphibolite from schist (loc.28).

GLACIATION: Glaciers modify the landscape by erosion as they advance and alter it by leaving behind deposits as they retreat. Materials carried by or deposited in water are layered, while other glacial deposits released directly from the ice are not (till).

STRATIFIED DRIFTS: Layered sediments deposited in streams and lakes derived from glaciers are classically collectively known as stratified drift. No deposits are observed within the park areas but sediment cores taken from the Harlem River along the position of the Henry Hudson Bridge reveal a rather thick variable sequence of varves (rhythmites) between depths of 18 to 25 m below the surface of the river. Rhythmites are sediments that form in layers, usually a thick summer layer when deposition is greatest and a thin winter layer when erosion and deposition drop to a minimum in the winter. Each pair represents one year of sedimentation. In the New York area, rhythmites were deposited between 17,000 and 13,000 years ago in the Hudson and Harlem Rivers, Hackensack Meadowlands and other low places in the region containing freshwater lakes (Reeds 1927). Above the varves are sand deposits laid down by streams after the lake drained. These have been subsequently covered by recent organic silts, muds, and peat deposited when estuarine conditions were introduced as a result of rising sea level flooding the former lake basins. It is at this time, 6000 or 7000 years ago, that Spuyten Duyvil Creek connected the Hudson and Harlem Rivers and made Manhattan an island.

During construction of the Harlem Ship Canal in the 1890s, near the site of the present-day 225th Street bridge a mastodon tusk was found 5 m

Photo: S. Horenstein

Fig. 11. Erratic boulders.

below mean low-water encased in a blanket of peat. This specimen is one of several found in the Inwood neighborhood (Horenstein 1989).

TILL: Till consists of a mixture of rock particles of many sizes ranging from clay to large boulders and forms a discontinuous cover over bedrock both in valleys and on hilltops. In general, the till is best seen on flat hilltops and gentle slopes, because recent sediments in valleys usually cover the till. Most rocks are rounded while some of the larger particles show distinct signs of abrasion, and usually resemble the bedrock beneath them indicating that they have not traveled far. However, in the parks, till exposures are infrequent, and much of the till eroded from the steeper hillsides (loc. 39). In all likelihood the till was more extensive at the time the glaciers receded but was subsequently removed by erosion when lower sea level increased erosion potential. The loss of till may also be related to human use of the parks.

ERRATIC BOULDERS: Erratic boulders are a type of till that differs from the bedrock it is in contact with or lies above (Press and Siever 1997). Gale (1839) mentions that "through this valley vast amounts of diluvial loam and gravel, with sand and pebbles and boulders, have been transported and piled up in conical hills east of the road…covered by abundance of boulders of limestone, granite, greenstone and sandstone." However, examination of boulders in the parks reveals that they are primarily Palisades diabase, with lesser amounts of schist and occasionally gneiss. Some erratic boulders lie free on the till surface or bedrock (loc. 40) and others are partially embedded within the till. However, at one locality on the south side of the park path, a series of boulders, approximately the same size but of different composition—slate, greenstone, pink gneiss, and quartzite—form the path border (loc. 41). Whether they are local erratics selected for their color or boulders imported from elsewhere for decorative purposes is not known at this time (Fig. 11).

TERMINAL MORAINE: The terminal moraine, another type of till, is a ridge of debris accumulated in front of the glacier as it melts at its furthest extent. Moraine contains material that the glacier picked up as it extended across the land to its most southerly position. This distinctive ridge extends through central Queens and Brooklyn across The Narrows to the southern tip of Staten Island. Although the terminal moraine is distant, it can be viewed from Inwood Hill, especially along the West Ridge Road looking east and southeast. Tall buildings block much of the far eastern view, but a few gaps between the buildings, especially just south of the silvery Kingsbridge Veterans Hospital, allow a view of the moraine, the most distant elevated area seen on a clear day (loc. 42).

Later, as the ice began to melt away, the moraine became a dam, impounding glacial meltwater to form a series of freshwater lakes that filled the low places in our region. Actually, the moraine is now missing at The Narrows, washed away when an influx of water from the Great Lakes came down the Mohawk and Hudson Rivers, causing the lakes to overflow and breach the moraine about 13,000 years ago. As a result, the lakes emptied rapidly and flooded down the exposed coastal plain to the edge of the sea, perhaps 80 to 100 km away. The rhythmites mentioned previously are the evidence for the lakes, their extent and age. How many times the area that is now New York City was glaciated is still debated, perhaps as many as five times, but the extant moraine was built by the last glacier that entered the New York region about 21,600 years ago and began melting away 19,000 years ago (Boothroyd et al. 1998, Merguerian and Sanders 1991).

GLACIAL EROSION: The best-known example of glacial erosion in Inwood Hill Park is a series of potholes located near the top of the Clove along the west side of Valley Road (loc. 43). During glaciation, turbulent, rock-fortified swirling water making its way through crevasses reached the underlying bedrock and drilled the holes. There are three successive depressions, but the lowest one below path level is usually filled with mud eroded from the slopes and decaying vegetation (New York Times 1931) (Fig 12).

Glacial striations are not abundant in the park: either they were not created or they have been weathered away. Homogenous fine-grained rocks

Photo: S. Horenstein

Fig. 12. Famous glacial potholes of Inwood Hill Park.

retain striations more easily than coarse-grained rocks with variable composition. Weathering also etches the weaker minerals, a process clearly seen where more resistant minerals stand up higher in the rock than the less resistant minerals (loc. 44) and many other sites in the park. The few striations, mostly faint, found in the parks have about a S40°E direction (loc. 45).

In addition, the glacier abraded the rock surfaces as it passed over them, usually streamlining the outcrops in the direction of ice flow. These topographic features are called whalebacks because of their characteristic shape (loc. 46), and from the distance Inwood Hill's entire profile appears similarly streamlined. In general, all surfaces of outcrops show evidence of glaciation, for most of them have relatively smooth surfaces honed by the passing glacier(s). Rock surfaces covered by till are another indication that glaciers once covered the area.

During the winter when the leaves are down, the view into the Clove from the adjacent ridges suggests a lovely U-shaped valley, a feature of glaciated regions, resulting from the conversion stream carved v-shaped valleys (loc. 46).

Other Geologic Features—Broadway, the Palisades and the Hudson Valley

One of the enduring aspects and attractions of Inwood Hill Park's location and topography is that it allows the visitor to view additional aspects of New York's geology. From many hilltop vantage points, when looking in an arc from north to east to south on the West Ridge Road, the middle ground reveals a series of hills and valleys whose location is determined by bedrock resistance to weathering and erosion. Both schist and gneiss form high places in the terrain while locations underlain by marble are low—just as we have seen locally in the area around the parks. Thus, in the western Bronx and northern Manhattan, the sequence of northeast-southwest trending ridges and valley results from the differences of these rocks types. The valley along Broadway between Fort George hill and Fort Washington hill extending to 181st Street is a larger version of the Clove Valley in Inwood Hill Park.

Across the Hudson River rise the spectacular cliffs of the Palisades Sill that marks the eastern edge of the Newark Basin of the Piedmont geomorphic province pleasantly visible from the seating area (loc. 47)—unfortunately, at present, in a state of disrepair—and from the fence at the cliff edge above the highway (loc. 48). The Palisades consists of the igneous rock diabase, which cooled from once molten material deep below the surface about 191 million years ago, during Early Jurassic time. Although its surface color ranges through various shades of tan and brown, it is actually dark gray to black when unweathered (as seen in some of the glacial erratics). Vertical cliffs, a sloping rampart of fallen rock debris and a flat upper surface are the main visual characteristics of the Palisades.

The molten material that formed the Palisades Sill rose upward through fractures in a great pile of sedimentary rocks. It eventually changed direction and flowed between horizontal layers of sediments, pushing them apart, and in several pulses grew, in places, to become 520 m thick. Intrusive igneous rocks conforming to the layers are called sills. However, further west, for example around Paterson, New Jersey, the molten rock poured out onto the surface, forming great lava flows. Although the cliffs in our view range from about 90 to 150 m high, the Palisades sill here was about 300 m thick before erosion removed the overlying sedimentary layers and a substantial amount part of the diabase itself. Today, the exposed part of the Palisades extends from just north of Haverstraw, New York, southward to the middle of Staten Island.

As molten material cooled slowly below the surface, it shrank and formed vertical cracks (columnar joints) which today are conduits for water freezing in winter. This process wedges blocks of rock out of the cliff face which eventually fall to the base, forming a rampart of talus. Where blocks have recently fallen, light-colored scars are left on the cliff face that become darker as they age and weather. Another reminder of rock falls are the places where the talus slope is free of vegetation, swept away by fast-moving gravity-propelled debris.

Where the talus is missing, 19th century quarrying, first with hand tools used by local inhabitants and later by more sophisticated operations, removed the loose blocks of this tough rock for construction material and paving stones. Eventually, when quarrying became more extensive and dynamiting the cliffs became the norm, it provided the incentive for the creation of the Palisades Interstate Park. Where you see precipitous vertical drops, for example, just north of the George Washington Bridge, they are reminders of the quarrying era. Comparison with 19th century paintings and lithographs reveals how much the cliff face has been altered.

Photo: S. Horenstein

Fig. 13. Hudson Valley from Inwood Hill Park.

Talus that accumulated during preglacial times is the source of most of the diabase glacial erratics found in many parts of the city. The present-day talus has accumulated since the glaciers receded. Glacial erratics are one of the indicator tools geologists use to determine the direction of glacial movement by matching these rocks to their sources.

Viewed from the park, the remarkable nearly flat profile of the top of the Palisades extending up and down the Hudson Valley is distinctive. Wave erosion created this feature when the continent's east coast subsided below the sea during Cretaceous time, 125 million years ago. Later, after it reimerged, glacial erosion fine-tuned the surface.

With a good pair of binoculars, the red sedimentary layers intruded by the diabase can be seen here and there below the base of the Palisades near river level, generally along the road. It was in these sedimentary rocks that a phytosaur was discovered and collected about a hundred meters south of the George Washington Bridge; it is now exhibited at the American Museum of Natural History (Horenstein 1982).

The viewing point at the edge of the cliff (loc. 48) also offers an excellent sweep of the majestically wide Hudson River. The river flows two ways with the tide, up and down and back and forth. Although marine water can reach northward beyond Haverstraw, depending on the amount of rainfall, the tides are felt for 210 km north to the Federal Dam near Troy, New York. The Hudson Valley, the southernmost fiord in the Northern Hemisphere, is a trough deepened below sea level by the glaciers, which subsequently became an arm of the sea as sea level rose following the glacial melt off. Depth to bedrock in the Hudson is about 122 m opposite Inwood Hill but the valley is now filled with glacial and postglacial sediments so that the depth of water is not great and dredging is required to keep the channels open (Fig. 13).

Weathering, Soils and Erosion

Weathering is the mechanical disintegration and chemical decomposition of rocks resulting in particles that are dissolved or washed away, while the residual material becomes a component of soil. In some disciplines soil is also be defined as any loose material or material that supports plants.

Inwood Marble, a carbonate rock, contains both calcitic (Ca) and dolomitic (Ca, Mg) layers, both of which are susceptible to solution by naturally occurring carbonic acid in rain (and enhanced by industrial acid rain). Dissolved calcitic marble and, to a lesser extent, dolomitic marble are washed away while most silicate minerals (e.g., tremolite) contained in the rock are much less susceptible to this process and are easily seen as white

Photo: S. Horenstein

Fig. 14. "Indian Caves" landslide.

nodular lumps standing up in relief (loc. 18). Differential weathering occurs not only within beds but also between layers of varying resistance (loc. 18).

Weathering processes also produce a granular texture on the marble surface, like sugar, that eventually falls apart, generating marble sand which mixes with quartz sand eroded from nearby glacial till (loc. 18).

As with marble, several types of schist respond differently to the weathering process. Differential weathering along foliation is obvious where some layers are raised and others are depressed, the result of the differences in composition (loc. 27).

Individual minerals, such as garnet, are usually more resistant to weathering than other minerals, such as feldspar, and stand up in relief. The garnets look like rough little black bumps on the surface until you get a several centimeters away from them and their red color becomes apparent (loc. 49). In all likelihood the garnets were even with the rest of the schist when glaciation smoothed the surface, but in the thousands of years since the glaciers have receded, weathering has favored the more resistant minerals. Wherever bedrock is newly exposed, it is generally clean, the result of previously weathered material removed by glacial action. Where the surface has been exposed for any length of time, it shows the effects of differential weathering.

Mechanical weathering includes frost wedging of fractures, a powerful force that breaks rocks apart. Once the block is separated from the outcrop, the influence of gravity takes over, pulling the rock down slope. On gentle inclines, the process is almost imperceptible: ice lifts a loose block at right angles to the slope, and when the ice melts, the block drops vertically, eventually reaching the base of the slope, sometimes aided by frozen ground. On steep slopes the downslope movement could be instantaneous. In Inwood Hill Park, large slabs of schist have fallen, forming the famous rock shelters, the "Indian Caves," along the west side of Clove Road. Exactly when this landslide(s) occurred is not known, but it happened sometime soon after glaciation, when the tempo of frost action was greater. Large slabs of rock fell from the cliff face crisscrossing each other, forming large spaces, utilized as shelters by Native Americans (loc. 37) (Fig. 14). Nearby a smaller landslide has enlarged in recent years as additional slabs have toppled over (loc. 51).

As fractures are opened, the extra space not only allows water to penetrate but also provides easier access for roots to grow and extend into the crack, contributing to the splitting process (loc. 52).

Exfoliation, another type of mechanical weathering, occurs in homogenous rocks such as diabase. As the rock surface is heated and cooled daily, the surface lifts and peels off in thin layers. Many of the diabase glacial erratics show this feature to some degree. At a much trampled section of the park where many diabase boulders occur, one boulder used to contain a "camp fire" has many thick flakes spalled off its surface, the exfoliation process enhanced by the flames (loc. 53).

Along many paths, asphalt and its underlying concrete base are severely disintegrated. Most of these occurrences take place on slopes or flat surfaces adjacent to persistent wet areas or seeps that provide water that freezes in the interstices of the materials, causing them to break up (loc. 50).

Geologically, soil is a residual deposit that forms from the chemical decomposition and physical disintegration of parent materials, which can be solid rock or an accumulation of loose rock fragments moved by glaciers, wind, gravity, water or people. As air, water and organic chemicals act on these materials, layers or soil horizons develop, grading from an organic rich upper layer (humus) down to unweathered parent rock. Together, these horizons make up the soil profile.

In Inwood and Isham Parks, soil is developing on bedrock, glacial deposits, landfill and "top soil" spread on the surface to create lawns for sitting and playing fields. All the soils in the parks are young. Glaciers scraped away previously formed soil, leaving behind fresh solid rock. In general, very little soil has formed on schistose rocks, except where the minerals are susceptible to rapid breakdown, forming very thin patchy deposits, and where soil has accumulated in joints (loc. 54). It is probable that glacial till once covered all the flat surfaces, but natural and human erosion has exposed the rock surfaces. Any loose material that formed subsequently on these surfaces has been carried away and/or deposited in cracks and fissures.

In many places, accumulation of leaves and encroachment by grass are covering some exposures, enabling soil formation to begin provided visitors stay on the paths and don't trample the surface. An example of this process can be seen on the concrete floor of a former comfort station, where after several decades, cracks have provided space for trees and shrubs, and several centimeters of plant litter have accumulated (loc. 55).

Often a soil profile is partially revealed when a large tree falls over, exposing yellowish sandy soil, often with roots entwined around glacial erratics (loc. 56). However, on southerly and western slopes of the western ridge, where land use was most intensive, the soil depth to bedrock is not known and outcrops are few. In several places where erosion has exposed the underlying material, it has the appearance of having been dumped and spread out when the surface was graded (loc. 57). Occasional fragments of bricks, terra cotta and other manufactured materials are exposed. It is on this "urban" parent material that soils are now forming. Fill can be placed directly on bedrock, on till, or on previous fill. The variety is substantial when taking into account the extent of work that occurred in the park.

At Isham Street, the edge of the till cover has eroded back at least 6 m in places during the last ten years. An approximately one meter profile is exposed that contains typical yellowish sand, some minor clay and boulders of diabase. With time, further erosion will expose more bedrock as the till cover continues to be eroded by human actions (trampling feet) (loc. 18).

On steeper slopes, erosion is an ongoing problem as loose material is continually carried down slope. In some places remedial work has not satisfactorily checked this process (loc. 58). After a heavy rain the bases of some slopes accumulate an apron of sediment, occasionally up to 2.5 cm thick. A clear sign of erosion are the numerous tree roots in various stages of exposure (loc. 60). Often roots sit directly on bedrock, the soil washed away, leaving the tree to hold on with roots extending into the cracks and crevices of bedrock until a strong wind topples it.

Off-road use of vehicles and shortcuts created by people wandering over the terrain contribute to soil compaction and erosion. Defective drainage systems along the western slope that should collect runoff from the highway have caused some severe gullying problems (loc. 59).

Autocompaction, perhaps enhanced by people running on the surface, is occurring along the north central part of the soccer field. The surface forms a shallow depression that is wet most of the time and supports a different type of vegetation (loc. 61). The railing along the adjacent path and the benches are no longer horizontal, forming a broad down warp adjacent to the depressed surface (loc. 62).

Springs and Wells

Normally, because of adequate rainfall, steep slopes and abundant jointed rocks such as those found in Inwood Hill, more springs and seeps would be expected in the park today. The dearth of springs is apparent in winter when spring water freezes on the surface and reveals their telltale occurrence. Perhaps this scarcity is a direct result of the landscaping performed in the 1930s that provided drains and sluices that carry water away, making it no longer available to soak into the ground.

The most vigorously flowing springs today are located along the south side of the path along the beginning of The Cove (loc. 64) and especially along Dyckman Street (loc. 34). At The Cove water emerges from the base of what appears to be a sand bank of unknown thickness and flows over a retaining wall and into a drain. An often repeated description reports that after it enters the drain, a pipe beneath the playing field carries the water and its sediment away northward and discharges it into the lagoon, building a delta that supports a variety of marsh plants.

Along the north side of Dyckman Street a strong flow of water issues from the rock outcrop in several places.

The other spring of note is the small seep that keeps the glacial pothole along the Valley Road filled with water. In the fall of 2002, its bowl-like depression was host to six goldfish.

The best record of springs and wells in New York City is found in Smith (1938), a compilation Smith accomplished during 1898-1901 as he traveled the city by bicycle. He measured and photographed each locality and whenever possible documented interviews with owners, neighbors and passersby. A number of springs were found in the Inwood area, most of which seem to be located within the Inwood Marble. The "White Stone Spring, the best-known and purest spring in the city," was located at the base of an 18 m vertical outcrop 90 m northeast of Payson Avenue and Dyckman Street. Cold Spring, the largest spring in New York City, flowed at a rate of six gallons a minute, at the time "three times as much as the flow from the usual bathroom faucet." The spring was found a short distance north of the celebrated tulip tree (City of New York, Department of Parks 1913), but no trace of it exists today, except for the culvert and drainage channel built to carry its waters to the lagoon. Surprisingly, today little water is found in the drain throughout the year, perhaps the result of the alteration made to the park during the 1930s. Smith reports that a Mr. Seeley put a padlock on the springhouse because it interfered with his sale of soft drinks to boatmen.

Smith mentions that near Cold Spring were two others, one nearly hidden at high tide and the other "cut out of a white rock." The Cove spring mentioned previously is probably one of these.

Another spring was "reached by following the road from Tubby Hook north along the Hudson. It is about 75 feet [23 m] from the river and 40 feet [12 m] above river level and "the water is cold and good to taste and so crystally clear…."

Smith writes that the last house on Bolton Road belongs to James McCreery and that "the well had not been used for a while and the rusted well is on a terrace and there are several terraces above it which appear to have once formed a serpentine road to the river but now are so grass grown that they look merely like sloping lawns…wild birds are singing in the large forests round about and no sound is heard that is foreign to the country."

His records indicate that another well is near the highest point in Inwood and "just beyond it the hill slopes down to Spuyten Duyvil Creek" over a half a kilometer from any current habitation.

Artificial Fill

Artificial fill consists of deposits made by human activities: these include roads, railroad beds, shore protection structures as well as large accumulations called dumps. Much of the fill was obtained from sources nearby, but part of it was brought from more distant sources. The largest fill areas are the sections of Inwood Hill Park west of the railroad tracks along the Hudson River, the flat ball field adjacent to Seaman Avenue and the soccer field adjacent to the eastern slope of Inwood Hill. Filling in the abandoned southern loop of Spuyten Duyvil required about 340,000 cubic meters of material. Some came from the removal of the peninsula and some from Baker Field, which was a repository for material removed from the 1895 canal cut. Outside sources would supply the remaining material. This work was done under the auspices of the War Department for the improvement of harbors and rivers.

One of the earliest records of fill is the use of stone from Fort Cock Hill recycled into terraces for the early nearby homes. Today there are no surface signs of terraces and other structures (except stonewalls), but where erosion from runoff from the highway has exposed the subsurface, a mixture of rock, tiles and other building debris appears. In one gully there is a large accumulation of glacial erratics of Palisades diabase (loc. 59). Whether this material was used previously for building stonewalls, terraces, road fill, etc. is unknown. For the park in general, the area developed the most for homes have the fewest rock outcrops.

Along the Hudson River edge, material dumped to create this part of the park is exposed, giving the visitor an appreciation of the variety of rock types found along part of the IND subway line route (loc. 65). Here, as well as along the Harlem River, stone riprap has been emplaced for erosion protection.

Brief Summary of Geologic History

The oldest rocks in New York City, the Precambrian Fordham Gneiss, Proterozic (1.1 billion years old), are metamorphosed volcanic rocks, formed during the Grenville Orogeny as the supercontinent Rodinia was assembling.

Near the end of Precambrian (Neoproterozoic, 570 million years ago), during the breakup of Rodinia, sediments and volcanic rock were deposited on the spreading seafloor in deep oceanic basins (Manhattan Schist).

During the Cambrian and early Ordovician periods, while fragments of the supercontinent were still drifting apart (diverging), the continental shelf of the ancestral North American continent subsided in Iapetus Ocean, accumulating shallow water sand, lime and mud (Inwood Marble and Walloomsac Formations).

Eventually, convergence replaced divergence. During the middle Ordovician Period beginning 440 million years ago, a volcanic arc-continent collision, metamorphosed the sediments and pushed the deep ocean basin rocks onto and over the edge of the continent along a thrust fault called Cameron's Line with embedded blocks of detached ocean basin rocks (serpentinite), resulted in uplift and formation of high mountains (Taconic Orogeny) that was soon followed by deep erosion.

During the Devonian Period Period, 380 million years ago, the continent, Avalon, collided and sutured with North America, causing additional folding, faulting and metamorphism and intrusion of granitic rocks resulting in renewed uplift.

During the Pennsylvanian, 300 million years ago, collision with ancestral Africa, continued the formation of the eventual supercontinent

Pangaea, subjecting the rocks to additional folding, faulting and perhaps some metamorphism. This event raised the Appalachians to high mountains.

Breakup of Pangaea after about 100 million years was marked by formation of Newark basin, which filled with lake and river sediments derived from surrounding high places in New York City and the Ramapo Mountains beginning about 200 million years ago. Sediments accumulated to 6.0 km plus thickness, and the basin was subject to igneous activity resulting in intrusions (Palisades sill) and lava flows (Watchung Mountain basalts) during the Lower Jurassic, 190 million years ago. After the formation of the sills and lava flows, the Newark Basin was tilted down to the west, faulted and profoundly eroded.

In the meantime, as Pangaea continued to split apart, the Atlantic Ocean basin formed and enlarged, and the eastern edge of North American subsided during the Cretaceous Period, about 125 million years ago, accumulating shallow water and near-shore sediments.

About 6-8 million years ago, a regional uplift occurred exposing the sediments and forming the coastal plain. The Hudson River established itself and its course changed position several times as erosion proceeded.

The last of at least two but perhaps as many as five advances of glaciation reached maximum extent 21,600 years ago, forming the terminal moraine. As the glacier began to melt away 19,000 years ago, it left behind a blanket of drift and till. The land began to rebound as the ice melted and its weight no longer pushed the surface down.

The terminal moraine acted as a dam, ponding glacial meltwater to form large lakes in low places of the terrain—Hackensack Meadowlands, Hudson River, East River, Upper Bay, and Long Island Sound. Deposition of rhythmites (varves) in the lakes occurred until about 13,000 years ago, when the dam was breached as result of influx of water from the Great Lakes via Mohawk River and Hudson Rivers.

Sea level rose as the glaciers melted invading low places in the terrain. By 10,000 years ago the Hudson Valley, had estuarine conditions, and the New York City area obtained their present configuration 4000 to 6000 years ago when sea level reached its present level.

Beginning about 1900, climatic warming has caused sea level to rise about 0.3 m (Brock and Brock 2001, Isachsen et al. 1991, Merguerian and Sanders 1991, Than et al. 2002).

Acknowledgments

I want to thank the Linnaean Society for inviting me to contribute this article and the American Museum of Natural History and the New York City Department of Parks and Recreation for inviting me to lead, over many years, field trips to the parks. It has been gratifying to introduce and show off the many features of these unique parks to the numerous participants.

Equally important are the wonderful resources of some of New York City's libraries including both electronic access as well as the actual places and especially the gracious help of the librarians of: American Museum of Natural History, The New York Public Library, The New York Historical Society, The Municipal Art Society, The Bronx County Historical Society and New York City Parks and Recreation.

They provided a wealth of material not all of which could be included in this report because of space constraints—as a result several aspects of the parks have been reduced in scope or left out entirely.

References

American Scenic and Historic Preservation Society. 1904a. *Petition for Public Park at Inwood, Manhattan Island.* May 1904.

————. 1904b. Proposed Park At Inwood, On Manhattan Island. *Ninth Annual Report, 1904*, American Scenic and Historic Preservation Society. p. 47-52.

————. 1907. Inwood Park. *Twelfth Annual Report, 1907*, American Scenic and Historic Preservation Society. p. 66-67

————. 1912. Inwood Park. *Seventeenth Annual Report, 1912*, American Scenic and Historic Preservation Society. p. 135-136.

————. 1916. Inwood Hill Park. *Twenty-First Annual Report, 1916*, American Scenic and Historic Preservation Society, p. 168-171.

Anderson, M. 1994. *Woodlands, Wetlands, and Wildlife: A Guide to the Natural Areas of New York City.* City of New York/Parks & Recreation and City Parks Foundation, New York.

Barlow, E. 1971. *The Forests and Wetlands of New York City.* Little Brown and Co., Boston.

Baskerville, C. A. 1982. The foundation geology of New York City. in Legget, R.F. ed., *Geology Under Cities, Geological Society of America Reviews in Engineering Geology*, 5: 95-117.

————. 1992. *Bedrock and Engineering Geologic Maps of Bronx County and Parts of New York and Queens Counties*, map I-2003. U.S. Geological Survey.

————. 1994. *Bedrock and Engineering Geologic Maps of New York County and Parts of Kings and Queens Counties, New York, and parts of Bergen and Hudson Counties, New Jersey*, map I-2306. U.S. Geological Survey.

Bolton, R. P. 1909. The Indians of Washington Heights. in Clark Wissler ed., *The Indians of Greater New York and the Lower Hudson.* American Museum of Natural History Anthropological Papers, no. 3, p. 77-113.

————. 1914. Guide to the named streets and avenues of Washington Heights, Inwood and Marble Hill. Reprinted from *Commonwealth Weekly*.

————. 1920. New York City in Indian Possession. *Indian Notes and Monographs*, vol. 2, no. 7. Museum of the American Indian, New York.

————. 1924. *Washington Heights, Manhattan: Its Eventful Past*. Dyckman Institute, New York.

————. 1932. *Inwood Hill Park*. Dyckman Institute, New York.

————. 1934. *Indian Life Of Long Ago in the City of New York*. Harmony Books, reprinted 1972.

Boothroyd, J. C., J. R. Stone, P. Craft, and J. Friedman. 1998. The glacial geology of southern Rhode Island. in Daniel P. Murray ed., *Guidebook to Field Trips in Rhode Island and Adjacent Regions of Connecticut and Massachusetts, Guidebook 90*, Annual Meeting, New England Intercollegiate Geological Conference. p. C5.1-5.25.

Britton, N. L. 1913. Notable Trees in New York City. *Eighteenth Annual Report*, American Scenic and Historic Preservation Association. p. 191-199.

Brock, P. C., and P. W. G. Brock. 1999. The Birth of Iapetus: Geochemical evidence for Late Neoproterozoic rifting from the metaigneous rocks of the Ned Mountain formation, Manhattan Prong. *Sixth Annual Conference on Geology of Long Island and Metropolitan New York*, Long Island Geologists, SUNY Stony Brook, April 24, 1999. p. 13-15,

————. 2001. Bedrock Geology of New York City: More than 600 M.Y. of Geologic History, *Field Guide for Long Island Geologists' Field Trip*, October 27, 2001.

Butler, W. A. 1868. Dobbs, his ferry. A legend of the lower Hudson. *Putnam's Monthly Magazine*, vol. 11, no. 1, January, 1868. p. 20 –25,

Calver, W. L. 1948. Recollections of northern Manhattan. *The New-York Historical Society Quarterly*, vol. 32:20-32.

Calver, W. L., and R. P. Bolton. 1950. *History Written with Pick and Shovel*. New-York Historical Society, New York.

Cantwell, A. E. and D. diZerega Wall. 2001. *Unearthing Gotham: The Archaeology of New York City*. Yale University Press, New Haven.

Caro, R. 1974. *The Power Broker: Robert Moses and the Fall of New York*. Knopf, New York.

City of New York, Department of Parks. 1913. *Annual Report for 1912*.

————. 1927. *Annual Report for 1927*.

————. 1931. *Annual Report for 1931*.

City of New York, Parks and Recreation. 1999a. *Inwood Hill Park*. (leaflet), July 1999.

————. 1999b. *Isham Park* (leaflet), July 1999.

Fenneman, N. M. 1938. *Physiography of Eastern United States*. McGraw-Hill, New York.

Fleming, T. 1997. *Liberty: The American Revolution*. Viking, New York.

Gale. L. D. 1839. Report on the geology of New York County. *Annual Report* 3, New

York Geological Survey. p. 177-199

Gody, L., ed. 1939. *New York City Guide*. Random House, New York. Reprinted as *The WPA Guide to New York City*. Pantheon Books, New York, 1982.

Gratacap, L. P. 1909. *Geology of the City of New York*. Henry Holt and Co., New York.

Graves, A. H. 1930. Inwood Park, Manhattan. *Torreya* 30:117-129.

Hall, L. M. 1968. Times of origin and deformation of bedrock in the Manhattan Prong. in Zen, E-an, ed., *Studies of Appalachian Geology, Northern and Maritime.*, Interscience, New York. p. 117-127

Hermalyn, G. 1983. The Harlem River Ship Canal. *Bronx County Historical Society Journal* 20:1-23.

Horenstein, S. 1982. Father Knickerbocker *The First. Natural History* 91:74-75.

————. 1989. Big Apple Tusks. Natural History 98:96-99.

Hudson River Railroad. 1851. *Hudson River, and the H.R.R.R., with a Complete Map, and Wood Cut Views of the Principal Objects of Interest upon the Line*. W.C. Locke & Co., New York.

Isachsen, Y. W., E. Landing, J. M. Lauber, L. V. Rickard, and W. B. Rogers. 1991. *Geology of New York: A Simplified Account*. New York State Museum, Albany.

Irving, W. 1880. *A History of New York from the Beginning of the World to the End of the Dutch Dynasty*. G. P. Putnam's Sons, New York.

Knight, W. D. 1932. *The Story of Mount Washington, 1844-1932*. Mount Washington Presbyterian Church, New York.

Kouwenhoven, J. A. 1953. *The Columbia Portrait of New York*. Doubleday and Co., Garden City, NY.

Linnaean News-Letter. 1956. Inwood Hill Park. *Linnaean News-Letter* 10(6).

Loeb, R. E. 1986. Plant communities of Inwood Hill Park, New York County, New York. *Bulletin Torrey Botanical Club* 113:46-52.

Long Island Geologists. Web page: pbisotopes.ess.sunysb.edu/lig/Conferences/abstracts_02/Mya-Mya-than.htm

McNamara, J. 1991. *History in Asphalt: The Origin of Bronx Street and Place Names*, rev. ed. The Bronx County Historical Society, Bronx, NY.

Merguerian, C. 1994. Stratigraphy, structural geology, and ductile and brittle faults of the New York City area. in Hansen, G.N., *Geology of Long Island and Metropolitan New York*. SUNY Stony Brook, NY.

Merguerian, C., and C. A. Baskerville. 1987. The geology of Manhattan Island and The Bronx, New York City, New York. in Roy, D.C., ed., *Northeastern Section: Centennial Fieldguide*, Geological Society of America. p. 137-140.

Merguerian, C., and J. E. Sanders. 1991. Geology of Manhattan and the Bronx: Guidebook for On-The-Rocks 1990-91. Fieldtrip Series, Trip 16, 21 April 1991. Section of Geological Sciences, New York Academy of Sciences, New York.

Moses, R. 1970. *Public Works: A Dangerous Trade*. McGraw-Hill, New York.

New York Sunday News. 1967. New York's changing scene. August 20, 1967.

New York Times. 1931. Glacial holes found in Manhattan Park, bored by icy torrents

30,000 years ago. July 5, 1931:21.

————. 1938. 'Taming' Inwood Hill. April 10, 1938.

Olmsted, F. L., and J. J. R. Croes. 1876. *Report of the Landscape Architect and the Civil and Topographical Engineer, Accompanying a Plan for Laying out That Part of the Twenty-fourth Ward Lying West of the Riverdale Road, City of New York.* Department of Parks.

Payson, G. S. 1914. *Forty Years in the Wilderness.* Jersey City Printing Co., Jersey City, NJ.

Pollara, G. 1997. Transforming the edge. in Bone, Kevin, ed., *The New York Waterfront.* The Monacelli Press, New York.

Press, F., and R. Siever. 1997. *Understanding Earth, 2nd ed.* W.H. Freeman and Co., New York.

Reeds, C. A., 1927. Glacial lakes and clays near New York City. *Natural History* 27(1):54-64.

Richards, T. A. 1861. New York circumnavigated. *Harper's New Monthly Magazine* 23:165-184.

Roberts, R. B. 1980. *New York's Forts in the Revolution.* Fairleigh Dickinson University Press, Rutherford, NJ.

Schuberth, C. J. 1968. *The Geology of New York City and Environs.* Natural History Press, Garden City, NY.

Skinner, A. 1909. Archeology of Manhattan Island. In Wissler, Clark, ed., The Indians of Greater New York and the lower Hudson. *American Museum of Natural History Anthropological Papers.* 3:113-275.

————. 1947. The Indians of Manhattan Island and Vicinity; 6th ed.. Guide Leaflet no. 41, American Museum of Natural History, New York.

Smith, J. R.. 1938. Springs and Wells of Manhattan and The Bronx, New York City. New-York Historical Society, New York.

Stern, R. A. M., T. Mellins, and D. Fishman. 1999. *New York 1880: Architecture and Urbanism in the Gilded Age.* The Monacelli Press, New York.

Than, M. M., T. Rasbury, P. Brock, P. C. Brock, and S. Hemming. 2002. The Timing of the Emplacement of the Tourmaline-Bearing Two-Mica Granites: U-Pb Monazite Dating. Web page: http://www.geo.sunysb.edu/lig/Conferences/abstracts_02/Mya-Mya-than.htm.

Thornbury, W. D. 1965. *Regional geomorphology of the United States.* John Wiley and Sons, New York.

Tieck, W. 1968. *Riverdale, Kingsbridge, Spuyten Duyvil.* Fleming H. Revell Co., Old Tappan, NJ.

————. 1971. *School and School Days in Riverdale, Kingsbridge, Spuyten Duyvil.* Fleming H. Revell Co., Old Tappan, NJ.

U.S. Works Progress Administration, Recreation Program. 1939. *A Trip Through Inwood Park.*

Wade, W. 1846. *Panorama of the Hudson River from New York to Albany.* J. Disturnell, New York.

New York City's Primeval Forest: A Review Characterizing the "Type Ecosystem"

Alexander R. Brash[1]
National Parks Conservation Association
731 Lexington Avenue
New York NY 10022
abrash@NPCA.org

Introduction

ONE OF THE MAJOR GOALS before undertaking ecological restoration efforts in New York City's parks has been to define, quantify and then measure the characteristics of the ecosystem one is attempting to recreate (Vogt et al. 1997). In order to do this, one must first attempt to denote a data set characterizing the system as it was at one time; indeed such a data set might be considered the site's "type ecosystem." This report examines the forest history of the New York City region and pursues the alluring idea of its primeval forest. While most people assume that New York City's forests resulted from a long and stable process, and that fundamentally, the forest first encountered by Henry Hudson had a history which unremarkably stretched back into the eons of time, nothing could be farther from the truth.

Current theory (Egler 1954, Bormann and Likens 1979, Pickett and White 1985, Oliver and Larson 1990, Vogt et al. 1997) holds that a forest ecosystem is an array of species each mechanistically driven by its own physiological adaptations, yet periodically subject to disturbances of differing scales. As a result, such an ecosystem is actually a mosaic of plant communities in endlessly varying combinations. As one might imagine, quantitatively

[1] Formerly, Chief, Natural Resource Group, City of New York Parks & Recreation.
1234 Fifth Avenue, New York N.Y. 10029

describing such an ecosystem is a rather intractable task. For the purposes here, I will narrow the focus and simply concentrate on describing what Oliver (1981) referred to as the last stage in a forest's development: the old-growth stage. I am fully cognizant, of course, that "disturbances" are no small matter. Even in recent times, New England has felt the impact of the 1938 hurricane on the great White Pines and Hemlocks of the Pisgah tract in New Hampshire (Whitney 1994) and the 1989 tornado in western Connecticut that flattened the magnificent cathedral pines of Cornwall (Peterson 2002). In sum, I am quite aware that even the greatest old growth stands never lasted forever and that significant disturbances regularly reset the structure of these forests.

Defining a forest with numbers is of course a herculean task, especially in its old-growth stage, for quantifying a forest is hardly limited to a simple listing of its species. A depiction of the system might rather include variables regarding the population biology of each species, such as size, age, structure, percent of composition and measures of various interactions like competition coefficients or predation probabilities. Additionally, as proposed by Bormann and Likens (1979) and later expanded on by others (O'Neill et al. 1986), this list of variables should also represent larger abiotic and biotic patterns and processes such as time, space, geomorphology, energy flows and nutrient cycles. However, the limitations of available data will curtail most such efforts, and ultimately I have simply focused on data available from palynological (pollen) cores, archeological studies, current ecological studies, early narratives and colonial land surveys.

Review Outline

Historical ecologists, forest scientists and numerous conservationists have all debated the concept, and especially the definition, of a "primeval" forest (for reviews see Whitney 1994 or Vogt et al. 1997). In this case I am simply looking for a period during which the forests of this area grew to an old-growth stage without *major* effects from human disturbance, yet obviously not so far back as to be in a period with significantly different geological or climatological characteristics.

I believe that once species' immigration and emigration rates finally stabilized in the Holocene after the last glacial retreat, which is not to say ceased, the forest itself would simultaneously have advanced to the old-growth stage. At this point it ought, perhaps, to have reflected a vision "dim and silent as a cavern, columned with innumerable trunks, each like an Atlas upholding its world of leaves, and sweating perpetual moisture down its dark and channeled rind" (Parkman 1983). Analytically, this vision of the primeval forest ought to translate into an old-growth stand where mature overstory trees individually "regenerate and grow without influence of external disturbances" (Oliver 1981, Oliver and Larson 1990).

Because the available data are rather limited, I will simply delineate the temporal boundaries of the forest and then estimate its species composition, the relative size of the individual trees by species and a stand's biomass. While modern ecologists now collect a great amount of data concerning stand development such as crown volume, total leaf area, horizontal or vertical spatial patterns, the first residents and early settlers were neither quantitative scientists nor even prolific in their detailed descriptions of the forest, as one might suspect.

Data Sets

Palynological data have been gathered as a result of coring sediments across the region and then examining the layers for the presence and prevalence of pollen of various tree species. It is a well-regarded method for a qualitative review of the species composition in an area over a great time span. Unfortunately, pollen data must always be regarded with great caution; adjacent samples may show significant quantitative differences, there is considerable interspecies variation in pollen dispersion, variation in decomposition, and finally, sampling and laboratory procedures vary greatly (Loeb 1989). Delcourt and Delcourt (1987) noted that "The representation of pollen…in sediments is a function not only of the abundance and distribution of plants but also of their pollen productivity; the timing and mode of pollen dispersal; the nature of processes associated with deposition; the incorporation and preservation of pollen within sediments; and the source area from which pollen assemblages are ultimately derived." However, these same authors, after exhaustive modeling with present-day forests and pollen counts, used regression analysis to create a theoretical model for the latitudinal advance of the Quaternary forests. I have relied most heavily on this study for a long-term post-glacial historical perspective of the forest's changing composition.

The second set of data I will examine is derived from archeological studies in the region. Clearly, what people eat, what they use to build their shelters, what they wear, or what they use in other cultural practices are tangible reflections of the resources available to them. Numerous studies on Native Americans provide solid qualitative data regarding the forest and its inhabitants (i.e., Ruttenber 1992, Trigger 1978, Grumet 1989, Ritchie 1994,

Weinstein 1994, Cantwell and Wall 2001). The dependence of various tribes on deer versus moose, or birch canoes versus Tulip Tree dugouts, and other assorted artifacts of their everyday life reflect the available natural resources. While these data do not create a detailed quantitative picture of the forests, the presence or absence of certain documented species is valuable in either buttressing or nullifying other findings. This same logic may be extended to the earliest European colonists, as they too made their tools, furniture and houses predominantly from materials gathered in the region.

The third set of data available derives from the Native American narratives collected by the earliest European settlers or narratives written by the settlers themselves. Numerous classic texts and manuscripts exist, such as those of the Roanoke voyages (Quinn 1991), the early English voyages (Quinn and Quinn 1983), the Drake (1996) manuscript, Ruttenber's (1992) work, Van der Donck's descriptions of New Netherlands (Van der Donck 1968), or the descriptions by many travelers on the Hudson River found in Van Zandt's *Chronicles* (1992).

Fourthly, there are indeed some truly quantifiable data in the form of witness trees, as identified by colonial land surveyors. Witness trees or boundary trees are those which the earliest surveyors used to mark property. Various authors (Greller 1972, Loeb 1987, Niering and Egler 1981, Whitney 1994) have all used survey records to describe the region's forests, but all noted that, like most studies used to reconstruct a forest, they must contend with numerous problems, both random and nonrandom, associated with the data. Early surveyors generally were not botanists and therefore certainly made errors in identification. Other introduced errors include the surveyors' biases for certain species (i.e., the surveyor picks conspicuous species), biases associated with attempts to inflate property values (the surveyor picks valuable species), and simple sampling biases (total study represents more trees in smaller, more valuable lots than in larger but less valuable lots). Additionally, the surveys themselves reflect the pattern of settlement by early colonists and thus are in no way random or statistically neutral. For instance, the initial settlers preferred flat lands over slopes (Smith et al. 1993), river valleys, south-facing slopes, and drier lands over swampy parcels (Whitney 1994). Targeting surveys on selected terrain would of course skew the species composition analyses, for example the results might reflect xeric versus mesic species.

Finally, to understand the forest's structure, I reviewed the available data from remnant old-growth stands in the Northeast (Davis 1996, Tyrrell et al. 1998, Bonnicksen 2000). In addition, as a basis for modeling the development of an average old-growth stand for the area, I performed a cluster analysis to find a young stand site of similar composition, using a forest stand from central Massachusettes (Spaeth 1920) from which to initiate such a time-series model.

Organizing the Findings

In combing through the various sets of data discussed above, a clear need became apparent for an outline by which to quantitatively characterize our "type ecosystem," the primeval forest. The first step was to detail the historical time frame for this forest. For this temporal definition, three clear parameters have been considered. The first parameter demarcates the time when the forest "type" began to manifest itself after climatic conditions had stabilized (i.e., in the Holocene). The second concerns the amount of time necessary for an old-growth forest to be fully established once species' immigration and emigration rates settled at a point closely reflecting the current species pool, and the third parameter marks the temporal end point of the primeval forest.

The second step in the outline was to detail the dominant tree species of the forest. Regardless of some complicating issues, this was clearly best determined by early land survey data. This evidence was then tested against secondary forms of evidence and their implications for either supporting or refuting the survey data. The third step involved quantifying the structural attributes of an old-growth forest typical of this region.

Finally, in order to test the results of our analysis, I created a time-series model depicting the basic trends that ought to reflect an old-growth stand as it developed to become New York City's mythical primeval forest.

The Forest's Temporal Framework

After the onset of the Wisconsin Glacial retreat, about 13,000 B.C., the northern half of what is now New York City was buried under mile-thick ice, and the southern half was a patchwork of tundra cut by torrential icy streams spewing glacial outwash. What followed has been well studied (Davis 1981 1983, Watts 1983, Delcourt and Delcourt 1987). In a geological time frame, the glacial retreat was rather rapid, for in less than 3000 years the glacier pulled back to Quebec from Long Island (Davis 1983), with the retreat averaging a little less than one-tenth of a mile per year. The wall of ice left behind the moraine which stretches northeast from Conference House Park on Staten Island through High Rock Park, Bensonhurst and Prospect Parks, forms the ridge of Forest Park and then continues east onto Long Island through Cunningham and Alley Pond Parks. As the ice wall moved north of the City's present-day limits, around 11,500 B.C., the vegetation of the area was essentially dominated by Dwarf Willow (*Salix herbacea*), Green Alder (*Alnus viridis*), shrubby birches (*Betula* sp.), and thickets of low blueberries (*Vaccinium* sp.).

Following the glacial retreat, an array of southern and western species moved northeast into the area. What few people realize is that in assembling the region's new species pool, great interspecies variation occurred during this broad northern movement (Delcourt and Delcourt 1987). Some, like spruce (*Picea* sp.), White Pine (*Pinus strobus*), and elm (*Ulmus* sp.) were moving northeast from the Appalachian highlands in the Blue Ridge Mountains. Other species, including Balsam Fir (*Abies balsamea*), Red Pine (*Pinus resinosa*), and oak (*Quercus* sp.) were moving due north along the coastal plain. Species also moved at different rates. Generation time and dispersal methods were presumably critical elements with respect to the movement of each species. For instance, while spruce and fir first reached this area about 10,000 B.C., oak, hemlock and maple did not reach New York until 8000 B.C., hickories arrived around 4000 B.C., and American Chestnut (*Castanea dentata*) only by 2000 B.C.

Finally, as is apparent even now, not all these species stayed. As the glacier continued its retreat and the colder climate receded northward, so too did many of these species continue to migrate north. For instance, hemlock's center of dominance moved from the southern Appalachians north past New York City to mid-Ontario between 6000 and 2000 B.C. (Delcourt and Delcourt 1987). This change is mirrored in the abrupt decrease in hemlock pollen found in lake sediments near New York City from 4800 B.C. (Davis 1983). In sum, we must realize that the region's forests were in a state of great flux due to substantive climatological changes until roughly 2000 B.C. It was only at this point that all the current tree taxa finally arrived in the area, and the importance of migration gave way to the processes of competition, disturbance and predation. This, then, denotes that point when the "primeval" forest's species assemblage is finally gathered.

Once the species pool was established for the primeval forest, the second step was establishment of the old-growth state. Part of the definition of old growth is that trees are replaced individually. This inherently means that we must allow at least two generations to pass before the trees *in situ* meet the definition. In remnant old-growth stands, numerous hemlocks, Black Gums and birches more than 350 years old have been found, and one hemlock was dated at 425 years of age, while a Black Gum came in at 510 years old. (Tyrrell et al. 1998). However, in a study of a virgin forest in Tennessee, McGee (1984) found that the *average age* of natural mortality, or senescence, for Red Oaks was 135 years and for ash 172 years. This implies that roughly 150 to 200 years after establishment, new seedlings would be emerging in their climb toward the canopy through gaps created by naturally senescing previously established trees. Therefore, somewhere between 300 and 500 years after the species pool was assembled, the forest would be well into its second generation, thus meeting the criteria for an old-growth stand.

The third and final parameter is the development of the primeval forest as determined by significant disruptions to its natural processes. In this case, major disruptions were due to the substantive impacts associated with anthropocentric causes. The first Native Americans with their Clovislike points moved into the area probably just as the glaciers withdrew, for the earliest dated finds place their arrival at roughly 8500 B.C. (Ritchie 1957, 1994). These early Native Americans focused on the big game animals associated with tundra and spruce woodlands found near the retreating glaciers, and as they were nomadic, their camps were few and far between. Not until after 6000 B.C., in the Archaic period, did Native Americans even began "settling" in the area, and probably really not until the late Archaic, roughly 2300 B.C. At this time, heavy steatite bowls first appear in archeological digs, indicating the probable establishment of more permanent camps (Funk 1978, Ritchie 1994).

When a strong warming period, the Hopewell Episode, arrived in about 300 B.C., prehistoric Native American populations were fairly well established throughout the region, and while still seasonally nomadic, they were certainly found all along the coastlines and inland along river valleys (Fitting 1978). From this point forward, over the next 1000 years, there were repeated migrations from the south and west as the culture associated with the Mound Builders of the Ohio Valley dissolved and elements then moved north and east into the region (Ritchie 1994). Changes in ceramics at various sites indicate a final influx of Algonquians as recently as A.D. 1300 (Bragdon 1996). In this period, the people now known as the Delawares or Lenapes moved up from the Delaware Valley and penetrated the established culture of the region to settle (Snow 1978). Probably not coincidentally, systemic agriculture is also first documented during this time. While obviously the widespread harvesting of numerous native plants such as hickories, blueberries and shadbush had long been practiced, maize, beans and squash first reached this area in roughly A.D. 1000 (Ritchie 1994, Bonnicksen 2000, Cantwell and Wall 2001). However, recent bone chemistry analyses have shown that initially these foods were not a major component of the regional diet (Cantwell and Wall 2001). But within another 500 years, systemic agriculture was clearly widespread. Henry Hudson's crew were offered "eares of Indian Corne, and Pompions [pumpkins], and Tobacco" near Katskill (Juet 1609).

The prevalence and type of agricultural practices combined with the population size are two of the key components in establishing the impact Native Americans may have had on the landscape. Unfortunately there are no known population data directly attributable to just the New York City region. Two estimates for the number of Native Americans in lower New England around 1600 both suggest about 20,000 individuals (Goddard 1978, Grumet 1989). Goddard more specifically estimated that at most 4500 Munsee-speaking Delawares occupied an area bounded by the Raritan River, the Catskill Mountains, Hempstead to the east and the Delaware River to the west. I estimate that the New York City area itself would at most have held only half of this population. Such an interpretation of this estimate is supported by three observations. First, when Verrazano stopped in New York Harbor in 1524, his crew noted that "about thirty of their small boats with innumerable people on board" came out to look at them (Wroth 1970). Even if only a quarter of the adults in the area had rowed out to view the first ship in the harbor, and if as many as 10 adults had been packed aboard each dugout, that would still indicate a population for the area only in the low thousands. Secondly, Grumet specifically noted that there were roughly 12 communities around the area just before Kieft's War in 1643. Even assuming that most such communities usually contained only a few hundred people, and along the coastline often far fewer (Cantwell and Wall 2001), this idea would again indicate only a few thousand people at most. Finally, after Kieft's War the Native Americans were effectively removed from the area between Oyster Bay on Long Island and Pound Ridge in Westchester, and estimates of the casualties from this war range between 1000 and 1600 (Grumet 1989, Cantwell and Wall 2001). Observers also noted the war left only a few hundred Munsees remaining alive, and these people soon fled westward.

Therefore, by the time of initial contact, Native American cultural practices already had at least five very tangible impacts on the region's forest. First, there would be the impact of simply having 12 village sites in the area. Secondly, combining Martin Pring's observation in 1603 that Native American families kept a garden that was "an acre of ground" (Quinn and Quinn 1983) and an implied population of nearly 2500 (or roughly 600 families) means that systemic farming would have covered about 1% of the City's 200,000 acres.

The third impact, the dependence of a large number of humans upon the surrounding countryside for their subsistence, would have been far more pervasive. Hunting, fishing, wood gathering and berry picking would certainly disrupt various ecological interrelationships, such as predator/prey, seed dispersal and pollination relationships. Fourthly, such impacts would also have trickle-down effects and ultimately increase or decrease species recruitment in the forest. For instance, if predators decreased as Native Americans preferentially trapped them for fur, then herbivores would presumably increase. Conversely, if herbivores were selectively hunted for food, then vegetative species recruitment would rebound. The final major impact most often discussed is that of fire. While the purposeful use of fire by Native Americans is well documented, its temporal and spatial impact on the landscape has long been the subject of debate (see Whitney 1994, Bonnicksen 2000). It is clear that fire was used to help drive game (e.g., Drake, 1996), clear fields and open up the understory for hunting (Cronon 1983, Russell 1983). The true frequency and spatial coverage of the annual burnings are very hard to determine, but no doubt by 1500 the use of fire dramatically affected the forests of the region. Patterson and Sassaman (1988) suggested that Native Americans more commonly used fire in the more densely populated coastal areas than in those villages located in the interior. Frequent fires in an area would indubitably have profound impacts on forest structure. Niering and Egler (1981) noted that fires would select for fire-resistant species, and indeed found that in early land surveys around Greenwich, Connecticut, 79% of the 937 trees noted were oaks and hickories. Less resistant species such as ash, maple and beech each made up less than 2%, and hemlock was nonexistent. In addition to selection pressure, frequent fires would also affect forest structure by leading to recruitment by cohorts instead of uneven age classes.

Following closely on these perturbations is the period of "initial contact" following John Cabot's claim of Newfoundland in 1497. Europeans quickly began visiting and fishing the waters of the New World in great numbers, so that by 1550, 30 French ships a year visited these waters, and by 1578, more than 300 ships arrived (Brasser 1978). Contacts increased, and with the arrival of the 17th century, colonies began sprouting all along the Atlantic coast: Cape Sable Island in 1598, Maine in 1604, Virginia in 1607, Massachusetts in 1620 and New Amsterdam (New York City) in 1624. However, even as hostilities erupted between the cultures, a plethora of European diseases that arrived with the fishermen and colonists effectively ended Native American domination of both the forests and the land. Epidemics of smallpox, measles and maybe even bubonic plague in 1617, 1633 and subsequent dates decimated their populations so that by 1700 the number of Native Americans in all of southern New England is estimated to have dropped by 85%, to less than 3000 (Goddard 1978, Grumet 1989). Bonnicksen (2000) estimated higher losses, and believed these epidemics accounted for the loss of 89% of the Native American population by this time.

With intercultural friction reduced to insignificance by depopulation, European settlers filled the vacuum. The demise of the region's forests as a whole functioning system occurred shortly thereafter as New Amsterdam/ New York grew rapidly. New York City was quickly settled after 1624, and by 1636, the land grab began when the Director General of the colony purchased Brooklyn's Flatlands. In the ensuing years the following purchases were made: Brooklyn in 1637, southern Bronx in 1639, eastern Bronx in 1640, Bushwick in 1641, Newton in 1642, Gravesend and Utrecht in 1643, Hempstead in 1644, and Flushing in 1645 (Seymann 1939). Between 1650 and 1776 the European population in the area increased from 5000 to more than 750,000 (Grumet 1989). Clearly there is no need here to further document or detail the effects of the City's growth, for cleared fields, cobble-stoned streets, brownstones and poured cement are hardly subtle in their impact on forest structure.

However, in addition to these obvious impacts, one should also not forget that throughout this period, and indeed consistently since then, a great array of pathogens and exotic species have been imported into the region. Each has taken a devastating toll on the area's ecology. For instance, plants such as the Norway Maple and Oriental Bittersweet now grow in the forests. Pathogens such as beech snap, Asian chestnut fungus, or blister rust have decimated certain species' populations, and insects such as the Gypsy Moth (*Lymantria dispar*), Woolly Adelgid (*Adelges tsugae*) and now the Tiger Beetles (*Cicindela* sp.) have also taken their toll (Feller 1994, Wessels 1997).

In summary, it is my belief that while early hunting and gathering life styles certainly affected the forests of the area, the arrival of systemic agriculture and the widespread use of fire after A.D. 1000 mark the beginning of the end of the primeval forest. Even allowing that mature trees and large stands would not immediately disappear, the fact remains that the forest ecosystem began to be disrupted. Certainly with the increased disturbances due to expanded Native American burning regimes, agricultural practices, and the arrival of European colonists in 1500, the primeval forest's ability to function suffered dramatically. The Europeans exploited and then settled the area, and their even greater demands as hunters and gatherers completed the disruption of established ecological interrelationships such as food webs, pollination and seed dispersal patterns. As they settled the region, they undertook even larger-scale clearing and burning that turned the forests into farmland. Finally, throughout this process they accidentally and purposefully introduced both pathogens and an array of exotic flora and fauna (Barbour and Christensen 1993). In sum then, I will categorize our primeval forest in New York City as that which existed from about 1500 B.C. until A.D. 1600, a scant 3000-year period.

The Forest's Composition

Having defined the temporal framework of the primeval forest, I will now sort the evidence to determine the forest's composition during that time period, and its trees' sizes, density and other associated facts. Table 1 presents data gathered from 16 sites surrounding New York City (compiled from Loeb 1987, Greller 1972, McIntosh 1962, Whitney 1994; Niering and Egler 1981). All but two of the sites lie between eight and 30 miles from Manhattan. The two outliers are from physiognomically similar environs in Ohio, included because they document well-known old-growth stands. As many of the surveys were themselves undertaken over a period of years, the date given for each survey represents the median year of the survey. The earliest survey began in 1669 and the most recent one ended in 1784, and the mean date for all surveys is 1735. Surveys ranged in size from 43 trees to one with 937

Table 1. Aggregate Forest Composition, New York City Region, circa 1735 AD
Note: * = Significant difference (P>0.01).

Species	North of Moraine		Outwash Plain	
	%	SD	%	SD
oak (*Quercus* sp.)	58.6	12.3	46.3	23.3
American Chestnut (*Castanea dentata*)	8.1	6.1	2.3	2.7
walnut (*Juglans* sp.)	5.3	5.4	1.0	1.4
hickory (*Carya* sp.)	4.2	5.3	1.8	2.9
maple (*Acer* sp.)	3.3	2.4	5.3	5.3
American Beech (*Fagus grandifolia*)	1.9	1.7	0.0	0.0
ash (*Fraxinus* sp.)	1.7	2.0	0.8	0.5
birch (*Betula* sp.)	1.4	2.0	0.5	0.6
elm (*Ulmus* sp.)	0.3	0.8	0.0	0.0
pine (*Pinus* sp.)	0.3	0.5	26.7*	21.3

trees. The mean number of trees for each sample was 255, while the total for all 16 surveys was 4084 trees.

In order to combine the data and then manage them so that they might best represent the region, yet still reflect physiognomic differences of the landscape, I divided the data in two ways. First, after Loeb (1987) I divided the surveys based on the five different physiographic provinces surrounding New York City, and secondly, I tried dividing the surveys simply into those sites north of the last terminal moraine and those south of it. Since the results were not significantly different for these two approaches, I then applied Occam's razor and kept with the second approach. Therefore, one group reflects upland areas, in essence north of the terminal moraine, and the other group represents forest types south of the moraine on the outwash plain.

As is unfortunately clear, these survey data were collected nearly 150 years past the conjectured demise of the functioning forest ecosystem. There are, however, several ways to at least "calibrate" if not verify the validity of the data, or perhaps refute them. For this purpose I have turned to the archeological evidence and the earliest narratives. While much of the archeological evidence concerning Native Americans within the boundaries of this City was lost to construction prior to academic interest in such matters, we know that the Delawares largely subsisted on foods characteristic of an oak-hickory forest (Kavasch 1994, Goddard 1978, Juli 1992, Grumet 1989). Table 2 includes data from a village in southern Connecticut. In addition, clothes, moccasins and war shields were all made predominantly from deer, and in this region beads and decorations were of wampum (clam shell), turkey feathers and snakeskins (Goddard 1978) but, for instance, not porcupine, a creature of more northern forests. From early colonial records we also know that furs were a major component of the initial contact period. In 1629, skins of 7520 beavers, 370 otters, 48 mink, and 36 wildcats were shipped out of the region's forests to Europe (Patterson 1978). This indicates that 100 years before the tree surveys, the animals inhabiting the forests were common in the type of forests described in the land surveys. The absence of either more northern or southern forest species at least suggests that there is no reason to suspect the forest's composition as recorded later in the mid-18th century.

It is also known that the Delawares used a great number of botanical products, and these, too, ought to reflect the forest's composition. Archeological evidence shows that numerous woody perennials were relied upon for food, including Black Walnut, Butternut Hickory, chestnut, oaks, Chokecherry, American Plum, blueberry, cranberry, strawberry, raspberry, Shadbush, hollies, dogwood, and currants (Kavasch 1994). While northern tribes

Table 2. Floral and Faunal Remains-Contact Period. Native American Site on Mamacoke Island, New London, CT (Modified from Juli 1992).

Species	No. of Fragments	% of Fragments
White-tailed Deer (*Odocoileus virginianus*)	212	67.30
Northern Raccoon (*Procyon lotor*)	5	1.58
American Beaver (*Castor canadensis*)	2	0.63
Eastern Gray Squirrel (*Sciurus carolinensis*)	9	2.85
Wild Turkey (*Meleagris gallopavo*)	2	0.63
Domestic Dog (*Canis familiaris*)	6	1.90
vole (*Microtus* sp.)	1	0.31
Northern River Otter (*Lontra canadensis*)	1	0.31
Muskrat (*Ondatra zibethicus*)	3	0.95
North American Porcupine (*Erethizon dorsatum*)	1	0.31
Red Fox (*Vulpes vulpes*)	2	0.63
Gray Fox (*Urocyon cinereoargenteus*)	1	0.31
Eastern Chipmunk (*Tamias striatus*)	1	0.31
Common Snapping Turtle (*Chelydra serpentina*)	2	0.63
Mallard (*Anas platyrhynchos*)	2	0.63
Eastern Cottontail (*Sylvilagus floridanus*)	2	0.63
mouse (*Peromyscus* sp.)	1	0.31
small-sized mammal	2	0.63
medium-sized mammal	9	2.85
large-sized mammal	7	2.22
unidentified bird	9	2.57
unidentified fish	7	2.00
American Holly (*Ilex opaca*)	1 (charred seeds)	
White Pine (*Pinus strobus*)	3 (charcoal)	
oak (*Quercus* sp.)	1 (charred seeds)	
Bayberry (*Myrica pensylvanica*)	10 (charred seeds)	
sumac (*Rhus* sp.)	37 (charred seeds)	

certainly tapped Sugar Maples, this practice is not mentioned, nor was it observed, as a food source for the New York City region (Goddard 1978). Other documented uses of native vegetation were utilizing the inner bark of basswood and ash to weave baskets, hickory saplings for long-house poles, chestnut and oak bark for roofing, Tulip Trees and White Pines to make dugout canoes (but notably *not* birch bark), and the meat of chestnuts for food (Goddard 1978; Juli 1992; Kavasch 1994).

Finally, several early European narratives also alluded to the composition of the forest. In 1656, Adriaen Van der Donck, a settler in upper Manhattan, noted that "the whole country is covered with wood…. There are several kinds of oak, such as white, smooth bark, rough bark, grey bark, and black bark…and nutwood [hickories] grow as tall as the oak, but not so heavy [thick]." A little later, Daniel Denton observed that the forests in the area held "oaks white and red,…[and] walnut-trees, chestnut-trees, which yield a store of mast for swine. Also maples, cedars sa[ssafras], beech, birch, holly, hazel, with many sorts more…. Grapes great and small, huckleberries, cranberries, plums of several sorts, raspberries and strawberries, of which the last is of such abundance in June that the fields and woods are died red" (Kieran 1959). European artifacts of the period also support this view of the forest's composition, as even a cursory examination of houses and furniture from the era reveals the woods from which they were derived. These early colonists depended upon the nearby forests for their needs, and notable early furniture was made from White Oak, other oaks, Black Cherry, Tulip, beech, walnut and lots of White Pine (Patterson 1978).

The Forest's Structure

Combining the views of various authors (Oliver and Larson 1990, Whitney 1994; White and Lloyd 1994, Smith et al. 1997), the structure of an old-growth stand in this region should have the following characteristics:

- Large, old trees. Individual trees established under mature trees, not in areas cleared due to a major disturbance.
- A reverse "J"-shaped diameter distribution (reflecting an implied and similar age distribution pattern).
- A solid canopy that effectively prohibits sunlight form reaching the forest floor, with only occasional gaps from individual mortality.
- A great diversity of tree species.
- A relatively uniform and continuous vertical distribution of foliage in the forest among the following layers: herbaceous, shrub, understory and canopy.
- An abundance of epiphytes, vines and mosses covering the trees, and established well up into the canopy.
- Living biomass of forest has reached a steady state; thus annual net pri-

mary production equals annual losses. Basal area remains a constant.

- Standing dead trees, and large dead trees on the forest floor.
- Forest floor pitted and mounded with a great amount of woody debris and organic matter. Very moist, except on ridges.

Early narratives certainly support many of the points above and evoke the myth of a seamless verdant forest canopy held aloft by ancient and gnarled giants. They tell of "the oak trees [that] are very large; from sixty to seventy feet without knots, and from two to three fathoms thick [a 12- to 18-foot diameter]" (Van der Donck 1968), or trees "to six feet in diameter and frequently not as many yards asunder" (Strickland 1971). South in Virginia, Captain John Smith wrote of trees "so tall and straight, that they will be two feet and a half square of good timber for 20 yards long" (Bonnicksen 2000). Even as late as 1872, Robert Ridgway described visiting an old-growth stand in Ohio: "Going into these primitive woods, we find symmetrical, solid trunks of six feet and upwards in diameter.... Now and then we happen upon one of those old sycamores…with a trunk thirty or even forty, possibly fifty or sixty feet in circumference [about 9.5 to 19 feet diameter]…and the tall shaft-like trunks of pecans (hickories), sweet gums or ashes…rise straight as an arrow for eighty or ninety, perhaps even over a hundred, feet before the first branches are thrown out" (Whitney, 1994). In this region, the canopy of this ancient forest was also punctuated by great emergents: white pines that were sometimes more than 200 feet tall. Indeed, as early as 1700, these great pines were reserved exclusively for the Royal Navy, and even after felling, one mast was still over 150 feet in length and 4.5 feet in diameter (Bromley 1935).

Unfortunately, as one closely examines the limited evidence that can be either gathered or surmised about the structure of the primeval forest, it is evident that the myth will at best remain conjectural. While there is no doubt that great giants existed, the mean was indubitably somewhat smaller and removed from the magnificent. Consider for a moment a stand of trees starting growth in a simple open field. Oliver and Larson (1990) neatly summarized a stand's development as the following process: when trees first occupy an open area they essentially grow unfettered. Their intrinsic growth rate depends upon such abiotic conditions as the available water, nutrients and sunlight. As the saplings grow, those which are closer to one another begin to experience competition (for nutrients, sunlight or water). In due course, as the trees reach the point where their crowns and roots begin to touch others, competition increases, and trees begin to change their shape in order to maximize their potential. During this phase, the number of trees in an area decreases as larger trees dominate. Eventually, the canopy completely closes, tree growth slows to negligible levels, and the size of each tree and the number of trees in an area reaches an average maximum, or the stand's maximum. Table 3 contains some recently recorded maxima taken from trees *within old-growth stands* for most of the tree species found in the region's primeval forest. There will, of course, always be "wolf trees" and others that manage to grow to unique proportions, but these are rare and do not fairly portray a forest's gestalt.

In order to create a quantitative time-series model of the development of a typical old-growth stand, I have turned to a comprehensive review of all extant old-growth stands in the eastern United States (Tyrrell et al. 1998). After reviewing all the data in this volume, I performed a hierarchical cluster analysis (Wilkinson et al., 1996) on 50 deciduous forest sites bounded by Massachusetts and New Jersey and then west to Ohio, and determined that, based on species composition, several stands in central Massachusetts were the nearest parallels to the stands of New York City. I used Spaeth's (1920)

Table 3. Average heights, and maximum known diameters and ages of regional tree species. Note: Measurements may be from different individuals. Diameters and ages from documented individuals in old growth stands. Heights are recorded maximum averages. (Grimm 1983, Bonnicksen 2000 and Tyrrell et al. 1998).

Species	Diameter in inches (BH)	Height in feet	Age in years
Acer rubrum (Red Maple)	38	70	310
Carya glabra (Pignut Hickory)	36	60	153
Carya o. ovata (Shagbark Hickory)	27	80	
Carya tomentosa (Mockernut)	36	75	
Castanea dentata (American Chestnut)	54	100	
Fagus grandifolia (American Beech)	42	100	366
Fraxinus americana (White Ash)	46	100	
Liriodendron tulipifera (Tulip Tree)	72	150	
Pinus strobus (White Pine)	52	200	460
Quercus alba (White Oak)	54	100	324
Quercus rubra (Red Oak)	41	150	189
Quercus velutina (Black Oak)	50	150	240
Ulmus americana (American Elm)	42	100	410

study of the development of a mixed deciduous forest in Massachusetts to create an initial data set for the time-series model. As Spaeth's data cover only the first 80 years of a stand's development, I then matched his data with a series of old-growth stands from the same physiographic area (Dunwiddie 1983) to create a 300-year time-series model.

The combination of these data sets roughly portrays the growth and development of an oak-hickory forest stand from its establishment phase to its maturity as an old-growth stand. Graphs 1, 2 and 3 are different facets of a time-series model created using a weighted polynomial regression with an Epanechnikov kernel (Wilkinson et al. 1996). While I realize that the species composition of such a forest would differ slightly from that of the New York City area, the structural attributes should be quite similar. Graph 1 depicts the well-known trend that as a stand ages, a great number of small saplings slowly give way to a much smaller number of large trees. This graph shows that a Northeastern old-growth stand will stabilize with roughly 200 to 400 trees per hectare. In Graph 2, the total basal area (i.e., volume) of a forest stand increases quickly and then also stabilizes, in this case at a point between 250 and 350 square feet per hectare. This graph also shows the greatest variability among the potential end points, but this is not surprising as the biomass of any stand is ultimately dependent upon the abiotic attributes (i.e., nutrients,

Graph 1.

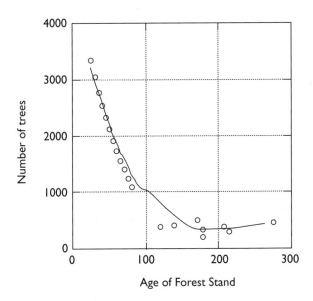

Age of Forest Stand

Graph 2.

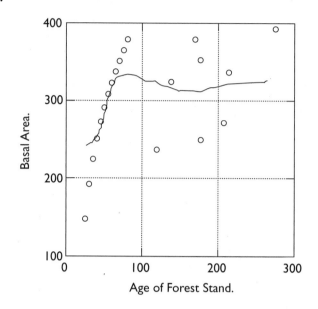

Graph 3.

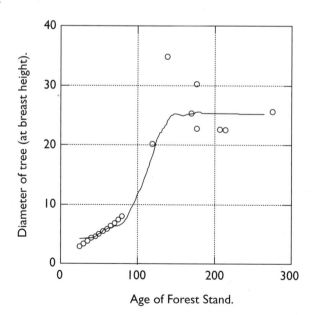

water) of the site. Finally, Graph 3 depicts the third element of this relationship. As the absolute number of trees declines and the volume of the stand remains constant, the average diameter of each tree at breast height increases asymptotically to a point that is just above 30 inches. This latter figure is a mean for a fully developed stand and thus, as already discussed, does not limit the notion of some great old giants "two to three fathoms thick" (Van der Donck 1968). It does, however, indicate that such giants were probably not uniformly found across the breadth of the landscape.

As a test of the time-series analyses, I went back to the larger pool of data from the 50 extant old-growth stands (Tyrrell et al. 1998). While these data, shown in Table 4, must be regarded cautiously, as they suffer from a great discrepancy of collection techniques, sampling regimes, and academic focus, they essentially validate the results derived from the time-series analysis. Tyrrell's review shows that current remnant old-growth sites have an average of 468 trees per hectare, and a mean basal area of 491 square feet per hectare. As the studies in the review were undertaken by ecologists rather than foresters like Spaeth, smaller stems and more detailed sampling methods probably account for the generally higher means, and certainly some sites were on generally more productive soils than those of central Massachusetts.

Conclusion

I have reviewed the palynological, ecological, archeological and early historical evidence to depict what constituted New York City's "primeval forest." To many, the idea of "a prodigious forest…[that] covered the whole face of the country" (Bonnicksen, 2000), or a great forest whose leafy boughs might bear aloft a squirrel from the Atlantic Ocean to the great Mississippi River is an attractive one. Indeed, certainly regional forest stands did reach mythical

Table 4. Structural Characteristics of Regional Old Growth Forests (From Tyrrell et al., 1998).

	Stems (>10 cm) per Ha.	Basal area (ft²/Ha.)	Maximum age for a tree on site
Mean	467.92	490.73	266.586
Standard Deviation	209.95	168.63	74.78
Range	171 - 907	211.50 - 756	119 - 450
Number of Cases	26	27	29

proportions in their old-growth stage, and they were something to behold. However, the evidence detailing the structure, temporal duration and geographic prevalence of these stands casts some shadows upon the myth.

I believe that the primeval forest which actually existed did so only during a brief period from roughly 1500 B.C. until A.D. 1600, though these boundaries are somewhat blurred by the glacial retreat at one end and the impacts of successive human invasions at the other. I would characterize the forest during this time as an oak-hickory association (after Barbour and Christensen 1993), with an increased representation of pine south of the terminal moraine. It is clear that great forest stands did develop and that these persisted in the face of the various perturbations. However, prior to major human impacts such as fire, agriculture or construction, how much of the landscape they actually covered will never be known. The old-growth stands that did exist would have had 200 to 400 canopy-level trees per hectare with an average diameter of more than 30 inches at breast height. Let there be no doubt, such a tree is a substantial tree, and a stand of them would be awesome to behold.

The forest was predominantly multistoried, as there were lush herbaceous and dense shrub layers, with a canopy roughly 100 to 120 feet high. In addition, great White Pines punctuated the canopy and soared as much as 200 feet into the air. However, it is equally clear that this overarching fabric was frequently torn asunder by fires, ice, hurricanes and wind storms sporadically toppling these splendid giants. Further, one must remember that gross averages do not reflect individual species' clear preferences for certain microhabitats. No doubt our regional view does not accurately portray the prevalence of hemlocks or sycamores along streams, the sumacs and Red Cedars that filled in openings after a hurricane's passage, or the White Cedars that dramatically lined the Hudson River in 1679 (Van Zandt 1992).

In sum though, I hope this expanded and historical view of the region's primeval forest will act as a "type ecosystem" and thus help set some basic guidelines for future restoration efforts. I have hopefully provided new insights into the range and proportional composition of the dominant tree species in the forest, their density, the size to which they might aspire, and lastly the time which our patience must provide them in order to reach a stature commensurate with our imagination.

Acknowledgments

I would like to thank Dr. Mark Ashton of Yale's School of Forestry and Environmental Studies and Neil Calvanese of the Central Park Conservancy for reviewing this paper and providing their thoughtful input, and Margaret Cooper for editorial review. I also want to thank all those in New York City's Department of Parks & Recreation, particularly in the Natural Resource Group and the Urban Park Rangers, who continue to pursue the preservation and restoration of such forests and other fragments of this City's natural heritage, and especially to Parks Commissioners Adrian Benepe, Henry Stern, and Betsy Gotbaum for supporting these efforts.

References

Barbour, Michael G., and Norman L. Christensen. 1993. Vegetation, in *Flora of North America* 1: 97-131, Oxford University Press, NY.

Bonnicksen, Thomas M. 2000. *America's Ancient Forests*, John Wiley & Sons, New York.

Bormann, F.H., and G.E. Likens. 1979. *Pattern and Process in a Forested Ecosystem. Disturbance, Development, and the Steady State Based on the Hubbard Brook Ecosystem Study.* Springer-Verlag, NY.

Bragdon, Kathleen J. 1996. *Native People of Southern New England*, 1500-1650, The Civilization of the American Indian Series, University of Oklahoma Press, Norman, OK.

Brasser, T. J. 1978. Early Indian-European contacts, in *Handbook of North American Indians: Northeast*, 15: 78-88. B.G. Tigger, Ed. Smithsonian Institution. Washington, D.C.

Bromley, S.W. 1935. The original forest types of southern New England. Ecol. Monographs 5:61-89.

Cantwell, Anne-marie, and Diana diZerega Wall. 2001. *Unearthing Gotham: The Archaeology of New York City*, Yale University Press, New Haven, CT.

Cronon, W. 1983. *Changes in the Land: Indians, Colonists, and the Ecology of New England*, Hill and Wang, NY.

Davis, M.B. 1981. Quarternary history and the stability of forest communities, pp. 1132-1153, in West, D.C., H.H. Shugart, and D.B. Botkin, eds., *Forest Succession: Concepts and Applications*, Springer-Verlag, NY.

Davis, M.B. 1983. Quarternary history of deciduous forests on eastern North America and Europe. *Annals of the Missouri Botanical Garden* 70: 550-563.

Davis, M.B., ed. 1996. *Eastern Old Growth Forests, Island Press*, Washington, D.C.

Delcourt, Paul A., and Hazel R. Delcourt. 1987. *Long Term Forest Dynamics of the Temperate Zone, Ecological Studies 63*, Springer-Verlag, NY.

Drake, Sir Francis. 1996. *Histoire naturelle des Indes. The Drake Manuscript in the Pierpont Morgan Library*, W.W. Norton & Co., NY.

Dunwiddie, Peter. 1993. *Survey of Old Growth Forest in Massachussettes*. Final Report.

Mass. Audubon Society. Nantucket, Mass.

Egler, F. E. 1954. Vegetation science concepts I. Initial floristic composition—a factor in old-field vegetation development. Vegetation 4:412-417.

Feller, M. 1994. *Forests of New York City*, City of New York, Department of Parks & Recreation, N.Y.

Fitting, James E. 1978. Regional cultural development, 300 B.C. to A.D. 1000, in *Handbook of North American Indians: Northeast* 15: 43-57. B.G. Tigger, Ed., Smithsonian Institution, Washington, D.C.

Funk, R.E. 1978. Post-Pleistocene adaptations, in *Handbook of North American Indians: Northeast*, 15: 16-27. B.G. Tigger, Ed. Smithsonian Institution, Washington, D.C.

Goddard, Ives. 1978. Delaware, in *Handbook of North American Indians: Northeast*, 15: 213-239. B.G. Tigger, Ed. Smithsonian Institution, Washington, D.C.

Greller, Andrew M. 1972. Observations on the forests of northern Queens County, Long Island, from colonial times to the present, *Bull. Torrey Bot. Club, 99*: 202-206.

Grimm, William C. 1983. *The Illustrated Book of Trees*, Stackpole Books, Mechanicsburg, PA.

Grumet, Robert S. 1989. *The Lenapes*, Chelsea House Publishers, New York, NY.

Juet, R., 1609 in Van Zandt, R., ed. 1992. *Chronicles of the Hudson. Three Centuries of Travel and Adventure*, Black Dome Press, Hensonville, NY.

Juli, Harold D. 1992. *Archaeology in the Connecticut College Arboretum*, The Connecticut College Arboretum, Bull. 33, New London, CT.

Kavasch, Barrie. 1994. Native Botanical and Contact History in Enduring Traditions, pp. 5-30.,L. Weinstein, Ed. Bergin & Garvey, Westport, CT.

Kieran, John F. 1959. *A Natural History of New York City*, Fordham University Press, NY.

Loeb, Robert E. 1987. Pre-European settlement forest composition in east New Jersey and southeastern New York, *Ame. Midl. Nat.* 118: 414-423.

Loeb, Robert E. 1989. The ecological history of an urban park, *Journ. of Forest Hist.* Vol. 87: 134-143. McGee, C.E. 1984. Heavy mortality and succession in a virgin mixed mesophytic forest, in *U.S. Forest Serv. Res. Paper* SO 209: 1-9, Washington, D.C.

McGee, C.E. 1984. *Heavy Mortality and Succession in a Virgin Mixed Mesophytic Forest*. USDA Forest Svc. Research Paper. SO-209, 9 pp.

McIntosh, R.P. 1962. The forest cover of the Catskill Mountain region, New York, as indicated by land survey records, *Amer. Midl. Nat.* 68: 409-423.

Niering, W.A., and F.E. Egler. 1981. *Vegetation of the Babcock Property*, Greenwich Conservation Commission, Greenwich, CT.

O'Donnell, T.F., ed. 1968. *A Description of the New Netherlands*, by Adriaen Van der Donck (originally published 1655), Syracuse University Press, Syracuse, NY.

Oliver, Chadwick D. 1981. Forest Development in North America following major disturbances, *Forest Ecol Manag.*, 3:153-168.

Oliver, Chadwick D., and Bruce C. Larson. 1990. *Forest Stand Dynamics*, McGraw-Hill, New York.

O'Neill, R.V., D.L. DeAngelis, J.B. Waide and T.F.H. Allen. 1986. *A Hierarchical Concept of Ecosystems*. Monographs in Population Biology, no. 23, Princeton University Press. Princeton, NJ.

Parkman, F. 1983. [Reprint of 1865-1892]. France and England in North America. *Literary Classics of the U.S.* New York, N.Y.

Patterson, Jerry E. 1978. *The City of New York*. Harry N. Abrams, New York.

Patterson, W.A., III, and K.E. Sassaman. 1988. Indian fires in the prehistory of New England, in *Holocene Human Ecology in Northeastern North America*, pp. 107-135. G.P. Nicholas, Ed., Plenum Publishing Co., New York.

Peterson, Chris J. 2002. Wind damage and re-vegetation across 10 years in a Hemlock-White Pine forest remnant, *www.dogwoodbotany.uga.edu*.

Pickett, Stewart, T.A., and P.S. White. 1985. *The Ecology of Natural Disturbance and Patch Dynamics*, Academic Press., Orlando, FL.

Quinn, David B., ed. 1991. *The Roanoke Voyages, 1584-1590: Documents to Illustrate the English Voyages to North America Under the Patent Granted to Walter Raleigh in 1584*, Hakluyt Society, 2nd Series, no. 104, London.

Quinn, David B., and Alison M. Quinn, eds. 1983. *The English New England Voyages 1602-1608*, The Hakluyt Society, London.

Ritchie, William A. 1957. *Traces of Early Man in the Northeast*, N.Y. State Mus. and Sci. Serv., Bull. 358, Albany, NY.

Ritchie, William A. 1994. *The Archaeology of New York State*, Purple Mountain Press, Fleischmanns, NY.

Russell, E.W.B. 1983. Indian-set fires in the forests of northeastern United States, *Ecol.* 64: 78-88.

Ruttenber, E.M. 1992 [1872]. *History of the Indian Tribes of Hudson's River*, J. Munsell, Albany, NY [Facsimile of original, Hope Farm Press, Saugerties, NY].

Seymann, J. 1939. *Colonial Charters Patents and Grants to the Communities Comprising the City of New York*, The Board of Statutory Consolidation of the City of New York. J.B. Lyon Co., Albany, NY.

Smith, Bryce E., P.L. Marks and Sana Gardescu. 1993. Two hundred years of forest cover changes in Tompkins County, New York, *Bull. Torrey Bot.* Club, 120(3): 229-247.

Smith, David M., B. C. Larson, M.J. Kelty and P.M.S.Ashton. 1997. *The Practice of Silviculture*, John Wiley & Sons, New York.

Snow, Dean R. 1978. Late prehistory of the East Coast, in *Handbook of North American Indians, : Northeast*, 15: 58-69. B.G. Trigger, Ed., Smithsonian Institution, Washington, D.C.

Spaeth, J. Nelson. 1920. *Growth study and normal yield tables for second-growth hardwood stands in Central New England*, Harvard Forest Bull. No. 2, Cambridge, Mass.

Strickland, W. 1971. *Journal of a Tour in the United States of America*, Strickland,

J.E., ed., New York Historical Society, New York.

Trigger, B. G. 1978. Early Iroquian Contacts with Europeans, in *Handbook of North American Indians: Northeast*, 15: 344-356, B. G. Trigger, Ed. Smithsonian Institution, Washington, D.C.

Tyrrell, Lucy E., G.J. Nowacki, T.R. Crow, D.S. Buckley, E.A. Nauertz, J.F.N. Niese, J.L. Rollinger and J.C. Zasada. 1998. *Information about Old Growth for Selected Forest Type Groups in the Eastern United States*, General Technical Report NC-197, North Central Forest Experiment Station, U.S. Forest Service, U.S. Department of Agriculture. St, Paul, Minn.

Van der Donck, Adriaen. 1968. [Reprint of 1656]. Edited by T.F. O'Donnell. Syracuse University Press. Syracuse, N.Y.

Van Zandt, R., ed. 1992. *Chronicles of the Hudson*. Three Centuries of Travel and Adventure, Black Dome Press, Hensonville, NY.

Vogt, Kristiina A., J.C. Gordon, J.P. Wargo, D.J. Vogt, H. Asbjornsen, P.A. Palmiotto, H.J. Clark, J.L. O'Hara, W.S.Keeton, T. Patael-Weynand and E. Witten. 1997. *Ecosystems, Balancing Science with Management*. Springer-Verlag, New York.

Watts, W.A. 1983. Vegetational history of the eastern United States 25,000 to 10,000 years ago, in *Late Quartenary Environments of the United States: Late Pleistocene*, 1: 294-310, S.C. Porter, Ed. University of Minnesota Press, Minneapolis.

Weinstein, L., ed. 1994. *Enduring Traditions: The Native Peoples of New England*, Bergin & Garvey Press, Westport, CT.

Wessels, T. 1997. *Reading the Forested Landscape*. A Natural History of New England, The Countryman Press, Woodstock, VT.

White, David L., and F. Thomas Lloyd. 1994. *Defining Old Growth: Implications for Management*, p. 51-62, Eighth Biennial Southern Silvicultural Research Conference, Auburn, AL.

Whitney, Gordon G. 1994. *From Coastal Wilderness to Fruited Plain*, Cambridge University Press, Cambridge, England.

Wilkinson, Leland, Grant Blank and Christian Gruber. 1996. *Desktop Analysis with Systa*, Prentice Hall, Upper Saddle River, NJ.

Wroth, Lawrence. 1970. *The Voyages of Giovanni da Verrazano* 1520-1528, Yale University Press, New Haven.

Forest Vegetation Along an Urban-Rural Gradient in the New York City Metropolitan Area: Patterns and Relationships to Ecosystem Processes

M.L. Cadenasso, *Department of Plant Sciences, University of California, Davis,*
S.T.A. Pickett, *Institute of Ecosystem Studies, Millbrook NY,*
M.J. McDonnell, *Australian Research Centre for Urban Ecology,*
Royal Botanic Garden: Melbourne and Cranbourne,
R.V. Pouyat, *USDA Forest Service, c/o Baltimore Ecosystem Study,*
University of Maryland Baltimore County, Baltimore MD
mlcadenasso@ucdavis.edu

Introduction

THE FOREST VEGETATION OF NINE CLOSED-CANOPY STANDS arrayed along a transect from urban New York City to rural western Connecticut was examined to test two hypotheses: 1) composition and structure of forest patches differ depending on their location relative to the urban core, and 2) forest composition and structure reflect differences in ecosystem processes previously quantified along the transect. No unique tree species assemblages were found in association with any particular region along the gradient, and no consistent trends in the distribution of tree dominance appeared along the gradient. Principal components ordination of plots revealed that species' basal area relations were organized along a gradient of mesic to xeric species—i.e., those requiring much to little moisture—and secondarily along a gradient of shade tolerance.

However, the principal components did not parallel the direct urban-rural transect. Ordination of tree species revealed a threshold in community organization occurring between urban and suburban stands as well as similar organization of suburban and rural stands. Stands throughout the gradient had similar basal area, but the largest trees were found in the urban stands. Urban

79

stands had the lowest tree and sapling density. Shifts in species abundance occurred in subcanopy layers: Black Cherry (*Prunus serotina*) saplings were significantly more common in urban than in suburban and rural stands. The herb layer was richer in rural than in suburban or urban stands, and herbs were particularly depauperate in urban stands, where bare soil and exposed rock were more common than in rural sites. Urban stands exhibited the greatest vine cover, while seedlings showed an opposing trend and appeared more commonly in rural forests.

We conclude that the composition of the forest canopy does not differ across the direct urban-rural transect. However, the structure of the forest as expressed in saplings, seedlings, vines and herbs does differ across the transect, with notable breaks in characteristics between rural forests and those closer to the urban core. The large differences in ecosystem processes observed in prior studies do not relate to compositional features of the forest canopy but do parallel structural trends in the understory components. Because the understory of all forests along the transect differs from the canopy, these forests are poised to undergo major changes. In order to determine what potential mechanistic relationships exist between the forest vegetation and ecosystem processes, long-term dynamic studies, improved linkage of biogeo-chemical and demographic studies, and studies of the landscape context of metropolitan forest stands are required. Because these forests offer important ecosystem services and amenities, and they may experience unprecedented shifts in the near future, continued integrated research is of importance to managers, restorationists and planners.

Background

New York's landscapes are becoming increasingly urbanized and natural areas consequently more fragmented and exposed to human development. The potential impacts of urbanization on the structure and function of natural areas such as forests need to be incorporated into the ecological understand-ing of these systems. Scientists, managers and urban planners require such information (Flores et al. 1997). "Urban" is defined as human settlements with populations denser than 620 people/km^2 (United States Bureau of Census 1980). McDonnell and Pickett (1990) defined urbanization as a four-part process: 1) increase in human population; 2) increase in energy consumption per capita; 3) landscape modification; and 4) a spatial expansion of the resource base such that the system does not rely on locally produced resources to sustain itself. However, the alteration of ecological processes as a result of the growth of cities and associated human activities must be quantified and relationships among them elucidated to determine the ecologically important impacts of urbanization (McDonnell et al. 1997).

The ecological influence of urban developments may manifest itself in changes in the structure, composition and function of pre-existing biophysical communities (Stearns and Montag 1974, Sukopp and Werner 1982, Rowntree 1988). Ecologists have increasingly incorporated humans into their research and understanding (McDonnell and Pickett 1993) and have done so from two angles. One approach is to study ecosystems embedded within urban areas, and the other is to study the entire urban area as an integrated system (Boyden et al. 1981, Pickett et al. 1997. Grimm et al. 2000). Our results focus on deciduous forest stands embedded within the metropolitan New York City area. We consider the influence of the urban area on the structure, composition and function of these forests across a spatial transect representing different degrees of urbanization. Therefore we have selected for study several forest stands arrayed on a direct gradient of urbanization, and the data presented address one time period, the year 1993.

The direct gradient approach is powerful for quantifying the spatially varying influences of urbanization (McDonnell and Pickett, 1990). This approach examines whether the spatial pattern of ecological variables controls the corresponding differences in structure, composition and function of systems. A gradient of urbanization has been described and quantified extending 140 km from New York City, one of the oldest and most densely populated cities in the U.S., to rural northwestern Connecticut. The urban core is taken to be Central Park in Manhattan, set as the starting point of the transect. The transect is restricted to the same geological substrate, and its location is the only one possible that maintains consistency of geology while permitting the greatest contrast between urban and rural land covers. Along this transect, measures of urbanization, such as human population density, density of roads and traffic volume on highways, decline logarithmically with distance from the urban core (Medley et al. 1995). In addition, land use shifts dramatically at 35-55 km from the urban core from an urban-residential mix of greater than 80% land cover to a land cover of greater than 70% of forest matrix (Medley et al. 1995). With these changes in land cover as distance from the urban center increases come changes in landscape metrics, such as an increase in mean forest patch size, a decrease in the number of forest patches and a decrease in the presence of forest edges adjacent to urban land uses (Medley et al. 1995). These results indicate that a strong linear gradient of urbanization exists between New York City and northwestern Connecticut.

In the past decade, a rich body of research has focused on the ecological impacts of urbanization on forests along the urban-rural gradient. This research, termed Urban-Rural Gradient Ecology (URGE), has focused primarily on ecosystem processes, particularly soil chemical and physical characteristics, biogeochemical cycling, including litter decomposition and atmospheric inputs of nutrients and pollutants, and invertebrate and mycorrhizal dynamics (McDonnell et al. 1997). All these studies have demonstrated spatial variation along the gradient in the focal process or variable. The research presented here was undertaken to investigate the obvious assumption that the gradient of urbanization measured in ecosystem processes would be reflected in the structure and composition of the plant community. Two main questions frame this research: 1) how do forest structure and composition change along the urban-rural transect? and 2) do differences in forest structure and composition reflect or predict ecosystem processes previously quantified along the urban-rural transect?

Study Sites

A belt transect 20 x 140 km was established extending from highly urbanized New York County (Manhattan) to rural Litchfield County in northwest Connecticut (Fig. 1). The transect resides within the southern portion of the Northeastern Upland Physiographic Province (Broughton et al., 1966). The bedrock, consistent throughout the transect, is composed of metamorphosed and dissected crystalline rocks including schist, granite and gneiss (Schuberth, 1968). The study sites lie on upland soils classified as Typic or Lithic Dystrochrepts (Hill et al., 1980).

Along the urban-rural transect, ten forest stands were selected for study. Within each stand, one to three plots were established for the description and quantification of vegetation (Fig.1). On the urban end of the transect, forests in the New York Botanical Garden, Van Cortlandt Park and Pelham Bay Park were used. All these forests are in the Bronx. We selected four forest stands to represent the suburban portion of the gradient: Saxon Woods Park, Calder Ecology Center, Mianus River Gorge and Mountain Lakes Park. Macedonia Brook State Park, Mohawk State Forest and Housatonic State Forest are in rural areas. Hereafter, the term "region" refers to urban, suburban or rural. Forest stands were selected using the following criteria: 1) closed canopy, 2) trees more than 60 years old, 3) similar species in both canopy and understory, 4) similar topography, 5) similar soil type to at least the subgroup classification category of the Charlton, Charlton/Chatfield, and Hollis series (Soil Survey Staff 1975), 6) no signs of obvious disturbance

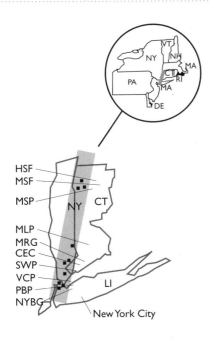

Fig. 1. Distribution of forest stands along the urban-rural transect in the New York metropolitan area. The transect extends from Central Park in New York City to rural sites in northwestern Connecticut. The number of plots in each stand and distance from the urban core are as follows: New York Botanical Garden (NYBG, n = 1; 10 km), Van Cortlandt Park (VCP, n = 2; 13 km), Pelham Bay Park (PBP, n = 1; 14 km), Saxon Woods Park (SWP, n = 3; 26 km), Calder Ecology Center (CEC, n = 1; 45 km), Mianus River Gorge (MRG, n = 1; 49 km), Mountain Lakes Park (MLP, n = 3; 63 km), Macedonia Brook State Park (MSP, n = 3; 110 km), Mohawk State Forest (MSF, n = 2; 123 km), and Housatonic State Forest (HSF, n = 2; 128 km).

by humans such as excavation or tree cutting, and 7) presence of exotic species in the canopy was avoided. The sample plots were originally selected to support soils and biogeochemical research. Detailed vegetation criteria were of secondary importance to soils and general ecosystem similarity.

We surveyed 19 plots of 20 x 20 meters in the 10 forest stands during the summer of 1993. Plots were surveyed to correct for slope and to achieve extremely high accuracy, allowing only 2 mm. of error in side length. This level of accuracy was required because vegetation data are compared on a per unit area basis and because it would also make possible relocating the exact plot boundaries at later sample dates. These plots are intended to be repeatedly sampled to capture long-term vegetation dynamics. Thus, plots were permanently labeled using markers placed on the four corners and the plot center and entirely sunk below the soil surface to safeguard them from removal. The markers were made of a metal electrical junction box cover, dipped in plastic to prevent corrosion and attached to a PVC conduit. Markers can be found for subsequent sampling using a metal detector. In addition, witness trees were selected around each corner and the identity and size of each tree noted as well as its angle and distance from the corner marker (McDonnell et al., 1990).

Sampling Method

To sample their vegetation and other features, the plots were divided into four 10 x 10 subplots, each further subdivided into four 5 x 5 m quadrats (Fig. 2). Thus, each plot consisted of 16 quadrats. Trees were defined as woody plants greater than 2.54 cm diameter at breast height (dbh) and taller than 1 m. All trees in each of the 16 quadrats were identified, tagged and mapped. We also measured the dbh and assessed the health of the tree, both crown and bole. Saplings were defined as woody plants smaller than 2.54 cm dbh and greater than 1 m tall. Within each of the four subplots, two quadrats were randomly selected, their saplings identified and stems counted. All other vegetation layers and nonliving features in the plot were sampled using transects (Fig. 2). Three transects were radiated from each corner of the plot, two extending down each side of the plot and the third at a 45-degree angle extending toward the plot center. The 12 transects, all 10 m long, made a total of 120 m of transects sampled in each plot. Along each transect, the cover of shrubs, vines, herbs, seedlings and nonliving features, such as rock,

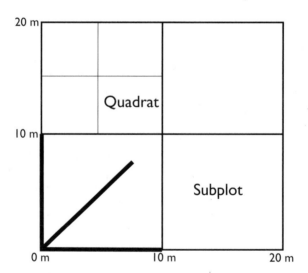

Fig. 2. The sampling design of the permanent plots in forest stands along the urban-rural gradient. The plots are subdivided as detailed in the text. Heavy lines shown in one subplot indicate sampling transects for understory and ground cover that were employed in all subplots. Modified from McDonnell et al. (1990).

bare soil, leaf litter, were quantified. Percent of cover was quantified by the number of centimeters each feature occupied on each meter of the transect. The feature had to cross the transect for at least 1 cm to be sampled, and its cover was considered continuous unless a break in cover greater than 5 cm occurred.

Data Analysis

Species importance values (Mueller-Dombois and Ellenberg, 1974) were calculated for each vegetation layer and for nonliving features in all plots. Because the importance value is a function of more than one variable, it provides an index for evaluating the overall importance of a species. For trees the importance values are calculated from relative values of density, basal area and frequency and can have a maximum value of 300. Importance values for saplings are based on relative density and relative frequency and can have a maximum of 200. Shrubs, herbs, seedlings and nonliving features can have a maximum importance value of 200 as well, and are calculated based on relative ground cover and relative frequency.

We used a two-factor multivariate analysis of variance (MANOVA) together with univariate two-factor ANOVAs to analyze the effects of forest and region on the density of trees and saplings. Density was calculated as the number of individuals per hectare. We did not consider ANOVA results for a particular factor (forest or region) unless MANOVA results for that factor were significant. A similar analysis was conducted to test the effect of forest and region on the 1) percent cover of shrubs, vines, seedlings and herbs, and 2) species richness of trees, saplings, seedlings, shrubs and herbs.

We used a two-factor ANOVA to analyze the effects of forest and region on the total basal area of trees. Total basal area was calculated from the measures of dbh of all trees present in the plots. Total basal area was also used in Principal Components Analyses (PCA) to ordinate stands in species space and vice versa. We subjected the PC scores from the stands in species space ordination to a MANOVA to determine whether any of the first four axes related significantly to either the distance of the forest from the urban core or the region of the transect that the stand occupies. This was done to assist interpretation of the PC1 axis (Pielou, 1984).

Results

FOREST COMPOSITION

The vegetation composition in all 19 of the forest plots varied, but not in a manner reflective of the linear urban-rural transect. Vegetation composition and structure were assessed using the calculated importance values. Similar magnitudes of importance values within a given plot indicated that no single species dominated the plots. Importance values of species can be compared across plots as a measure of patterns in composition and structure. No single species dominated the tree layer across all the plots. Species richness of trees and saplings did not differ significantly among plots or regions of the transect (Table 1). A similar suite of woody species (Table 2a, b) was present in all the plots, but at varying abundances, and urban stands were not distinguished by a unique assemblage of species. While oak (*Quercus*) species dominated plots on the urban and rural ends of the gradient, plots in the middle of the gradient tended to maintain mixed species canopies. Species in the sapling layer were also relatively evenly distributed, with no single species dominating across the plots. Though *P. serotina* is present in all regions of the transect, on average it contributed 40% of the sapling density in the urban plots but only 1.4% of sapling density in suburban forests and 0.7% of sapling density in the rural forests. Jaccard's index of similarity (Pielou, 1984) was calculated to compare the species composition of the tree and sapling layer in each plot.

Table 1. MANOVA and univariate ANOVAs for effects of region and forest on the species richness of trees, saplings, seedlings, shrubs, and herbs.

a) Multivariate analysis	Source	df	Wilks' λ	F	P
	Region	10	0.00487	13.33	0.0002
	Forest	35	0.00333	1.93	0.049
b) Univariate analyses	Source	df	ss	F	P
Trees	Region	2	6.8139	0.41	0.6739
	Forest	7	17.2738	0.3	0.9373
Saplings	Region	2	89.2303	2.74	0.1174
	Forest	7	80.5417	0.71	0.6685
Seedlings	Region	2	132.1767	18.68	0.0006
	Forest	7	46.0952	1.86	0.1896
Shrubs	Region	2	31.6438	6.24	0.02
	Forest	7	66.4702	3.74	0.035
Herbs	Region	2	70.3477	4.63	0.0414
	Forest	7	81.8452	1.54	0.2675

Forest Vegetation along an Urban-Rural Gradient in the New York City
Metropolitan Area: Patterns and Relationships to Ecosystem Processes

87

Table 2. Species present in each plot.

a) TREES

FOREST	NYBG	VCP		PBP	SWP			CEC	MRG	MLP			MSP			MSF		HSF	
PLOT	1	1	2	1	1	2	3	1	1	1	2	3	1	2	3	1	2	1	2
Acer pensylvanicum										X	X	X				X			
Acer platanoides																			
Acer rubrum	X	X			X	X	X	X	X	X	X	X	X	X	X	X	X	X	X
Acer saccharum					X			X	X				X	X	X				
Amelanchier canadensis				X						X	X	X	X	X			X		
Betula allegheniensis										X						X			
Betula lenta	X	X	X	X	X	X	X	X	X		X	X	X	X	X		X	X	X
Carpinus caroliniensis					X	X		X	X				X	X		X	X		
Carya cordiformis																X			
Carya ovata					X	X			X										
Castenea dentata					X											X	X	X	
Cornus florida		X	X		X	X		X											
Fagus grandifolia	X				X	X	X	X	X	X	X	X				X			
Fraxinus americana										X	X		X	X				X	
Liquidambar styraciflua	X	X			X												X		
Liriodendron tulipifera		X	X		X														
Ostrya virginia													X	X			X		
Nyssa sylvatica				X															
Prunus serotina	X	X	X	X													X		
Quercus alba		X		X	X	X	X				X			X		X	X		
Quercus palustris	X								X								X		
Quercus prinus								X											X
Quercus rubra	X		X		X	X	X	X	X	X	X	X	X	X	X	X	X	X	X
Quercus velutina		X		X	X	X							X	X					
Robinia pseudoacacia				X															
Sassafras albidum		X		X															

Table 2. Species present in each plot.

b) SAPLINGS

FOREST	NYBG	VCP		PBP	SWP			CEC	MRG	MLP			MSP			MSF		HSF	
PLOT	I	I	2	I	I	2	3	I	I	I	2	3	I	2	3	I	2	I	2
Acer pensylvanicum													X	X	X	X			X
Acer platanoides		X	X			X													
Acer rubrum	X	X			X	X	X	X	X	X	X	X		X			X	X	
Acer saccharum			X					X	X	X	X		X	X					
Ailanthus altissima	X																		
Amelanchier canadensis										X	X	X	X	X	X	X	X	X	X
Betula allegheniensis										X									
Betula lenta			X							X	X		X	X		X			X
Carpinus caroliniensis					X	X		X	X				X	X		X	X	X	
Carya cordiformis			X						X							X			
Carya glabra																X			
Carya ovata					X	X										X			
Carya tomentosa																X			
Castenea dentata					X	X									X	X	X	X	X
Cornus florida		X	X													X			
Fagus grandifolia					X	X	X	X	X							X			
Fraxinus americana	X	X	X		X												X		
Liquidambar styraciflua		X	X																
Liriodendron tulipifera		X	X		X				X										
Ostrya virginia						X													
Nyssa sylvatica		X	X	X															
Prunus serotina	X	X	X	X		X				X			X	X			X	X	
Quercus alba				X									X			X			
Quercus prinus								X							X				X
Quercus rubra			X							X	X		X		X		X		
Sassafras albidum				X									X			X			

The index varied between 0.11 and 0.67 and did not differ significantly among forests (p = 0.0807) or among regions (p = 0.6243). This indicates that the suite of species in the two canopy layers do not directly match and that regeneration is not replacing canopy species. In addition, species in the sapling layer tend to be shade-intolerant species.

The composition of the understory vegetation layers, however, does differ significantly among regions and among forests (Table 1, Fig. 3). The herbaceous layer in rural forests contained significantly more species than in suburban forests (Table 1, Fig. 3). Plots in the NYBG forest and in the forest at CEC had very minimal herb cover. These two sites also contained the most bare soil and exposed rock. The seedling community contained significantly more species in rural forests than in either suburban or urban forests (Table 1, Fig. 3). The forest plots in the city were particularly depauperate in seedling species. The shrub layer differed significantly among forests (Table 1) due to the high number of species present in Van Cortlandt Park.

The abundance of understory vegetation, measured as percent of cover, differed significantly among regions and forests (Table 3). All vegetation layers, with the exception of shrubs, differed significantly in cover along the gradient (Table 3). The percent cover of vines in urban stands signifi-

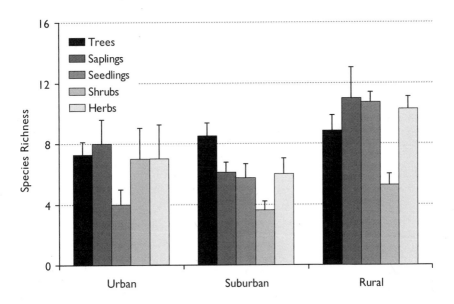

Fig. 3. Species richness of vegetation layers. Each bar represents the average +1 S.E. For the urban region n = 4, n = 8 for the suburban region and n = 7 for the rural region.

Table 3. MANOVA and univariate ANOVAs for effects of region and forest on the percent cover of shrubs, vines, seedlings, and herbs.

a) Multivariate analysis	Source	df	Wilks' λ	F	P
	Region	8	0.01746	9.85	0.0003
	Forest	28	0.01139	2.03	0.0439
b) Univariate analyses	**Source**	**df**	**ss**	**F**	**P**
Shrubs	Region	2	34.4504	0.41	0.6734
	Forest	7	470.4348	1.61	0.2472
Vines	Region	2	181.5163	15.05	0.0013
	Forest	7	176.4177	4.18	0.0253
Seedlings	Region	2	210.5638	22.75	0.0003
	Forest	7	55.5775	1.72	0.2212
Herbs	Region	2	463.7806	8.46	0.0086
	Forest	7	292.049	1.52	0.2725

cantly exceeded that of suburban and rural stands. Conversely, seedlings had significantly higher percent cover in rural stands compared to suburban and urban stands. The herbaceous layer had a greater cover in rural stands than in suburban stands (Fig. 4).

FOREST STRUCTURE

Total basal area of the trees did not differ within or among regions of the transect. However, plots in the rural forests tended to lack trees in the larger size classes more frequently than plots in either the urban or suburban stands. The density of both trees and saplings differed significantly among urban, suburban and rural stands (Table 4). Densities of trees and saplings were significantly greater in rural stands than in urban and suburban stands (Fig. 5). This indicates that the forests in the rural end of the gradient are more complex structurally, with greater development of vegetation layers. It also indicates that, though tree density was greater in rural stands and there was no difference in basal area, urban forests contain fewer, but larger trees. All forest plots contained downed logs, which suggests that the woody debris is not being removed from these sites, allowing it to decay in place and contribute to the nutrient pool and habitat structure of the site.

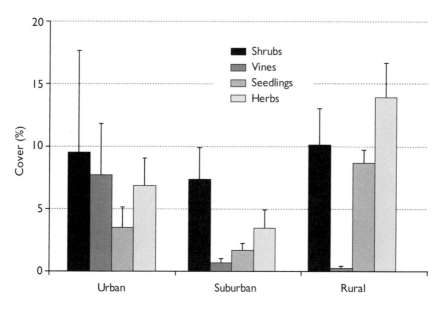

Fig. 4. Percent cover of ground vegetation. Each bar represents the average +1 S.E.
Replication is as described in Fig. 3.

The basal area of all tree species was subjected to a principal components
analysis to ordinate species in plot space. The first principal component
(PC1) explained 60% of the variation, and the second (PC2) explained an
additional 20%. Negative loadings on PC1 corresponded to *Quercus rubra*,
while *Q. velutina* loaded positively. *Q. rubra* and *Q. velutina* both loaded

Table 4. MANOVA and univariate ANOVAs for effects of region and forest on the
density of trees and saplings.

a) Multivariate analysis	Source	df	Wilks' λ	F	P
	Region	4	0.2093	4.74	0.0102
	Forest	14	0.1381	1.93	0.1036
b) Univariate analyses	**Source**	**df**	**ss**	**F**	**P**
Tree Density	Region	2	1208932.7	5.82	0.0239
	Forest	2	3517191.2	4.83	0.0162
Sapling Density	Region	2	15304907	11.34	0.0035
	Forest	2	24134851	0.51	0.806

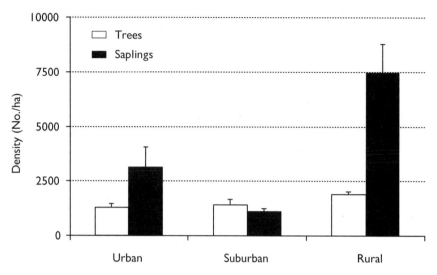

Fig. 5. Tree and sapling density across the urban-rural transect. Means represent the numbers of plots as described in Fig. 3.

positively on PC2 and *Betula lenta* loaded negatively. The separation of the *Quercus* spp. and *B. lenta* represent a separation in light-demanding species from more shade-tolerant species. The MANOVA to determine whether distance or region was significantly related to the PC scores indicated that the first axis was significantly related to both distance and region (Table 5). This significant finding results from the fact that rural stands differ from both suburban and urban stands, while suburban and urban stands do not differ from each other. Plots were also ordinated in species space, again using the total basal area of all tree species. The first axis explained 47% of the variation, and PC2 explained an additional 37%. All sites loaded positively on PC1, and the three sites that loaded the highest and the three that loaded the lowest were from each of the three regions. The site in PBP loaded the most positively on PC2, and many sites loaded negatively on PC2. The stands do not array along a linear urban-rural transect (Fig. 6).

Discussion

There are few consistent patterns in vegetation composition which correspond to a direct gradient of urbanization. Some variables, such as species richness in the understory and the density of woody stems, do vary significantly among regions, with rural stands more species rich and having a greater

Table 5. MANOVA and univariate ANOVAs for effects of region and distance from urban core on Principal Component axes PC1, PC2, PC3, and PC4.

a) Multivariate analysis	Source	df	Wilks' λ	F	P
	Region	8	0.06161	4.54	0.0096
	Distance	28	0.00595	2.59	0.0113
b) Univariate analyses	**Source**	**df**	**ss**	**F**	**P**
PC1	Region	2	740.8257	11.2	0.0036
	Distance	7	1627.9257	7.03	0.0046
PC2	Region	2	72.4303	0.89	0.4449
	Distance	7	453.5839	1.59	0.254
PC3	Region	2	90.7829	3.09	0.0952
	Distance	7	117.1874	1.14	0.4177
PC4	Region	2	12.5029	1.37	0.3013
	Distance	7	89.6159	2.82	0.0753

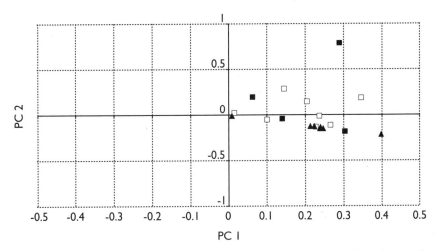

Fig. 6. Principal components ordination of stands in species space over the urban-rural transect. Urban stands are solid squares, suburban stands are open squares and rural stands are represented by solid triangles.

density of trees and saplings. Notable differences in community structure are the high cover of *Prunus serotina* saplings in the city and the significant increase of vine cover in urban stands. However, at this point it is difficult, if not impossible, to attribute all of these differences to anthropogenic influences represented by urbanization. McDonnell et al. (1997) suggest that the individual components of the system need to be quantified and correlations among them assessed to determine the ecological impacts of urban development and change on natural areas. To achieve this goal, research over the last decade has been conducted on a suite of ecological processes along the urban-rural land use gradient in the New York metropolitan area. This body of research includes chemical and physical properties of soil, biogeochemical processes, invertebrate communities, soil mycorrhizae, litter decomposition and atmospheric deposition of nutrients and pollutants. Many ecosystem properties and dynamics exhibit clear patterns that coincide with the urban-rural land use gradient. In contrast, the conservatism of tree species composition along the gradient does not appear to reflect or predict the variation in ecosystem processes that have been elucidated. Here we will briefly summarize the trends in ecosystem processes (see McDonnell et al. 1997 for a detailed review) and suggest when aspects of the vegetation may be mirroring those patterns.

An assessment of vegetation change in the NYBG forest concluded that the forest experienced an increase in disturbance to the understory including trampling, vandalism and arson (Rudnicky and McDonnell 1989). The understory was also colonized by shade-intolerant species, and it was suggested that urban stresses to the forest resulted in a more open canopy (Rudnicky and McDonnell 1989). Here we quantified a sparse understory in the NYBG plot in particular, and a lower density of trees and saplings in urban and suburban stands in general, compared to rural stands. The increase in vine cover in the urban stands presents a notable contrast with suburban and rural forests. Such a shift in vines has also been identified along an urban-rural transect in Baltimore, MD (Thompson 1999). In addition, it was noted that species in the lower forest layers are primarily shade-intolerant species, adding support to the suggestion that urban forest canopies are more open. The abundance and composition of seeds stored in the soil seed bank were also quantified in urban forest stands. A greater number of emergents and a greater presence of exotic species were found in urban seed banks compared to seed banks in rural stands (Kostel-Hughes et al. 1999). However, a more abundant seed bank does not appear to be reflected in a more abundant ground layer.

Soil chemical properties tightly correlated with distance from the urban core. Higher concentrations of Pb, Cu, Ni, Ca, Mg and K, high total soluble salt concentrations, high organic matter and high total N were documented in urban soils (Pouyat et al. 1995a). These concentrations decreased dramatically at approximately 30 km from the urban center (Pouyat et al. 1995a). In addition, concentrations and fluxes of NO3, NH4, Ca, Mg, SO4 and Cl entering the systems as throughfall all declined with distance from the city. Deposition of inorganic N, a form readily available to the biotic community, was twice as great in urban as in suburban and rural stands (Lovett et al. 2000). The decreases in chemical concentrations in soil and atmospheric inputs correspond to the change in landscape structure from predominantly urban-residential land cover to a dominance of land cover described as forest matrix (Medley et al. 1995). The forest matrix may include many houses and other structures in the suburban region. In addition, soils were more hydrophobic in urban stands than rural stands (White and McDonnell 1988). It is difficult to ascertain whether and how these differences in soil chemical properties and nutrient and pollutant inputs influence the structure and composition of the vegetation. The dynamics of vegetation change and the feedback between vegetation structure and biogeochemical pools and fluxes remain to be investigated in the New York metropolitan area.

Biogeochemical cycling also exhibited patterns along the urban-rural gradient. Higher rates of litter decomposition occurred in urban than in rural stands, and both the loss of litter mass and the amount of N released from litter were greatest in urban stands (Pouyat et al. 1995b, 1997). These results are surprising given that the biomass of litter fungi (Pouyat et al. 1994) and litter quality (Pouyat et al. 1995b) are lower in these stands. In general, lower microinvertebrate densities occur in urban soils than in rural soils (Pouyat et al. 1994). However, earthworms are an exceptional case, and earthworm abundance and biomass was 10 times greater in urban compared to rural soils (Steinberg et al. 1997). An experimental manipulation of earthworm abundance demonstrated that urban soil with earthworms had greater rates of N-mineralization and nitrification compared to urban soils without earthworms (Steinberg et al. 1997). Therefore, the higher rates of mineralization and nitrification in urban relative to rural soils (Pouyat et al. 1995a, 1997, Zhu and Carreiro 1999), may be due to the ability of earthworms to compensate for the lower litter quality and the lower densities of other soil invertebrates and litter fungi.

The structure and composition of the mycorrhizal community have been investigated along the gradient. This information complements that on the broader fungal community, discussed above. Mycorrhizae are an important component of forest soils because they benefit their host trees and contribute to forest functioning through enhancement of nutrient acquisition, drought tolerance and pathogen resistence. They are also sensitive to anthropogenic stresses such as acid deposition, N deposition, and heavy metals. Therefore, mycorrhizae may be good indicators of the ecological implications of biogeochemical alterations on the performance of the plant community. Urban soils have lower ectomycorrhizal richness and evenness as well as lower levels of colonization (Baxter et al. 1999).

It may be that the increased input of nutrients and the higher rates of N mineralization and nitrification facilitated by earthworm abundance may translate into tangible benefits to the plant community. Those benefits, though, are difficult to ascertain with a single snapshot of vegetation composition and structure. The effect of these differences may become visible with repeated sampling, which would better determine the performance and survival of the vegetation. Only repeated sampling, too, would capture a possible temporal lag between environmental changes caused by urbanization and their manifestation in vegetation structure and composition. This lag was anticipated because the lifespan of the target indicators—trees—greatly exceeds the temporal scale of recent changes in ecosystem processes brought about by urbanization. The enhanced nutrient input and processing may have negative effects through runoff and soil leaching on other components of the urban ecosystem, such as stream and stormwater quality. However, these linkages have yet to be explored.

The data presented here suggest that no overwhelming difference exists in forest stand composition along the urban-rural gradient. Notably, the strong trends in ecosystem processes along the gradient occur in spite of the fact that tree species do not correspond to the urban-rural gradient. However, there are more subtle structural differences among stands along the gradient that may reflect the influence of urbanization. These vegetational differences reside in the sapling, vine, seedling and herbaceous layers and therefore may become functionally significant during forest regeneration. In the urban forests, the mature trees of the canopy layer are the first generation to have experienced the full force of the urban environment. We do not know how these forests will regenerate given the differences in soil fauna and flora, altered atmospheric deposition and new distributions of life forms, exotics and dominants in the understory. Repeated measuring of permanent plots, such as those reported here, is needed to answer the question of how forest dynamics will differ under urbanization.

To fully understand the role of urbanization on forest structure and dynamics, more information is needed on the history of these sites as well as the present human use through either management or recreation. In addition, most work on urban forests has focused on structures and processes within the stand (Pickett et al. 2001), and the understanding of the structure and dynamics of the landscape in which these stands are embedded may increase our understanding of the effects of urbanization on these natural areas.

The urban forests of the New York City metropolitan region constitute a valuable amenity and source of ecosystem services (Flores et al. 1997) for the people of the region. Our studies have indicated that many of the compositional and structural features of these forests continue to reflect regional and historical environmental factors. However, ecosystem processes have already been strongly affected in urban stands, and contrasts between the understories of urban versus rural forests suggest that the urban and suburban stands are poised to undergo major compositional and structural changes in the near future. In order to inform the management, restoration and planning that maintain the ecosystem services of the forests in the metropolitan area, long-term research, studies that link community and ecosystem processes and studies of the landscape context of these stands must be increased.

Acknowledgments

Data collection was supported by a grant from the Lila Wallace-Reader's Digest Fund. The Baltimore Ecosystem Study-LTER through NSF DEB-97-14835 supported analysis. The authors thank Jennifer Haight, Nicholas Lewin, Peter Wycoff and Amy Hayes for assistance in the field. This project is a contribution to the program of the Institute of Ecosystem Studies with partial support from the Mary Flagler Charitable Trust and the Andrew W. Mellon Foundation.

References

Baxter, J.W., S.T.A. Pickett, M.M. Carreiro and J. Dighton. 1999. Ectomycorrhizal diversity and community structure in oak forest stands exposed to contrasting anthropogenic inputs. *Canadian Journ. Bot.* 77: 771-782.

Boyden, S., S. Millar, K. Newcombe and B. O'Neill. 1981. *The Ecology of a City and Its People: The Case of Hong Kong.* Australian National University Press, Canberra.

Broughton, J.G., D.W. Fisher, Y.W. Isachsen and L.V. Richard. 1966. Geology of New York: a short account. *New York State Mus. Sci. Ser., Educational Leaflet* no. 20.

Flores, A., S.T.A. Pickett, W.C. Zipperer, R.V. Pouyat and R. Pirani. 1997. Adopting a modern ecological view of the metropolitan landscape: The case of a greenspace system for the New York City region. *Landscape and Urban Planning* 392:95-308.

Grimm, N.B., J.M. Grove, S.T.A. Pickett and C.L. Redman. 2000. Integrated approaches to long-term studies of urban ecological systems. *BioSci.* 50:571-584.

Hill, D.E., E.H. Sauter and W.N. Gonick. 1980. Soils of Connecticut. *Connecticut Agric. Exper. Sta. Bull.* no. 787.

Kostel-Hughes, F., T.P. Young and M.J. McDonnell. 1999. The soil seed bank and its relationship to the aboveground vegetation in deciduous forests in New York City. *Urban Ecosys.* 2: 43-59.

Lovett, G. M., M. M. Traynor, R. V. Pouyat, M. M. Carreiro, W. Zhu, and J. W. Baxter. 2000. Atmospheric deposition to oak forests along an urban-rural gradient. *Environmental Science & Technology* 34:4294-4300.

McDonnell, M.J. and S.T.A. Pickett. 1990. Ecosystem structure and function along urban-rural gradients: An unexploited opportunity for ecology. *Ecol.* 71:1232-1237.

McDonnell, M.J. and S.T.A. Pickett. eds. 1993. *Humans as Components of Ecosystems: The Ecology of Subtle Human Effects and Populated Areas.* Springer-Verlag, New York.

McDonnell, M.J., J.L. Rudnicky, J.M. Koch and E.A. Roy. 1990. Permanent forest reference system: Pelham Bay Park and Van Cortlandt Park, Bronx, New York. *Protocol for Establishing Permanent Forest Reference Plot*, vol.1, Institute of Ecosystem Studies, Millbrook, NY.

McDonnell, M.J., S.T.A. Pickett, P. Groffman, P. Bohlen, R.V. Pouyat, W.C. Zipperer, R.W. Parmelee, M.M. Carreiro and K.Medley. 1997. Ecosystem processes along an urban-to-rural gradient. *Urban Ecosys.* 1:21-36.

Medley, K.E., M.J. McDonnell and S.T.A. Pickett. 1995. Forest-landscape structure along an urban-to-rural gradient. *Profess. Geogr.* 47: 159-168.

Mueller-Dombois, D., and H. Ellenberg. 1974. *Aims and Methods of Vegetation Ecology.* John Wiley & Sons, New York.

Pickett, S.T.A., W.R. Burch Jr., S.E. Dalton, and T.W. Foresman. 1997. Integrated urban ecosystem research. *Urban Ecosystems* 1:183.

Pickett, S.T.A., M.L. Cadenasso, J.M. Grove, C.H. Nilon, R.V. Pouyat, W.C. Zipperer and R. Costanza. 2001. Urban ecological systems: Linking terrestrial ecological, physical, and socioeconomic components of metropolitan areas. *Ann. Rev. Ecol. Syst.* 32.

Pielou, E.C. 1984. *The Interpretation of Ecological Data: A primer on Classification and Ordination.* John Wiley & Sons, New York.

Pouyat, R.V., R.W. Parmelee and M.M. Carreiro. 1994. Environmental effects of forest soil-invertebrate and fungal densities in oak stands along an urban-rural land use gradient. *Pedobiol.* 38:385-399.

Pouyat, R.V., M.J. McDonnell and S.T.A. Pickett. 1995a. Soil characteristics of oak stands along an urban-rural land-use gradient. *Journ. Envir. Qual.* 24:516-526.

Pouyat, R.V., M.J. McDonnell, S.T.A. Pickett, P.M. Groffman, M.M. Carreiro, R. W. Parmelee, K.E. Medley and W.C. Zipperer. 1995b. Carbon and nitrogen dynamics in oak stands along an urban-rural gradient, pp. 569-587, in Kelly, J.M., and W.W. McFee, eds. *Carbon Forms and Functions in Forest Soils.* Soil Science Society of America, Madison, WI.

Pouyat, R.V., M.J. McDonnell and S.T.A. Pickett. 1997. Litter decomposition and nitrogen mineralization along an urban-rural land use gradient. *Urban Ecosys.* 1:117-131.

Rowntree, R.A. 1988. Ecology of the urban forest: Introduction to Part III. *Landscape and Urban Planning* 15:1-10.

Rudnicky, J.L. and M.J. McDonnell. 1989. Forty-eight years of canopy change in a hardwood-hemlock forest in New York City. *Bull. Torrey Bot. Club* 116:52-64.

Schuberth, C.J. 1968. *The Geology of New York City and Environs.* Natural History Press, New York.

Soil survey staff. 1975. *Soil taxonomy: A basic system of classification for making and interpreting soil surveys, Soil Conservation Service Agricultural Handbook 436.* Government Printing Office, Washington, DC.

Stearns, F., and T. Montag. 1974. *The Urban Ecosystem: A Holistic Approach.* Dowden, Hutchinson, and Ross, Stroudsburg, PA.

Steinberg, D.A., R.V. Pouyat, R.W. Parmelee and P.M. Groffman. 1997. Earthworm abundance and nitrogen mineralization rates along an urban-rural land use gradient. *Soil Biol. Biogeochem.* 29:427-430.

Sukopp, H., and P. Werner. 1982. *Nature in Cities: A Report and Review of Studies and Experiments Concerning Ecology, Wildlife, and Nature Conservation in Urban and Suburban Areas.* Council of Europe, Strasbourg, France.

Thompson, H.C. 1999. Study finds adjacent land uses are key to predicting the number and type of exotic species in forest gaps (Maryland). *Ecolog. Restor.* 17:159-160.

United States Bureau of Census. 1980. *Number of Individuals: New York.* Government Printing Office, Washington, DC.

White, C.S., and M.J. McDonnell. 1988. Nitrogen cycling processes and soil characteristics in an urban versus rural forest. *Biogeochem.* 5:243-262.

Zhu, W.-X., and M.M. Carreiro. 1999. Chemoautotrophic nitrification in acidic soils along an urban-to-rural transect. *Soil Biol.Biochem.* 31:1091-1100.

Wildflowers and Flowering Shrubs of Forest Hills, Queens, 1984-2005

Guy Tudor
111-14 76th Ave
Forest Hills NY 11375

THIS REPORT ENCOMPASSES 20 YEARS OF OBSERVING flowers in the Forest Hills area, Queens County, a borough of New York City where I live—all on foot in my own "patch."

Encompassed here are:

1. Forest Park: east end, from the "Overlook" (park headquarters) to about Myrtle Ave.
2. Willow Lake, the southern terminus of Flushing Meadow-Corona green belt, bordered on the north by Jewel Ave.
3. Forest Hills lots: hereinafter applied to various vacant lots, street verges or garden edges in and around built-up Forest Hills.

I am no trained botanist, and many of my sightings have been convergent with bird and/or insect surveys. I employ Newcomb's *Wildflower Guide* (1977) as my basic guide, augmented with several more technical manuals.

This report's list follows, in taxonomic sequence and nomenclature, Mitchell's checklist of New York State plants (1986), a handy reference. English names are nearly all from Newcomb. Intermittently, I've added older scientific names to avoid confusion: like almost every other discipline, plant taxonomy is in great flux. Some plants have been identified only at the genus level.

Forest Park (East End)

As this Park is quite well known, I'll confine myself to selected comments. Basically, it is a quite uniform, wooded park typical of morainal Long Island.

Some principal or commoner trees include: Tulip Tree (*Liriodendron tulipifera*), Sassafras (*Sassafras albidum*), Pignut Hickory (*Carya glabra*), White Oak (*Quercus alba*), Black Oak (*Quercus velutina*), Northern Red Oak (*Quercus rubra*) (very common), Black (Sweet) Birch (*Betula lenta*) and Black Cherry (*Prunus serotina*). Occurring less commonly, or more locally, are: Eastern White Pine (*Pinus strobus*) (mostly planted), Sweetgum (*Liquidambar styraciflua*), Black Walnut (*Juglans nigra*), American Chestnut (*Castanea dentata*) (a few), American Beech (*Fagus grandiflora*), Gray Birch (*Betula populifolia*), American Basswood (*Tilia americana*), Black Locust (*Robinia pseudoacacia*), Flowering Dogwood (*Cornus florida*), Norway Maple (*Acer platanoides*) (edges), Red Maple (*Acer rubrum*), Catalpa (*Catalpa* sp.), Cork-tree (*Phellodendron* sp.) and American Holly (*Ilex opaca*) (a few). The Park is essentially waterless, with only a few manmade pools; the birders' "waterhole" at the east end is dry most of the year. The main "gully" lies west of the railroad tracks which bisect my area.

My general impression over two decades is that this Park is gradually losing its plant diversity, at least among the forbs. Some of the more "desirable" species are disappearing or becoming rare, while the invasive "weed" species are gaining ground, even (or especially) deep within the woods. Such tolerant species as Garlic Mustard (*Alliaria officinalis* = *petiolata*), Jumpseed (*Polygonum (Tovara) virginianum*), Enchanter's Nightshade (*Circaea quadri-sulcata* = *lutetiana*), Oriental Bittersweet (*Celastrus orbiculatus*), Jewelweed (*Impatiens capensis*), Maple-leaved Viburnum (*Viburnum acerifolium*), White Snakeroot (*Eupatorium rugosum*) and White Wood Aster (*Aster divaricatus*), in my recollection, seem to have remained stable or increased—note that many of these are native species.

Part of this change may be due to the woodland reaching a climax condition. It is worth noting that human-set fires were more frequent in the 1980s, when there were several large "burns"; however, this often allowed various flowers (not to mention certain birds and butterflies) to flourish. Probably there has been an overall drying out due to increasing human and horseback traffic. Another assault has been the repeated application of herbicides along the open railroad banks; these once held various flowers but are now more of a wasteland. However, most of all, the park may be experiencing the sadly familiar "island effect": diminishing of the rarer species within a circumscribed area. This effect has been documented for the Middlesex Fells reservation in Massachusetts, while our own John Kieran wrote of similar "winking-out" over the years in the Bronx's Van Cortlandt Park.

Nevertheless, I continue to discover surprises in out-of-way spots or on unfamiliar trails. Since my first draft in 2002, a more concerted effort has been made to botanically explore Forest Park. A number of new sites have been found for various scarcer species, and about 13 new species have been added in the last three seasons.

Willow Lake

This obscure and neglected "park" has experienced fluctuations of fortune—mostly downhill—over my years here. Originally built on landfill (during the 1939 World's Fair), this is essentially a small, Phragmites-fringed lake surrounded by weed-filled waste lots and dense vegetation along the borders. It may represent one of the very few associations of wetland and open fields in central Queens County. The southern end of the lake is rather swampy, with small stands of cattails along a tiny creek; this creek was ditched and cleared in 1984, but the vegetation here has since recovered. In 1983, the park lost about 4 hectares of upland fields which were appropriated by the IND Subway yards.

Water quality here has clearly deteriorated both in the lake and the "swamp." Wintering waterfowl visited in much better numbers in the early 1980s than at present but various fish, Painted Turtles and Muskrat continue to live here. I have never found any interesting aquatic plants in the lake. The vegetation along the edges of the park is often quite lush—indeed impenetrable. Among the commoner trees noted (at least formerly) have been: Sweetgum, White Mulberry (*Morus alba*), Pin Oak (*Quercus palustris*), White Poplar (*Populus alba*), Eastern Cottonwood (*Populus deltoides*), Weeping (*Salix babylonica*) and Crack (*Salix fragilis*) Willows, Black Cherry, Red Maple, Black Locust and Buckthorn species (*Rhamnus* sp.). Trees seen less commonly, or locally, would include: Austrian Pine (*Pinus nigra*), Hackberry (*Celtis occidentalis*), Willow Oak (*Quercus phellos*) (northend), American Hornbeam (*Carpinus caroliniana*), Hawthorn species (*Crataegus* sp.), Honeylocust (*Gleditsia triacanthos*) and Green Ash (*Fraxinus pennsyl-vanica*) (north end). An assortment of shrubs have seldom been adequately identified by me.

Without going into details, I will note that the Parks Department has alternately abused or tried to improve Willow Lake. There was an effort in the mid-1990s to create more wetland habitat; a shallow pool was dug out at the south end and certain "nice" flowers were introduced. These plants appear on my list, although some/most of them expired following a drought the next year. A "nature trail" was completed across the south end, but this too was not maintained properly and was overly seeded with *Rudbeckia*. Before and after these alterations, numerous adventive flowers appeared on disturbed soil only to subsequently vanish. Accordingly, my Willow Lake list contains some sightings which were not found again.

My impression is that the entire park is slowly sinking, or at least the upland fields are being invaded by Phragmites, Purple Loosestrife, etc. My old trails, on either side of the lake, are now so overgrown with brush that exploration is difficult. As a final indignity, in the past few years some City Department (?) has effectively barred any access with fences across the Grand Central Parkway overpasses. I did make one effort to enter at the north end (Jewel Ave) but was dismayed to find the fields here totally smothered by the invasive Porcelainberry. All things considered, I have rather given up on Willow Lake and have not really visited it since 1998.

What follows is mostly anecdotal observations made during my sojourn in Forest Hills. There was much less effort on my part to correctly identify all the nonflowering trees and decidedly still less for other floristic organisms (e.g., ferns, etc.). Some of the trees were identified many years ago by the late John Farrand, Jr.

My *total* list for Forest Hills to date includes about 280 species of wildflowers and flowering shrubs.

Annotated List

FP = Forest Park; WL = Willow Lake; FHL = Forest Hills lots, etc. No annotation means simply that the species is widespread here, or that I had nothing useful to add. * denotes Not native to New York State, (*) denotes Uncertain (following Mitchell (1986))

LAURACEAE		
	Lindera benzoin Spicebush	
RANUNCULACEAE		
	Anemone quinquefolia Wood Anemone	FP: uncommon and local; 4 sites around east end (April 2004)
*	*Clematis terniflora* Yam-leaf Clematis	Escaped along fence, Forest Hills lot (Oct 5, 2003)
	Ranunculus abortivus Kidneyleaf Crowfoot	FP: locally fairly common, mainly in "gully"; still present
*	*Ranunculus ficaria* Lesser Celandine	FP: recent; 3 sites in 2005-6; WL: several at south end (April 1993)

RANUNCULACEAE (continued)	
* *Ranunculus repens* Creeping Buttercup	FP: one plant on bridle trail (1984-5)
* *Ranunculus sceleratus* Cursed Crowfoot	WL: one plant in "swamp" (June 1996)
BERBERIDACEAE	
* *Berberis thunbergii* Japanese Barberry	FP: not very invasive yet
PAPAVERACEAE	
* *Chelidonium majus* (Greater) Celandine	FP: 3-4 along bridle trails west of railroad tracks (2003-6)
HAMAMELIDACEAE	
Hamamelis virginiana Witch-Hazel	FP;WL (flowering Nov 1989, 1998)
URTICACEAE	
Boehmeria cylindrica False Nettle	FP: very common at "waterhole"
Pilea pumila Clearweed	FP: locally common but not in wet areas
PHYTOLACCACEAE	
Phytolacca americana Pokeweed	
CHENOPODIACEAE	
Atriplex patula Orach	WL: uncommon
* *Chenopodium album* Pigweed	FHL, etc.
* *Chenopodium ambrosioides* Mexican Tea	Occasionally FHL
AMARANTHACEAE	
* *Amaranthus hybridus* Slender Amaranth	
PORTULACACEAE	
* *Portulaca oleracea* Purslane	Locally FHL and streets
MOLLUGINACEAE	
* *Mollugo verticillata* Carpetweed	FHL and streets; not uncommon

CARYOPHYLLACEAE

*	*Cerastium fontanum* Mouse-ear Chickweed	FHL (May 2002)
*	*Dianthus armeria* Deptford Pink	WL: several in field (1992)
*	*Sagina procumbens* Bird's-eye Pearlwort	FHL (identified by NW)
*	*Silene latifolia* White Campion (Evening Lychnis)	
*	*Silene noctiflora* Night-flowering Catchfly	WL: very local at north end (up to 1996)
	Silene stellata Starry Campion	FP: still occurs; 4 sites July 2001, 2 new sites west of railroad (Aug 2003)
*	*Stellaria graminea* Lesser Stitchwort	WL: fairly common
*	*Stellaria media* Common Chickweed	FP; also FHL
*	*Saponaria officinalis* Bouncing Bet	WL: fairly common

POLYGONACEAE

*	*Fagopyrum esculentum* Buckwheat	Obvious escape, several in flower FHL (2003)
*	*Polygonum cespitosum* Long-bristled Smartweed	FP: common along edges
*	*Polygonum cuspidatum* Japanese Knotweed	
*	*Polygonum lapathifolium* Nodding Smartweed	FP: not uncommon; WL: fairly common
*	*Polygonum persicaria* Lady's Thumb	WL; FP: local and uncommon
	Polygonum scandens Climbing False Buckwheat	
	Polygonum (Tovara) virginianum Jumpseed	FP: abundant; increasing
*	*Rumex crispus* Curly Dock	WL
*	*Rumex obtusifolius* Broad Dock	FP: fairly common throughout; also WL

CLUSTIACEAE

*	*Hypericum perforatum* Common St. Johnswort	Widespread, even on FHL

CLUSTIACEAE (continued)	
Hypericum punctatum Spotted St. Johnswort	FP: recent (2003-6); viable small colony just west of railroad tracks
MALVACEAE	
* *Abutilon theophrasti* Velvet-leaf	WL: one plant (Aug 1995); recent colony along edge of Grand Central Pkwy (Nov 2004)
Hibiscus moscheutos Swamp Rose-Mallow	WL: fairly common (*peckii* noted)
* *Hibiscus syriacus* Rose-of-Sharon	Occasional escapes, both parks at edges
* *Malva neglecta* Cheeses or Common Mallow	Local; FHL and street edges
VIOLACEAE	
Viola sororia Common Blue (Dooryard) Violet	FP: fairly common at edges, mainly east end; also FHL
CUCURBITACEAE	
Sicyos angulatus One-seeded Bur-Cucumber	FP: invaded "waterhole" (1996), later gone; recently discovered (a few) along Park Dr
BRASSICACEAE	
* *Alliaria officinalis = petiolata* Garlic Mustard	Very common; increasing in FP
* *Arabidoposis thaliana* Thale Cress	Recent on FHL
* *Barbarea vulgaris* Common Wintercress	WL: widespread
* *Brassica rapa* Field Mustard	WL: not common
* *Capsella bursa-pastoris* Shepherd's Purse	
* *Cardamine hirsuta* Hairy Bittercress	Recently noted, FHL
* *Diplotaxis tenuifolia* Perennial Wall-Rocket	Appeared on FHL (fall 1998); several new sites in May 2002 (identified by KA)
Lepidium virginicum Poor-man's-pepper	
* *Lepidium campestre* Cow-cress	WL

BRASSICACEAE (continued)	
* *Lunaria annua* Money-plant	Escapes on lot near WL; presently gone
* *Raphanus raphanistrum* Wild Radish	WL: formerly very common at north end of lake; also FP edges
Rorippa palustris Marsh Yellowcress	WL: noted infrequently in 1990s
* *Rorippa sylvestris* Creeping Yellow Cress	FHL (several sites)
* *Sinapsis arvensis* (B. kaber) Charlock	WL: south end of lake (June 1996)
* *Sisymbrium officinale* Hedge Mustard	Several FHL (2001-6); often mowed
* *Thlaspi arvense* Field Pennycress	WL: noted locally
PYROLACEAE	
Chimaphila maculata Spotted Wintergreen	FP: several newly found (July 2002) in old "burn"; 15 plants noted here in wet summer 2003
Pyrola americana Round-leaf Pyrola	FP: Large colony (45+ plants) found recently (2001) west of railroad tracks in woods; several other sites (July 2002-3) east of tracks
MONOTROPACEAE	
Monotropa uniflora Indian Pipe	FP: one or two seen in early 1980s; found again in old "burn" (July 2002); also at 2 new sites in wet summer 2003
PRIMULACEAE	
Lysimachia ciliata Fringed Loosestrife	FP: formerly, uncommon; at present, nice colony at "waterhole"
* *Lysimachia nummularia* Moneywort	FHL: recent (2006) escape, blooming
Lysimachia quadrifolia Whorled Loosestrife	FP: formerly common throughout park, but appears to be seriously declining of late
ROSACEAE	
Agrimonia gryposeptala Common Agrimony	FP: presumably this species; not common
Crataegus sp. Hawthorn	WL

ROSACEAE (continued)

	Geum canadense White Avens	FP: widespread and fairly common; WL: occasional
*	*Potentilla argentea* Silvery Cinquefoil	WL
	Potentilla canadensis Dwarf Cinquefoil	FP: local; also, FHL/lawns
	Potentilla norvegica Rough Cinquefoil	WL: fairly common locally (1990s)
*	*Potentilla recta* Sulphur (Rough-fruited) Cinquefoil	FP: local; not lately
	Potentilla simplex Common Cinquefoil	FP: local; uncommon
	Prunus serotina Black Cherry	
*	*Rhodotypos scandens* Jetbead	FP: formerly, occasionally at edges; now spreading invasively into park
*	*Rosa multiflora* Multiflora Rose	Both parks; spreading
	Rubus allegheniensis Common Blackberry	
*	*Rubus phoenicolasius* Wineberry	FP: locally common; spreading?

* CAESALPINIACEAE

	Cassia nictitans Wild Sensitive-plant	FP: colony present west. of railroad (1990-1); now gone

* FABACEAE

	Amphicarpea bracteata Hog-peanut	FP: local, but good colony in "gully" still present
*	*Coronilla varia* Crown Vetch	FP: colony invaded along Interboro Pkwy edge in 1990s; now gone; never found at WL
	Desmodium nudiflorum Naked-flowered Tick-trefoil	FP: always very uncommon, in west woods; several found in 2001, but not in 2005-6
	Desmodium paniculatum Panicled Tick-trefoil	FP: 4 to 5 sites (1990); still present locally
*	*Lespedeza cuneata* Chinese Bush-clover	WL: local, spreading?
	Lespedeza intermedia Wandlike Bush-clover	FP: found once in 1992

* **FABACEAE (continued)**		
*	*Lotus corniculatus* Bird's-foot Trefoil	WL: common
*	*Medicago lupulina* Black Medick	Found in FHL (Aug 2003)
*	*Melilotus alba* White Sweet-clover	Common and widespread
*	*Melilotus officinalis* Yellow Sweet-clover	More local; mainly WL
*	*Trifolium arvense* Rabbit's-foot Clover	WL: locally common
*	*Trifolium campestre* Low (Smaller) Hop-clover	Local; both parks
*	*Trifolium dubium* Least Hop-clover	
*	*Trifolium hybridum* Alsike Clover	Both parks, but only edges of FP
*	*Trifolium pratense* Red Clover	
*	*Trifolium repens* White Clover	
*	*Vicia cracca* Cow Vetch	WL common; FP: Interboro Pkwy edge, but now gone
* **LYTHRACEAE**		
*	*Lythrum salicaria* Purple Loosestrife	WL: very common and spreading
* **ONAGRACEAE**		
	Circaea quadrisulcata = lutetiana Enchanter's Nightshade	FP: abundant throughout; also WL
	Epilobium glandulosum = ciliatum Northern Willow-herb	WL: became very common at southwest end following wet year of 1990; present status?
	Oenothera biennis Common Evening Primrose	WL: common; also FP edge
CORNACEAE		
	Cornus florida Flowering Dogwood	FP: remains fairly common, but scattered
	Cornus amomum Silky Dogwood	FP: one shrub, east of railroad, budding on 14 May 2006

CELASTRACEAE	
*	*Celastrus orbiculatus* Oriental Bittersweet	Spreading invasively, even in FP woods
*	*Euonymus alata* Winged Euonymus	FP: flowering shrub found in "gully" (May 2003)
EUPHORBIACEAE		
	Acalypha rhomboidea Three-seeded Mercury	Common; FHL, etc.
*	*Chamaesyce maculata (E. supina)* Milk-purslane	FHL and streets
	Poinsettia (E.) dentata Green Poinsettia (Toothed Spurge)	Found recently at several FHL, including Queens Blvd divider
RHAMNACEAE		
*	*Rhamnus frangula* Glossy (Smooth) Buckthorn	FP: one blooming (May 2005); WL: buckthorns never identified
***VITACEAE**		
*	*Ampelopsis brevipedunculata* Porcelain-berry	WL: formerly, locally decorative; now invasively blankets north end of lake
	Parthenocissus quinquefolia Virginia Creeper	
	Vitis aestivalis Summer Grape	FP: recently identified (June 2004) at "water- hole" and along Park Lane South
	Vitis labrusca Fox Grape	
LINACEAE		
*	*Linum usitatissimum* Common Blue Flax	Present in FHL (Austin St) in 1996-97; now extirpated
ANACARDIACEAE		
	Rhus copallinum Dwarf Sumac	WL
	Rhus glabra Smooth Sumac	WL: common
	Toxicodendron radicans Poison Ivy	Recently spreading in FP; WL: fairly common
OXALIDACEAE		
	Oxalis stricta Yellow Wood-Sorrel	

GRANIACEAE		
*	*Erodium cicutarium* Storksbill	FHL: Recent (2000-6) colonies on sandy lots
	Geranium maculatum Wild Geranium	FP: formerly more common; 3 sites in 1993; now seen only in "gully," where declining (10-12 plants in May 2004)
*	*Geranium pusillum* Small-flowered Cranesbill	WL: small colony on disturbed soil (June 1996); now probably gone
* BALSAMINACEAE		
	Impatiens capensis Jewelweed	FP: locally very common
* ARALIACEAE		
	Aralia nudicaulis Wild Sarsaparilla	FP: large colony long suspected east of railroad; confirmed May 2006 with several in flower
	Aralia racemosa Spikenard	FP: first found in July 2002; then, 2 more large plants seen in 2003 and one at least remains
	Aralia sp. Hercules'-club	FP: noted once in 1980s; uncertain which species, perhaps Japanese *elata*?
APIACEAE		
	Cryptotaenia canadensis Honewort	FP: fairly common locally, especially east end
*	*Daucus carota* Queen-Anne's-Lace	
*	*Heracleum sphondylium* European Hogweed	FP: 2 huge plants appeared along well-used bridle trail east of railroad, flowering in May 2006; identified by KA
	Osmorhiza longistylis Aniseroot	FP: locally, at various sites, especially east end
*	*Pastinaca sativa* Wild Parsnip	WL: fairly common, at least formerly
	Sanicula gregaria Clustered Snakeroot	FP: common, especially at east end (often with Honewort); identified by KA
APOCYNACEAE		
	Apocynum androsaemifolium Spreading Dogbane	FP: very local (not lately)
	Apocynum cannabinum Indian-hemp	

APOCYNACEAE (continued)		
*	*Vinca minor* Periwinkle	FHL

ASCLEPIADACEAE		
	Asclepias incarnata Swamp Milkweed	WL: introduced 1995; still present 1997 (but current status unknown)
	Asclepias syriaca Common Milkweed	WL: very common; FP: local, declining and now gone?

SOLANACEAE		
	Datura stramonium Jimsonweed	WL: local; present status?
	Solanum carolinense Horse-Nettle	WL
*	*Solanum dulcamara* Bittersweet Nightshade	
*	*Solanum nigrum* Black (Garden) Nightshade	

CONVOLVULACEAE		
	Calystegia sepium Hedge Bindweed	WL: very common; FP: local, at edges
(*)	*Convolvulus arvensis* Field Bindweed	WL: locally fairly common; present status?
*	*Ipomoea purpurea* Common Morning-Glory	WL: escaped along edges; large vine noted (2001) on fence along Grand Central Pkwy

POLEMONIACEAE		
	Phlox paniculata Perennial (Fall) Phlox	FP: noted once (Oct 1992) at landfill edge

* BORAGINACEAE		
	Hackelia virginiana Virginia Stickseed	FP: first found in 2001, in west woods; large new colony (25+ plants) found nearby in July 2005

VERBEACEAE		
	Verbena hastata Blue Vervain	WL: fairly common
	Verbena urticifolia White Vervain	Fairly common in both parks

LAMIACEAE

	Collinsonia canadensis Horse-balm	FP: several colonies in woods west of railroad tracks; still present; one new site (Oct 2003)
*	*Glechoma hederacea* Gill-over-the-ground	FP: locally common; several sites
*	*Lamium purpureum* Purple Dead-nettle	Along building lots on Queens Blvd in early spring
*	*Leonurus cardiaca* Motherwort	FP: fairly common in "gully"; occasionally noted WL
	Lycopus americanus Cut-leaved Water-horehound	WL: very common in wet years
	Lycopus virginicus Virginia Bugleweed	FP: local, at several sites in 1990s; not seen recently
*	*Mentha spicata* Spearmint	WL: one patch near lake (Sept 1990)
	Monarda fistulosa Wild Bergamot	FP: surprise of last season were 4 flowers blooming on slope east of railroad in early July (note: 2006 was 'banner year' in Orange Co)
	Prunella vulgaris Heal-all	FP: fairly common locally; perhaps declining
	Scutellaria lateriflora Mad-dog Skullcap	FP: large colony appeared at "waterhole" in Aug 1990; extirpated by 1996

PLANTAGINACEAE

*	*Plantago lanceolata* English Plantain	
*	*Plantago major* Common Plantain	

OLEACEAE

*	*Ligustrum vulgare* Common Privet	FP: blooming in "gully" (2002); also edges and FHL

*SCROPHULAIACEAE

	Linaria canadensis Blue Toadflax	WL: local in field (May 1991)
*	*Linaria vulgaris* Butter-and-eggs	WL: fairly common
*	*Mazus pumilus* Japanese Mazus	Found on several lawns (May 2002-5) in Forest Hills; identified by KA; blooms in May

*SCROPHULAIACEAE (continued)	
* *Verbascum blattaria* Moth Mullein	WL: local in FP
* *Verbascum thapsus* Common Mullein	WL: common
* *Veronica arvensis* Corn Speedwell	On lawns and lots in Forest Hills; may get mowed
Veronica americana American Brooklime	WL: one patch in bloom (May 1983), in cattail swamp; never seen again
Veronica peregrina Purslane Speedwell	WL: small colony on disturbed soil (June 1996), south end; probably gone
* OROBANCHACEAE	
Epifagus virginiana Beechdrops	FP: one patch newly found near Beech trees (July 2002), but not recently
BIGNONIACEAE	
* *Campsis radicans* Trumpet Creeper	WL: very recently (July 2006), on fence along Grand Central Pkwy
* *Paulownia tomentosa* Paulownia	FP: flowering tree; noted a few blooming in May 2000
CAMPANULACEAE	
Lobelia inflata Indian-tobacco	FP: local and uncommon; along railroad banks in recent years
Lobelia siphilitica Great Lobelia	WL: first appeared at south end 1990; by Oct 1996 (wet year) 20+ flowers counted; present status?
Triodanis (Specularia) perfoliata Venus' Looking-glass	On various FHL (including 76 Ave); not uncommon; also, noted WL
RUBIACEAE	
Cephalanthus occidentalis Buttonbush	WL: north end of lake; FP: "waterhole"
(*) *Galium aparine* Cleavers	FP: local, especially in "gully", but declined lately; WL: noted occasionally
* *Galium mollugo* Wild Madder	Status similar to Cleavers; both parks
Mitchella repens Partridge-berry	FP: recently (2003) found at 2 adjacent sites east of railroad tracks; not flowering

* CAPRILIFOLIACEAE	
* *Lonicera japonica* Japanese Honeysuckle	
* *Lonicera* spp. "Bush" Honeysuckles	Probably *morrowii* but possibly (also) *tatarica* never identified satisfactorily; mainly at WL?
Sambucus canadensis Common Elderberry	Both parks; common at WL
Viburnum acerifolium Maple-leaved Viburnum	FP: abundant
Viburnum lentago Nannyberry	FP: recently noted: 4 blooming at different sites (May 2005)
Viburnum sp. Arrowwood	Both parks, commoner at WL; exact species not identified
* *Viburnum plicatum* Japanese Snowball	FP: not recognized until 2001; occasional escapes along edge at east end
ASTERACEAE	
* *Achillea millefolium* Common Yarrow	WL: common
Ambrosia artemisiifolia Common Ragweed	
Ambrosia trifida Great Ragweed	Fairly common in both parks; abundant along Forest Park Dr (east end)
* *Anthemis* sp. Mayweed or Field Chamomile	WL: common on disturbed soil in 1996; present status?
* *Arctium minus* Common Burdock	Common in both parks, especially WL
* *Artemesia vulgaris* Mugwort	
Aster cordifolius Heart-leaved Aster	FP: locally common
Aster divaricatus White Wood Aster	FP: by far the commonest aster; frequent at edges
Aster dumosus Bushy Aster	WL: fairly common locally
Aster lanceolatus (simplex) Panicled Aster	FP: local at edges; WL: one of commonest asters

ASTERACEAE (continued)

	Aster lateriflorus Calico Aster	Identified once, on FHL
	Aster macrophyllus Large-leaved Aster	FP: small, discrete colony west of railroad tracks; seems to have declined lately (blooming late July-Aug)
	Aster novae-angliae New England Aster	WL: several patches of this showy species at south end of lake (Oct 1997); present status? A similar "garden" aster escaped into FP on dry trails
	Aster patens Late Purple Aster	FP: noted only once, in woods west of railroad tracks (Oct 1997)
	Aster pilosus Heath Aster	WL: common; FP: along edges
	Aster puniceus Purple-stemmed Aster	WL: locally fairly common
	Baccharis halimifolia Groundsel-tree	WL: noted occasionally; scarce
	Bidens frondosa Common Beggar-ticks	
	Bidens tripartita (connata) Swamp Beggar-ticks	WL: noted at southwest end (1985); present status?
	Bidens coronata Northern Tickseed-sunflower	WL: noted once, at northeast end (Sept 1991)
*	Carduus nutans Nodding (Musk) Thistle	WL: several plants in south field in 1980s; extirpated by 1991
*	Centaurea maculosa Spotted Knapweed	
*	Centaurea nigra Black Knapweed	More widespread here than Spotted Knapweed
*	Cichorium intybus Chicory	
*	Cirsium arvense Canada Thistle	WL: common and invasive
	Cirsium discolor Field Thistle	FP: one flower recently (2003) found along edge; may not persist
*	Cirsium vulgare Bull Thistle	WL: fairly common; FP: occasionally at edges
	Conyza canadensis Horseweed	

ASTERACEAE (continued)		
*	*Coreopsis lanceolata* Lance-leaved Coreopsis	WL: noted only twice, on disturbed soil (1991, 1996)
	Erechtites hieracifolia Pilewort	WL: common locally; FP: very local
	Erigeron annuus Daisy Fleabane	
	Erigeron philadelphicus Philadelphia Fleabane	WL: local, uncommon
	Eupatorium dubium Eastern Joe-pye-weed	WL: not uncommon
	Eupatorium fistulosum Hollow-stem Joe-pye-weed	Both parks; now common in FP
	Eupatorium perfoliatum Boneset	WL: common
	Eupatorium rugosum White Snakeroot	Very common, both parks
	Eupatorium serotinum Late-flowering Boneset	WL: local colony at south end; noted through Oct 1996
	Euthamia graminifolia Lance-leaved Goldenrod	WL: very common; FP: only at edges
*	*Galinsoga ciliata (quadriradiata)* Common Galinsoga	Very common, FHL and streets
	Gnaphalium obtusifolium Sweet Everlasting	Recent, one on FHL (Sept 2005); origin unknown
*	*Helianthus annuus* Common Sunflower	WL: occasional
*	*Heterotheca subaxillaris* Camphorweed	WL: uncommon and local; few records
*	*Hieracium caespirosum (pratense)* King-devil	WL: uncommon
	Hieracium kalmii (canadense) Canada Hawkweed	FP: formerly fairly common along railroad tracks; now reduced and local, mainly in nearby woods
	Hieracium paniculatum Panicled Hawkweed	FP: remains locally fairly common
*	*Hieracium pilosella* Common Mouse-ear	WL: recorded at south end (1996)
	Hieracium scabrum Rough Hawkweed	FP: one record, in woods (Sept 2000)
*	*Hypochoeris radicata* Cat's-ear	WL: oddly, only once (Aug 1991)

ASTERACEAE (continued)

	Lactuca biennis Tall Blue Lettuce	FP: formerly along railroad tracks; extirpated by herbicides and not seen recently
	Lactuca canadensis Wild Lettuce	
*	*Lactuca serriola (scariola)* Prickly Lettuce	WL: fairly common.; also FHL
*	*Lapsana communis* Nipplewort	FP: recently, a few in flower along trails west of railroad (June-July 2005-6)
*	*Chrysanthemum leucanthemum* Ox-Eye Daisy	WL
*	*Matricaria matricarioides* Pineappleweed	Occasional, FHL
	Mikania scandens Climbing Hempweed	WL: common
	Pluchea odorata (purpurascens) Saltmarsh Fleabane	WL: very local and sporadic; 4-5 plants seen in wet year 1990
*	*Rudbeckia hirta* Black-eyed Susan	WL: normally common, but became abundant from "seeding" in 1996
*	*Senecio vulgaris* Common Groundsel	WL; also fairly common FHL
	Solidago bicolor Silver-rod	FP: formerly fairly common; decreased lately
	Solidago caesia Blue-stemmed Goldenrod	FP: remains very common and widespread; blooming in Oct
	Solidago canadensis Canada Goldenrod	Local in both parks
	Solidago junecea Early Goldenrod	Locally fairly common in both parks
	Solidago nemoralis Gray Goldenrod	Status same as Solidago junecea
	Solidago rugosa Rough-stemmed Goldenrod	FP: local; but fairly common; WL: recorded at south end
	Solidago sempervirens Seaside Goldenrod	WL: commonest goldenrod here
*	*Sonchus asper* Spiny-leaf Sow-thistle	Much scarcer than next species
*	*Sonchus oleraceus* Common Sow-thistle	Widespread, even in FHL

ASTERACEAE (continued)	
* *Taraxacum officinale* Common Dandelion	
Vernonia noveboracensis New York Ironweed	WL: appeared at south end of lake Aug 1996 (10+ plants); present status?
Xanthium strumarium (chinense) Common Clotbur	WL: very local; sandy areas
* ALISMATACEAE	
Alisma plantago-aquatica (subcorda-tum) "Small" Water-plantain	WL: introduced (?) or colonized shallow pool in 1996; present status?
ARACEAE	
Arisaema triphyllum Jack-in-the-pulpit	FP: not uncommon locally; but seems to be declining
COMMELINACEAE	
* *Commelina communis* Asiatic Dayflower	
SPARGANIACEAE	
Sparganium sp. Bur-reed	WL: introduced (?) or more likely colonized 1996; present status?
* TYPHACEAE	
Typha angustifolia Narrow-leaved Cattail	WL: Fairly common, at least in 1980s, south end of lake
Typha latifolia Broad-leaved Cattail	WL: Common, at least formerly; cattails have declined following construction; invaded by Phragmites
PONTEDERIACEAE	
Pontederia cordata Pickerelweed	WL: apparently introduced into pool in 1996; presumably gone following drought
LILIACEAE	
* *Allium vineale* Field Garlic	WL: locally common
* *Convallaria majalis* Lily-of-the-valley	FP: small colony established in woods west of "waterhole" (May 2005-6); also escaped (?) at edges
* *Hemerocallis fulva* Day-lily	WL: occasional escapes along edges

LILIACEAE (continued)	
Hypoxis hirsuta Yellow Stargrass	FP: for years a small colony west of railroad tracks still persists; a stable new colony east of tracks (2003-6)
Maianthemum canadense Canada Mayflower	FP: always local but a number of new sites recently discovered
* *Ornithogalum umbellatum* Star-of-Bethlehem	FP: occasional, along edges, especially Park Dr
Polygonatum pubescens Hairy Solomon's-seal	FP: oddly, uncommon; not many sightings
Smilacina racemosa False Solomon's-seal	FP: very common
Uvularia sessilifolia Sessile Bellwort	FP: one or 2 near "waterhole" in early 1980s; large stable colony discovered at east end off Park Dr in 2003; blooming in late April
IRIDACEAE	
Iris versicolor Large Blue Flag	WL: presumably introduced (?) by bridge in 1996; present status?
Sisyrinchium angustifolium Stout Blue-eyed Grass	FP: few records; not lately
SMILACACEAE	
Smilax rotundifolia Common Catbrier	
ORCHIDACEAE	
* *Epipactis helleborine* Helleborine	FP: not noted until early 1990s; now present at many sites, undoubtedly spreading, with colony near "Overlook"

Addendum

In spring of 2007, two unexpected flowers were discovered by Mike Feder in Forest Park, and subsequently seen by me; both in bloom. *Asarum canadense*, Wild Ginger—very few modern records for LI and *Erythronium americanum*, Trout-Lily—at the southeast corner.

Acknowledgments

Occasionally I have submitted "voucher specimens" to Nick Wagerik (NW) or Karl Anderson (KA) of the Rancocas Nature Center, NJ, both very competent botanists. I would also like to thank Dr. Skip Blanchard and Rich Kelly of the Long Island Botanical Society for their help.

References

Anderson, K. 1989. *A Checklist of the Plants of New Jersey*. New Jersey Audubon Society, Rancocas Nature Center. Mount Holly, NJ.

Clemants, S. and K. A. Barringer. 1999. *New York Metropolitan Flora: Woody Plant Workbook*. Brooklyn Botanic Garden, Brooklyn, NY.

Conolly, B. and G. Lotowycz. 2004. *Illustrated Field Guide to Shrubs and Woody Vines of Long Island*. Waterline Books, Hardwick, MA. (brand new and very useful; Queens is on L.I.!)

Fitter, R., A. Fitter and M. Blamey. 1996. *Wild Flowers of Britain and Northern Europe* (5th edition). Harper Collins, London.

Gleason, H.A. and A. Cronquist. 1991. *Manual of Vascular Plants of Northeastern United States and Adjacent Canada* (2nd edition). New York Botanical Garden, Bronx, NY.

Mitchell, R. S. 1986. A checklist of New York State plants. *New York State Museum Bulletin* No. 458.

Newcomb, L. and G. Morrison. 1977. *Newcomb's Wildflower Guide*. Little Brown & Co., Boston.

Petrides, G. and J. Wehr. 1988. *A Field Guide to Eastern Trees*. Houghton Mifflin Co., Boston.

Symonds, G. W.D. 1963. *The Shrub Identification Book*. William Morrow & Co., New York.

One Hundred Fifty Years of Change in the Orchid Flora of Brooklyn and Queens, New York

Eric Lamont
Honorary Research Associate, Institute of Systematic Botany,
The New York Botanical Garden, Bronx NY
elamont@optonline.net

Introduction

DURING THE PAST 150 YEARS, 24 species of native orchids from Brooklyn and Queens have been well documented by voucher specimens, although in recent years only three native species have been observed in the field from Queens and none in Brooklyn. Before the beginning of the 20th century, seven orchid species probably had been extirpated from Brooklyn and six others were known from only one population. The last verified report of a native orchid from Brooklyn dates from 1911. Historically, the orchid flora of Queens was somewhat richer and more diverse than that of Brooklyn. Several orchid populations persisted in Queens into the first quarter of the 20th century but soon thereafter drastically declined in numbers. The greatest diversity of orchids in Queens was concentrated in the vicinity of Flushing. In the 20th century's last quarter, the nonnative Helleborine Orchid (*Epipactis helleborine*) invaded Brooklyn and Queens and vigorously colonized disturbed roadsides and woodland borders. This report also presents a brief summary of the native orchids of each of the five boroughs of New York City.

History

Giovanni da Verrazano was the first European to set eyes on the land we now know as New York City. The year was 1524, and the Italian explorer was drawn across the vastness of the Atlantic Ocean by stories of virgin lands overflowing with riches and schools of fish so thick they could thwart a ship's passage. On April 17 of that year, Verrazano piloted his ship, the *Dauphine*, through a narrow cut between two land masses he did not know were islands and entered a wide, deep bay sheltered by thickly forested lands. He had reached what would later be called New York Harbor; he was the first European to see the wooded western end of Long Island on the harbor's eastern shore.

Describing his trip in a letter to his patron king of France, Francis I, Verrazano spoke of a land "covered with immense forests of trees, more or less dense, various in colors and delightful and charming in appearance." The land was so filled with an abundance of animals, forests and flowers that its "rich perfume wafted out to sea at great distance." The letter was written in an almost breathless tone.

Years later, other explorers and settlers confirmed the land's rich natural history and beauty. Eventually, botanists visited the land that we now call Brooklyn and Queens (Kings County and Queens County, respectively). They observed plants of southern affinities that had migrated northward on the sandy soils of the Atlantic coastal plain. They also found species growing in the rich soils of northern Brooklyn and adjacent Queens, soils deposited by glaciers originating far to the north. Small streams flowed southward from the humble Brooklyn hills and fanned out to form vast swamps and marshlands on the flat coastal lowlands before flowing through endless salt marshes that eventually emptied into the Atlantic Ocean. Such diversity of habitats provided the opportunity for the development of a rich and diverse flora.

Today, Brooklyn and Queens constitute two of the five boroughs of New York City. Located in the southwestern extremity of Long Island, Brooklyn occupies a relatively small land area. The irregularly shaped borough extends over only 71 square miles; if Brooklyn were rectangular, it would extend less than nine miles from east to west and less than eight miles from north to south. Queens, the largest in area of the five New York City boroughs, occupies 108 square miles, extending from Brooklyn to Long Island Sound. Combined, these two counties constitute less than 0.5% of the total land mass of New York State, but within this small area the 24 species of native orchids documented by our botanical forefathers represent an impressive 42% of the total orchid flora of New York State (57 species).

Methods

The following analysis and discussion of the past and present status of native orchids of Brooklyn and Queens is based exclusively upon a study of voucher specimens deposited at the following herbaria: Brooklyn Botanic Garden (BKL), Cornell University (CU), Harvard University Herbaria (HUH, including AMES), New York Botanical Garden (NY), New York State Museum (NYS) and Planting Fields Arboretum (OBPF). Label data from all voucher specimens were recorded and entered into a database; this information obtained from herbarium collections provided the foundation for the discussion that follows. Tables 1 and 2 present abbreviated summaries of the herbarium searches; more specific information on the orchids of Brooklyn and Queens is available upon request from the author.

The information presented in Table 3, which includes a summary of initial investigations in Bronx, Manhattan and Richmond boroughs,

Table 1. Selected Herbarium Collections of Native Orchids from Brooklyn, New York.

Species	Year Collected	Location	Name of Collector	Herbarium
Arethusa bulbosa	1871	New Lots	Leggett	NY
Calopogon tuberosus	1888	Canarsie	Eccles	NYS
Coeloglossum viride	1879	New Lots	?	CU
Corallorhiza maculata	1859	Brooklyn	Calverley	BKL
Corallorhiza odontorhiza	1857	Brooklyn	Calverley	BKL
Cypripedium acaule	1890	Forbells Landing	Hulst	BKL
Cypripedium parviflorum	1866	Greenwood	Brainerd	BKL
Goodyera pubescens	1890	Flatbush	Zabriskie	BKL
Isotria verticillata	1891	Forbells Landing	Hulst	BKL
Liparis lilifolia	1890	Cypress Hills	Hulst	BKL
Malaxis unifolia	1889	Flatbush	Zabriskie	BKL
Platanthera blephariglottis	1892	New Lots	Hulst	BKL
Platanthera ciliaris	1890	New Lots	Zabriskie	BKL
Platanthera flava var. herbiola	1877	New Lots	Schrenk	NY
Platanthera lacera	1867	New Lots	Brainerd	BKL
Platanthera psycodes	1863	New Lots	Brainerd	BKL
Pogonia ophioglossoides	1888	Canarsie	Eccles	NYS
Spiranthes cernua	1889	New Lots	Fernie	BKL
Spiranthes lacera var. gracilis	1889	Cypress Hills	Fernie	BKL
Spiranthes vernalis	1911	Coney Island	McCallum	BKL

Table 2. Selected Herbarium Collections of Native Orchids from Queens, New York.

Species	Year Collected	Location	Name of Collector	Herbarium
Arethusa bulbosa	1864	Queens	Calverley	BKL
Calopogon tuberosus	1899	Aqueduct	Seelman	BKL
Corallorhiza maculata	1927	Bayside	Ferguson	NY
Corallorhiza odontorhiza	1905	Jamaica	Bicknell	NY
Cypripedium acaule	1910	Jamaica	McCallum	BKL
Cypripedium parviflorum	1866	Flushing	Webb	BKL
Goodyera pubescens	1889	Flushing	Eccles	NYS
Goodyera repens	1866	Jamaica	Brainard	BKL
Isotria verticillata	1864	Jamaica	Leggett	NY
Liparis lilifolia	1889	Flushing	Eccles	NYS
Liparis loeselii	1896	Rockaway Park	Mulford	BKL
Platanthera blephariglottis	1890	Woodhaven	Hulst	BKL
Platanthera ciliaris	1902	Rosedale	Bicknell	NY
Platanthera clavellata	1881	Flushing	Bisky	BKL
Platanthera cristata	?	Queens	Calverley	BKL
Platanthera flava var. herbiola	1864	Queens	Calverley	BKL
Platanthera lacera	1904	Springfield	Bicknell	NY
Platanthera psycodes	1885	Kissena	Bisky	BKL
Pogonia ophioglossoides	1899	Aqueduct	Seelman	BKL
Spiranthes cernua	1927	Newtown	Ferguson	NY
Spiranthes lacera var. gracilis	1885	Flushing	Bisky	BKL
Spiranthes tuberosa	1902	Springfield	Bicknell	NY

was derived from both herbarium and literature searches. No discussion is presented here on the changes in the orchid flora of these boroughs, because research on those topics has not yet been completed. The historical occurrence of orchids in the three boroughs is exclusively based on the following sources: for Bronx Borough (Bronx Co.), a herbarium search at the New York Botanical Garden and information provided in *Preliminary Vouchered Atlas of New York State Flora* (New York Flora Association 1990); for Richmond Borough (Richmond Co.; Staten Island), information provided in *A Comparative Flora of Staten Island, 1879-1981* (Buegler and

Parisio 1982); for Manhattan Borough (New York Co.; Manhattan Island), information provided in *Native Orchids of Manhattan Island* (Denslow 1924). Throughout this report, scientific nomenclature follows *Revised Checklist of New York State Plants* (Mitchell and Tucker 1997).

The Orchids of Brooklyn

Probably the most significant collection of all the Brooklyn orchids is the Spotted Coral-root (*Corallorhiza maculata*). The genus *Corallorhiza* was first delimited in 1760 by the French botanist Jean Jacques Chatelain. In the same 1760 publication, he designated the Northern Coral-root (*Corallorhiza trifida* [=*Ophrys corallorhiza Linnaeus*]) as the type species for the genus. Sometime during the early 1800s, a large robust specimen of coral-root was collected from the "shady woods of Long Island, near Flatbush [Brooklyn]." Eventually, the orchid collection from Brooklyn made its way into the hands of the eccentric French botanist Constantine Samuel Rafinesque who, in 1817, proclaimed it to be an undescribed species, new to science. Rafinesque initially placed the new orchid from Brooklyn in the genus *Cladorhiza* but then transferred it to *Corallorhiza* where we still know it today as *Corallorhiza maculata*, the Spotted Coral-root.

The last verified report of the Spotted Coral-root from Brooklyn was documented by S. Calverley, who collected a specimen in 1858. Calverley also collected the inconspicuous, more southern Autumn Coral-root, *Corallorhiza odontorhiza*, from Brooklyn in 1857. Calverley's Brooklyn collections of the two species of *Corallorhiza* have been deposited in the herbarium at the Brooklyn Botanic Garden (BKL).

It is impossible for present-day botanists to determine the exact locations of the historical orchid collections from Brooklyn. Almost all of our information comes from hand-written notes recorded on herbarium labels, and these records are scanty and incomplete at best. Most herbarium labels from the late 1800s provide locality data that simply state "Brooklyn," or "swampy places" near a named town, or rarely (as in the case of a collection of the Small Purple Fringed Orchid, *Platanthera psycodes*) "meadow near bone boiling factory, New Lots, Brooklyn."

We can deduce, however, that the rich woodland-loving orchids probably occurred in the morainal hills of northern Brooklyn, in the vicinity of present-day Cypress Hills and Brooklyn Heights. Sometimes these locations were listed on herbarium labels, as in the collection of the Lily-leaved Twayblade (*Liparis lilifolia*); but most often we are left to speculate, as in the Brooklyn collections of the Long-bracted Orchid (*Coeloglossum viride*

Table 3. Native Orchids of the Five Boroughs of New York City, New York
Key: "X" = the presence of species. The information presented in this table was derived from both herbarium and literature searches (see Methods Section for more details).

Species	New York City Borough				
	Bronx	Kings	Manhattan	Queens	Richmond
Arethusa bulbosa		x		x	
Calopogon tuberosus	x	x	x	x	x
Coeloglossum viride		x			
Corallorhiza maculata	x	x	x	x	x
Corallorhiza odontorhiza	x	x	x	x	x
Cypripedium acaule	x	x	x	x	x
Cypripedium parviflorum	x	x	x	x	
Galearis spectabilis	x		x		x
Goodyera pubescens	x	x	x	x	x
Goodyera repens				x	
Isotria verticillata		x	x	x	x
Liparis lilifolia		x	x	x	x
Liparis loeselii	x		x	x	x
Listera cordata					x
Malaxis unifolia	x			x	
Platanthera blephariglottis		x		x	x
Platanthera ciliaris		x		x	x
Platanthera clavellata	x		x	x	x
Platanthera cristata				x	
Platanthera flava var. herbiola		x	x	x	x
Platanthera lacera	x	x	x	x	x
Platanthera psycodes	x	x	x	x	x
Pogonia ophioglossoides	x	x	x	x	x
Spiranthes cernua	x	x	x	x	x
Spiranthes lacera var. gracilis	x	x	x	x	x
Spiranthes lucida			x		
Spiranthes tuberosa				x	x
Spiranthes vernalis	x	x			x
Tipularia discolor			x		x
Triphora trianthophora					x
TOTAL: 30	**15**	**20**	**19**	**22**	**24**

var. virescens), Pink Lady's Slipper (*Cypripedium acaule*), Yellow Lady's Slipper (*C. parviflorum*) and Large Whorled Pogonia (*Isotria verticillata*).

The "Brooklyn Barrens" was a stretch of land located between the rich hills of northern Brooklyn and the sandy outer coastal plain to the south. The town of Flatbush sprang up in The Barrens, and orchid collections from this vicinity include the Downy Rattlesnake Plantain (*Goodyera pubescens*) and Green Adder's Mouth (*Malaxis unifolia*).

As the human population of Brooklyn significantly increased during the late 1800s, land suitable for development became more and more scarce. The extensive system of swamps and marshlands located in the southeastern portion of Brooklyn became the last safe haven for orchids. A rich diversity of orchid species occurred in this region, including Dragon's Mouth (*Arethusa bulbosa*), Grass-pink Orchid (*Calopogon tuberosus*), White-fringed Orchid (*Platanthera blephariglottis*), Yellow-fringed Orchid (*P. ciliaris*), Tubercled Rein-orchid (*P. flava var. herbiola*), Ragged-fringed Orchid (*P. lacera*), Purple-fringed Orchid (*P. psycodes*) and Rose Pogonia (*Pogonia ophioglossoides*).

The last orchid specimen collected from Brooklyn dates to 1911, when J. McCallum collected Spring Ladies' Tresses (*Spiranthes vernalis*) from moist sands at world-famous Coney Island. Nodding Ladies' Tresses (*S. cernua*) and Slender Ladies' Tresses (*S. lacera var. gracilis*) were also known to occur in Brooklyn; the final collections date to 1892 and 1889, respectively.

Sadly, all the Brooklyn wetlands were filled in by the beginning of the 20th century, and today, of the 20 species of native orchids historically known to have occurred in Brooklyn, not a single species has survived (see Table 1). Ironically, during the last two decades of the 20th century, the nonnative Helleborine Orchid (*Epipactis helleborine*) had invaded Brooklyn and vigorously colonized disturbed roadsides and the borders of woodlands.

The Orchids of Queens

Historically, the orchid flora of Queens was somewhat richer and more diverse than that of Brooklyn. Altogether, 22 orchid species have been documented with voucher specimens from Queens compared with the 20 species known from Brooklyn. Queens supported populations of five orchid species (Dwarf Rattlesnake-plantain, *Goodyera repens*; Yellow Twayblade, *Liparis loeselii*; Green Woodland Orchid, *Platanthera clavellata*; Crested Fringed Orchid, *P. cristata*; and Little Lady's Tresses, *Spiranthes tuberosa*) that were never reported from Brooklyn; conversely, Brooklyn supported populations of three orchid species (*Coeloglossum viride, Malaxis unifolia* and *Spiranthes vernalis*) that were never known to occur in Queens. Populations of 17 orchid species were common to both Brooklyn and Queens (Tables 1 and 2).

Although the total numbers of orchid species from Brooklyn and Queens are relatively similar (20 and 22, respectively), significantly more individual populations of native orchids occurred in Queens than in Brooklyn during the second half of the 19th century. More than 50 individual orchid populations (of all species) have been documented with voucher specimens from Queens, whereas only about 30 populations have been documented from Brooklyn during the same time period. The lower number of orchid populations from Brooklyn during the 19th century probably resulted from the earlier destruction of natural habitats there and development of the land for human use. Before the beginning of the 20th century, seven orchid species had probably been extirpated from Brooklyn and six other species were known from only one population, whereas most of the orchid species from Queens consisted of several populations. In 2000, no native orchid species were known from Brooklyn, whereas three extant orchid populations still occurred in Queens (*Cypripedium acaule, Platanthera lacera* and *Spiranthes cernua*).

At the beginning of the 20th century, the greatest diversity of orchids in Queens was concentrated in the vicinity of Flushing and College Point. Twelve orchid species occurred in this region of northern Queens. Especially noteworthy was the area surrounding and including Flushing Meadows, which drained north into Flushing Creek and ultimately into Flushing Bay; this area provided habitat for a rich diversity of orchid species, including *Corallorhiza maculata, Cypripedium parviflorum, Goodyera pubescens, Liparis lilifolia, L. loeselii, Plantanthera blephariglottis, P. clavellata, P. lacera, P. psycodes, Spiranthes cernua* and *S. lacera* var. *gracilis*. Other localities in northern Queens that also supported populations of orchids included Astoria, Bayside, Idlewild, Kissena, Maspeth and Newtown.

A second significant area in Queens that supported a rich orchid flora in the early 1900s was in the vicinity of Jamaica. Seven orchid species are known to have occurred in that region, including *Corallorhiza odontorhiza, Cypripedium acaule, C. parviflorum, Goodyera repens, Isotria verticillata, Liparis lilifolia* and *Spiranthes cernua*. Widely distributed populations of orchids in southern Queens also occurred in the vicinity of Aqueduct, Laurelton, Richmond Hill, Rockaway, Rosedale, Springfield and Woodhaven.

At the beginning of the 21st century, only three populations of native orchids still persisted in Queens. One small population of *Cypripedium acaule* was known to occur at Alley Pond Park south of Little Neck Bay.

Jamaica Bay Wildlife Refuge also provided suitable habitat for populations of *Platanthera lacera* and *Spiranthes cernua*. During the last two decades of the 20th century, the nonnative Helleborine Orchid (*Epipactis helleborine*) had vigorously invaded and colonized disturbed roadsides and the borders of woodlands throughout Queens.

Sources

Britton, N.L. 1899. List of plants growing in Bronx Park, in Report of the Director-in-chief of the New York Botanical Garden for 1898. *Bull. New York Botanical Garden* 1:171-242.

Brown, P.M. 1992. *Platanthera pallida* (Orchidaceae), a new species of fringed orchis from Long Island, New York, USA. *Novon* 2:308-311.

Brown, P.M. 2007. Wild Orchids of the Northeast. Univ. Press of Florida, Gainesville.

Buegler, R. and S. Parisio. 1982. Orchidaceae, pp. F16-17 in Hollick, Arthur, and Nathaniel Lord Britton, *A Comparative Flora of Staten Island 1879-1981, Including the 1879 and 1930 Floras*. Staten Island Institute of Arts and Sciences, Staten Island, NY.

Chapman, W.K. 1997. Orchids of the Northeast. Syracuse Univ. Press, Syracuse.

Correll, D.S. 1950. *Native Orchids of North America north of Mexico, (2nd edition)*. Chronica Botanica Co., Waltham, MA.

Denslow, H.M. 1919. Reminiscences of orchid-hunting. *Torreya* 19:152-156.

Denslow, H.M. 1920. Further reflections of an orchid hunter. Journ. New York Botanical Garden 21:145-156.

Denslow, H.M. 1924. Native orchids of Manhattan Island. *Journ. New York Botanical Garden* 25:290-293.

Denslow, H.M. 1927. Native orchids in and near New York. *Torreya* 27:61-63.

Gleason, H.A., and A. Cronquist. 1991. Orchidaceae, pp. 849-863 in: *Manual of the Vascular Plants of the Northeastern United States and Adjacent Canada*, The New York Botanical Garden, Bronx, NY.

Hollick, C.A. 1928. *Isotria verticillata* on Staten Island. *Torreya* 28:75-77.

House, H.D. 1924. Orchidaceae, pp. 234-252 in: Annotated list of the ferns and flowering plants of New York State. *New York State Mus. Bull.* no. 254.

Jelliffe, S.E. 1899. Orchidaceae, pp. 79-81 in: *The Flora of Long Island*. Lancaster Press (privately printed).

Kalbfleisch, A.S. 1898. Orchids on Long Island. *Plant World* 1:177-179.

Flora of North America Editorial Committee, eds. 2002. Orchidaceae, pp. 490-651 in: Flora of North America, North of Mexico, vol. 26. Oxford Univ. Press, NY.

Lamont, E.E. 1992. East Hampton orchids: Will they survive? *Long Island Bot. Soc. Newsletter* 2: 4-5.

Lamont, E.E. 1994. The weed orchid (*Epipactis helleborine*) on Long Island, New York. *Long Island Bot. Soc. Newsletter* 4:12.

Lamont, E.E. 1995. Fanny Mulford's orchid collections from the late 1890's. *Long Island Bot. Soc. Newsletter* 5:7-9.

Lamont, E.E. 1996. Atlas of the orchids of Long Island, New York. *Bull. Torrey Bot. Club* 123: 157-166.

Lamont, E.E. 1996. One hundred years of change in the orchid flora of Long Island, New York. *Program and Abstracts, Proc. New York Nat. Hist. Conf.* 4:20.

Lamont, E.E. 1998. Notes on wild orchids of Long Island, New York. *Long Island Bot. Soc. Newsletter* 8:36.

Lamont, E.E. 2000. Historical orchid collections from Brooklyn, New York. *North Amer. Native Orchid Journ.* 6:93-102.

Lamont, E.E. 2001. Notes on the white-fringed orchid on Long Island, New York. *Long Island Bot. Soc. Newsletter* 11:46.

Lamont, E.E. 2001. An additional note on the white-fringed orchid on Long Island, New York. *Long Island Bot. Soc. Newsletter* 11:47.

Lamont, E.E., J.M. Beitel, and R.E. Zaremba. 1988. Current status of orchids on Long Island, New York. *Bull. Torrey Bot. Club* 115:113-121.

Latham, R. 1940. Distribution of wild orchids on Long Island. *Long Island Forum* 3:103-107.

Luer, C.A. 1975. *The Native Orchids of the United States and Canada Excluding Florida*. New York Botanical Garden, Bronx, NY.

McGrath, R.T. and J.L. Turner. 1985. Some orchids of the Long Island pine barrens. *The Heath Hen* 2:32-39.

Mitchell, R.S., and G. C. Tucker. 1997. Orchidaceae, pp. 345-352 in: *Revised Checklist of New York State Plants*. New York State Mus. Publ. 490, Albany, NY.

New York Flora Association. 1990. Orchidaceae, pp. 469-477 In: *Preliminary Vouchered Atlas of New York State Flora, 1st edition*. The New York State Museum Institute, Albany, NY.

Taylor, N. 1915. Orchidaceae, pp. 245-261 in: Flora of the Vicinity of New York. *Mem. New York Bot. Gard.* 5.

Torrey, J. 1819. *A Catalogue of Plants Growing Spontaneously within Thirty Miles of the City of New York*. The Lyceum of Natural History of New York, Albany, NY.

Torrey, J. 1843. Orchidaceae, p. 266-288 in: *A Flora of the State of New-York*, 2. Carroll & Cook Printers, Albany, NY.

The Butterflies of Staten Island Revisited

Harry Zirlin
235 Rock Creek Lane
Scarsdale NY 10583
hzirlin@debevoise.com

Introduction

STATEN ISLAND SUPPORTS A COLLECTION of residential and commercial centers that would qualify as cities and towns in their own right if they were not already part of this outlying borough of New York City. Although nearly the entire island has been more or less modified by human activity, it still has open areas. These undeveloped areas form a crazy quilt patchwork of salt marshes, freshwater wetlands, beach habitats, serpentine balds and barrens, arid scrub and various types of deciduous woodland. Mixed in with these more natural habitats are backyard gardens, vacant urban lots and botanical gardens. All these areas support a large variety of both native and introduced plant species and these plants, in turn, serve as sources either of caterpillar food or adult nectar for Staten Island's butterflies.

Data from 1989-2006 record 76 species of butterflies seen on Staten Island, including three native North American species and two introduced European species not recorded in the two prior published surveys dated 1910 and 1973. The changing conditions in this rapidly developing part of the city have allowed a few species to increase in numbers since the earlier studies, while many others have declined or disappeared.

The butterflies of Staten Island have been the subject of two important articles: "List of the Macrolepidoptera of Staten Island," by William T. Davis (1910) and "The Ecological Associations of the Butterflies of Staten Island," by Arthur and Miriam Shapiro (1973). Both of these articles listed records for each species that the authors knew had been recorded previously on the island, and both, particularly the latter article, noted the habitat preferences of each species. The authors of both articles, too, recognized that the fauna

133

was changing before their eyes and, for the most part, becoming diminished from loss of habitat. In 1910 Davis wrote:

> Some of the species mentioned will probably not again be found, owing to the city conditions which are prevailing over an ever wider area of the island.

And more than 60 years later the Shapiros wrote:

> Many of the species which Davis regarded as widespread, common Island residents have undergone great reductions of population size and restriction of ranges. A number of these are obviously endangered [on Staten Island]; known today only from one or two localities, they could be eliminated from the Island by a few hours' work with a bulldozer.

The Shapiros then commented that "most or all of them" were doomed and listed 21 species "likely to become extinct on Staten Island within five years," i.e., by 1978. They also listed the species which they believed would persist either in urban areas or in the protected upland forest—"the green belt"—and concluded:

> This leaves us a fauna of some 21 species to look forward to by the year 2000....If there are more discoveries to be made in the Staten Island fauna, they had better be made soon.

The passing of the year 2000 seemed an opportune time to assess once again the island's butterfly fauna and compare it to the faunas known to Davis in the late 19th and early 20th centuries and to the Shapiros in 1970-71. The survey also provides a look at the fate of the 21 species that the Shapiros predicted would disappear from Staten Island. Finally, a survey at this time can provide important data regarding the remaining species that elected officials, regulatory agencies, conservationists and members of the public can consider when deciding land use issues on Staten Island.

Study Area

Staten Island occupies approximately 181 square kilometers between latitudes 40° 29' and 40° 16' west (Shapiro and Shapiro 1973.). The highest point is the summit of Todt Hill at 126 meters (see Shapiro and Shapiro for summary of geology). The island's flora has suffered to a large degree from development and invasive alien species (Shapiro and Shapiro 1973). Although all of Staten Island lies within the study area, a number of localities are consistently visited by butterfly seekers, as follows (Table 1):

a. Sailor's Snug Harbor (SSH): 33.7 hectares of botanical gardens, lawns and woods, including a butterfly garden with Buddleia (*Buddleia davidii*) and Joe-pye-weed (*Eupatorium dubium*).

b. Clay Pit Ponds State Park (CPP); [dimensions unavailable] sandy soil with scrub oaks, ponds and natural wetlands.

c. Conference House Park in Tottenville (CHP); 108 hectares of Hackberry (*Celtis occidentalis*) thickets, deciduous forest and scrubby beach vegetation at the southernmost tip of the island.

d. Sea View (SV): [dimensions unavailable] Serpentine barrens, with some acid scrub and woodlands.

e. Wolfe's Pond Park (WPP): 138 hectares of open recreational areas of typical lawn grasses with some wooded areas, a bog, ponds, salt marsh and beach areas.

f. Blue Heron Pond Park (BHPP): 90 hectares of old fields growing up to woods, some wetlands; gardens.

g. Eltingville (JF): The backyard butterfly garden of John Flynn deserves special mention here. Mr. Flynn has been carefully recording the butterflies in his yard since 1994. All records designated "JF" are from Mr. Flynn's backyard in Eltingville.

A few other sites are mentioned in the table without abbreviation, e.g., Mount Loretto, Great Kills Park, etc.

Methods

The data for this survey, which cover the years 1989 through 2006, come from the following sources: (1) records published in the Mulberry Wing (a data compilation of the New York City Butterfly Club, and Cech, 1993); (2) records published in the North American Butterfly Association (NABA)/ Xerces Society 4th of July Butterfly counts ("4JBC") (held on Staten Island for most years beginning in 1991); (3) my personal records (HZ); and (4) personal records of New York City area avocational and professional naturalists, including Rick Cech (RC), Tom Fiore (TF), John Flynn (JF), Edward Johnson (EJ), Jeff Ingraham (JI), Cliff Hagen (CH), Guy Tudor (GT), Nick Wagerik (NW), and Steve Walker (SW). Thus, most of the data are derived from sight records. Fortunately, the vast majority of Staten Island species are distinctive and easily recognized by experienced naturalists, and for many of the records photographic documentation exists.

In compiling the data, emphasis was placed on using the most recent records available. For many widespread and common species, only the data for one or two records are noted. For less common species, a wider range of data is set out in Table 1.

One of the problems with a survey of this type is that Staten Island has very few species not more readily seen somewhere else within easy traveling distance of the city. Thus, when many New York City area butterfly enthusiasts want to see or photograph the spring-flying univoltine species such as Cobweb Skipper (*Hesperia metea*) or Dusted Skipper (*Atrytonopsis hianna*) they will more likely visit the many well-known New Jersey Pine Barrens or Long Island Pine Barrens localities than trouble to scour the few hard-of-access spots on Staten Island. These spring-flying species are also unlikely to reach backyard butterfly gardens where they might be seen by a casual observer. They need to be sought out.

On the other hand, there are a few attractions for the avid butterfly seeker that consistently draw observers to the island. Three factors account for much of the data in this survey:

a. The geographical placement of Staten Island as the southernmost point in New York State, and its location on the Atlantic coastal flyway, makes it an ideal spot to observe southern immigrant species in the late summer through the fall.

b. The Hackberry thickets at Tottenville make that location a reliable spot to view the three Hackberry feeders in the Northeast (*Asterocampa celtis, A. clyton and Libytheana carinenta.*)

c. The widespread and growing interest in butterfly watching has resulted in a number of resident observers on the island who search for, and record, the species present and conduct an annual Fourth of July Butterfly count.

Results

Of the 110 species recorded from Staten Island, there are recent records (1989-2005) for 76 species. As noted above, these include three native North American species not recorded by either Davis or the Shapiros as well as two introduced European species not previously recorded. Of the 76 species recorded, 51 were recorded from a single locality, John Flynn's backyard.

Table 1. List of butterfly species known from Staten Island, with an indication of their current status. Note: 1: D = Davis reference; 2 = Shapiro reference. Initials in parentheses are those of observers. Abbreviations not in parentheses refer to localities. Nomenclature for both the scientific and common names follows NABA's revised checklist (2001).

	Species	D[1]	S[2]	Recent Records/Comments
1	*Enodia anthedon* Northern Pearly-eye		x	No recent records; may still persist in small numbers in the Greenbelt
2	*Satyrodes appalachia* Appalachian Brown	?	x	June 16,1991 WPP (NW); July 29, 1992 CPP (NW); Aug 7, 1994 CPP (RC); July 25, 1998 (JF); Aug 16, 1998 (JF); June 19, 1999 (4JBC)
3	*Satyrodes eurydice* Eyed Brown	x	x	No recent records; an unconfirmed sighting reported; a more northern species than Appalachian Brown
4	*Megisto cymela* Little Wood-Satyr	x	x	June 23, 1997 (JF); June 19, 2000 (4JBC); numerous records.
5	*Cercyonis pegala* Common Wood-Nymph	x	x	July 17, 2000 (JF); numerous records.
6	*Coenonympha tullia inornata* Common Ringlet			June 21, 1997 (4JBC). This species has been expanding its range north to south.
7	*Danaus plexippus* Monarch	x	x	Aug 17, 2000 SSH (HZ); numerous records.
8	*Agraulis vanillae* Gulf Fritillary		x	No recent records; a southern species; often bred for butterfly houses; any future records will be difficult to assess because of this.
9	*Euptoieta Claudia* Variegated Fritillary		x	June 26, 2000 (JF); numerous records.
10	*Speyeria idalia* Regal Fritillary	x	x	No recent records; extirpated from the entire NYC area and most of the northeast.
11	*S. cybele* Great Spangled Fritillary	x	x	July 19,1999 (JF); July 12, 1994 (JF); Aug 15, 1996 (JF)
12	*S. aphrodite* Aphrodite Fritillary	x	x	No recent records; another species in general decline in the northeast
13	*Boloria selene* Silver-bordered Fritillary	x	x	No recent records; may persist in some wet areas; this species, too, has had a general decline
14	*B. bellona* Meadow Fritillary	x	x	No recent records; may persist. Declining to the north

Table I continued.

	Species	D¹	S²	Recent Records/Comments
15	*Euphydryas phaeton* Baltimore Checkerspot	x	x	July 1991 (CHP) (JI)
16	*Chlosyne nycteis* Silvery Checkerspot		x	No recent records; probably no longer present; a good population persists in Van Cortlandt Park in the Bronx.
17	*Phyciodes tharos* Pearl Crescent	x	x	July 18, 1999 (JF); numerous records
18	*Polygonia interrogationis* Question Mark	x	x	May 8, 2000 (JF); numerous records.
19	*P. comma* Eastern Comma	x	x	July 2, 1999 (JF); numerous records.
20	*P. progne* Gray Comma	x	x	No recent records; a northern species; a recent record from Cape May NJ demonstrates that it can occasionally turn up south of its normal range.
21	*Nymphalis vau-album* Compton Tortoiseshell	x		Sept 20, 1996 (JF); a northern species, rare in NYC area, although sometimes there are outbreak years where it is present in some numbers.
22	*N. antiopa* Mourning Cloak	x	x	April 12, 1996 (JF); June 17, 2000 (4JBC); numerous records.
23	*N. milberti* Milbert's Tortoiseshell	x		No recent records; a northern species that has disappeared from the entire NYC area
24	*Vanessa atalanta* Red Admiral	x	x	Aug 17, 2000 SSH (HZ); numerous records.
25	*V. cardui* Painted Lady	x	x	Sept 13, 1997 (JF)
26	*V. virginiensis* American Lady	x	x	July 28, 1997 (JF); numerous records.
27	*Junonia coenia* Common Buckeye	x	x	July 13, 1997 (JF); numerous records.
28	*Limenitis arthemis astyanax* Red-spotted Purple	x	x	July 14, 2000 (JF); numerous records.
29	*L. archippus* Viceroy	x	x	July 30, 1999 (JF)
30	*Asterocampa celtis* Hackberry Emperor	x	x	Aug 17, 2000 CHP (HZ); numerous records

Table I continued.

	Species	D¹	S²	Recent Records/Comments
31	*A. clyton* Tawny Emperor			Aug 17, 2000 CHP (HZ)
32	*Libytheana carinenta* American Snout	x	x	Aug 17, 2000 CHP (40+) (JI, HZ); July 27, 2000 (JF)
33	*Parrhasius m-album* White-M Hairstreak	x	x	Aug 17, 2000 CHP (4) (JI, HZ); Aug 19, 1992 SV (EJ)
34	*Calycopis cecrops* Red Banded Hairstreak		x	Aug 17, 2000 CHP (HZ); June 28, 2003 (4JBC); numerous records. Range expanding south to north.
35	*Strymon melinus* Gray Hairstreak	x	x	Aug 17, 2000 CHP (HZ); numerous records
36	*Satyrium titus* Coral Hairstreak	x	x	June 22, 1991 (4JBC); June 26, 2004 (4JBC)
37	*S. acadica* Acadian Hairstreak		x	No recent records; may persist in small numbers in wetlands.
38	*S. edwardsii* Edwards Hairstreak		x	July 23, 2005 CPP (25+) (TF) July 29, 2006 CPP (TF). Declining.
39	*S. calanus falacer* Banded Hairstreak	x	x	July 9, 1995 (JF); numerous records.
40	*S. caryaevorum* Hickory Hairstreak		x	June 25, 1989 CHP (4) (GT). Also present in CPP. (TF).
41	*S. liparops* Striped Hairstreak		x	July 17, 1996 (JF); July 6, 1996 (JF)
42	*Callophrys gryneus* Olive Juniper Hairstreak	x		No recent records; probably no longer present.
43	*C. augustinus* Brown Elfin	x	?	No recent records; may persist in small numbers in barrens. Shapiro noted an unconfirmed sighting.
44	*C. henrici* Henry's Elfin			No recent records; unconfirmed reports of its presence.
45	*C. irus* Frosted Elfin	x	x	No recent records; probably no longer present
46	*C. niphon* Eastern Pine Elfin	x		No recent records; unconfirmed reports of its presence.
47	*Lycaena phlaeas* American Copper	x	x	Aug 17, 2000 CHP (HZ)

Table I continued.

	Species	D[1]	S[2]	Recent Records/Comments
48	*L. hyllus* Bronze Copper	x	x	No recent records; this species has suffered a general decline in the northeast.
49	*Everes comyntas* Eastern Tailed-Blue	x	x	July 16, 1999 (JF); numerous records.
50	*Celastrina ladon* Spring Azure	x	x	April 12, 1998 Greenbelt (SW)v
50a	*Celastrina ladon neglecta* Summer Azure	x	x	June 17, 2000 (4JBC) (23); numerous records.
51	*Feniseca tarquinius* Harvester	x	x	Sept 3, 1996 (JF); Aug 20, 1989 Great Kills (NW)
52	*Papilio polyxenes* Black Swallowtail	x	x	July 16, 1997 (JF); numerous records.
53	*P. glaucus* Eastern Tiger Swallowtail	x	x	Aug 17, 2000 SSH (HZ); numerous records.
54	*P. troilus* Spicebush Swallowtail	x	x	Aug 17, 2000 CHP (HZ); numerous records.
55	*P. cresphontes* Giant Swallowtail	x		No recent records; no longer present.
56	*Battus philenor* Pipevine Swallowtail	x	x	July 29, 2000 (JF); July 25, 1998 (JF); July 17, 1999 (JF); June 19, 1999 CHP (CH)
57	*Eurytides marcellus* Zebra Swallowtail	x		No recent records; no longer present.
58	*Colias eurytheme* Orange Sulphur	x	x	Aug 17, 2000 SSH (HZ); numerous records.
59	*C. philodice* Common Sulphur	x	x	June 20, 1998 (4JBC); numerous records.
60	*C. cesonia* Southern Dogface	x		No recent records; no reported sightings of this stray in the NYC area for many years.
61	*Phoebis sennae* Cloudless Sulphur	x		Aug 30, 1998 Mount Loretto (CH); Sept 1, 1998
62	*Eurema nicippe* Sleepy Orange	x	x	June 12, 2004 Mount Lorretto (TF); a rare stray to NYC area.
63	*E. lisa* Little Yellow	x	x	July 18, 1993 (4JBC)

Table I continued.

	Species	D[1]	S[2]	Recent Records/Comments
64	Pieris rapae Cabbage White	x	x	Aug 17, 2000 SSH (HZ); numerous records.
65	Pontia protodice Checkered White	x	x	July 25, 1992 Great Kills Pk (NW)
66	Pieris brassicae Large White			Aug 17, 2000 SSH (HZ, JI) (photo)
67	Epargyreus clarus Silver-spotted Skipper	x	x	Aug 17, 2000 SSH (HZ); numerous records.
68	Achalarus lyciades Hoary Edge	x	x	June 20, 1998 (4JBC)
69	Thorybes pylades Northern Cloudywing	x	x	June 20, 1991 Great Kills Pk (NW)
70	T. bathyllus Southern Cloudywing	x		No recent records; may still be present in small numbers.
71	Pholisora catullus Common Sootywing	x	x	July 18, 1993 (4JBC); numerous records.
72	Pyrgus communis Common Checkered-Skipper	x		Sept 4, 1995 SSH (NW); Sept 26, 1998 BHPP; Aug 28, 1999 SSH (NW); Sept 27, 2000 Crooke's Pt (CH)
73	Erynnis icelus Dreamy Duskywing	x	x	May 7, 1994 Greenbelt (SW)
74	E. brizo Sleepy Duskywing	x		No recent records; may persist in oak barrens.
75	E. martialis Mottled Duskywing	x	x	No recent records; probably no long present; another species that has declined drastically in the northeast.
76	E. horatius Horace's Duskywing		x	July 22, 2000 (JF)
77	E. juvenalis Juvenal's Duskywing	x	x	May 7, 1994 Greenbelt (SW)
78	E. baptisiae Wild Indigo Duskywing	x	x	July 18, 1993 (4JBC) June 26, 2004 (4JBC)
79	Ancyloxypha numitor Least Skipper	x	x	Aug 17, 2000 CHP (HZ); numerous records.
80	Thymelicus lineola European Skipper		x	June 21, 1997 (4JBC); numerous records.

Table I continued.

	Species	D¹	S²	Recent Records/Comments
81	*Hesperia sassacus* Indian Skipper	x		No recent records; probably no longer present.
82	*H. leonardus* Leonard's Skipper	x	x	No recent records; may persist in serpentine areas.
83	*H. attalus* Dotted Skipper		x	No recent records; probably no longer present.
84	*H. metea* Cobweb Skipper	x	x	May 7, 1994 Greenbelt (SW) (4)
85	*Hylephila phylaeus* Fiery Skipper		x	July 10, 1999 BHPP (CH); Oct 16, 1999 (JF); Sept 30, 2000 BHPP (CH); July 27, 1997 (JF)
86	*Atalopedes campestris* Sachem		x	July 18, 1999 BHPP (CH); July 10, 2000 (JF)
87	*Pompeius verna* Little Glassy-wing	x	x	June 21, 1997 (4JBC); numerous records.
88	*Polites origenes* Crossline Skipper	x	x	June 21, 1997 (4JBC); numerous records.
89	*P. themistocles* Tawny-edged Skipper	x	x	July 12, 1989 SV Seaview (NW); numerous records.
90	*P. pekius* Peck's Skipper	x	x	June 20, 1998 (4JBC); numerous records.
91	*P. mystic* Long Dash	x	x	No recent records; may still persist in wetlands.
92	*P. vibex* Whirlabout		x	No recent records; a very rare stray from the south.
93	*Wallengrenia egeremet* Northern Broken Dash	x	x	June 20, 1998 (4JBC); numerous records.
94	*Poanes viator* Broad-winged Skipper	x	x	Aug 17, 2000 CHP (HZ); numerous records.
95	*P. massasoit* Mulberry Wing	x	x	No recent records; may persist in small numbers in wetlands.
96	*P. hobomok* Hobomok Skipper	x	x	June 20, 1998 (4JBC)
97	*P. zabulon* Zabulon Skipper	x	x	Aug 17, 2000 CHP (HZ); numerous records.
98	*Atrytone arogos* Arogos Skipper		x	No recent records; almost certainly extirpated; a candidate for federal protection throughout its range.

Table I continued.

	Species	D[1]	S[2]	Recent Records/Comments
99	*Anatrytone logan* Delaware Skipper		x	July 13, 1997 (JF); numerous records.
100	*Euphyes dion* Dion Skipper		x	No recent records; probably present in very small numbers in wetlands.
101	*E. conspicua* Black Dash	x	x	No recent records; may persist in wetlands.
102	*E. bimacula* Two-spotted Skipper		x	No recent records; may be present in one or two bogs.
103	*E. vestris* Dun Skipper	x	x	June 20, 1998 (4JBC); July 13, 1999 (JF)
104	*Lerema accius* Clouded Skipper		x	No recent records; a rare stray from the south
105	*Atrytonopsis hianna* Dusted Skipper		x	May 29, 1992 SV (SW) (2)
106	*Nastra lherminier* Swarthy Skipper	x	x	June 22, 1991 (4JBC)
107	*Panoquina panoquin* Salt Marsh Skipper		x	August 20, 2006 (TF) Lemon Creek on the southeast shore.
108	*P. ocola* Ocola Skipper	x	x	Aug 17, 2000 SSH (HZ); Sept 13, 1997 (JF); Sept 12, 2000 (JF); Oct 13, 1995 (JF); Aug 18, 1999 (JF)
109	*Urbanus proteus* Long-tailed Skipper			Sept 5, 1994; Oct 1, 1995; July 19, 1997; Sept 23, 1994; Oct 13, 1995; Sept 1, 1998 (all JF)
110	*Inachus io* Peacock			Sept 30, 1995 (JF)

Species Declining and Species Increasing

Thirty-six species recorded by either Davis or the Shapiros were not recorded in this survey. However, a number of these previously recorded species were clearly accidentals and not part of the island's regular fauna, at least in historical times, if ever. *Agraulis vanillae, Nymphalis milberti, Eurytides marcellus, Colias cesonia, Hesperia attalus,* and *Polites vibex* are all very rare strays in the New York City area, *N. milberti* from the north and the rest from the south. To my knowledge none of these species has been recorded within 80.5 kilometers of New York City since 1971. Another group of butterflies recorded previously from the island have suffered drastic regionwide reductions in range that appear unrelated to particular conditions in any one locality. *Speyeria idalia, S. aphrodite, Boloria selene, Lycaena hyllus, Atrytone arogos* and *Erynnis martialis* are in this category. See Table 1 for further notes on each of the 36 species.

The species recorded in this survey as increasingly seen are primarily of Southeastern affinities. Davis did not record *Euptoieta claudia, Parrhasius m-album, Calycopis cecrops, Hylephila phylaeus* or *Atalopedes campestris.* The Shapiros did not record *Pyrgus communis* or *Phoebis sennae,* and neither survey recorded *Asterocampa clyton* and *Urbanus proteus. Libytheana carinenta* was recorded twice by Davis and listed as rare by the Shapiros, and *Panoquina ocola* was also listed as rare, with only one record by Davis.

It is tempting to attribute the increase in numbers of southern species to the reported warming trend in global temperatures. Many more carefully controlled data are required, however, before any such conclusions can be validly drawn. Moreover, several species of southern affinities reported by Davis or the Shapiros have not been recorded recently. Indeed, the Shapiros had the last known sightings of *A. vanillae* and *P. vibex* anywhere in the New York City area. Davis, too, had *C. cesonia* and *E. marcellus,* both of southeastern origins.

Along with *A. clyton* and *U. proteus,* the other native North American species recorded in this survey but not recorded by Davis or the Shapiros is *Coenonympha tullia inornata,* a satyrid of northern and western affinities which has been experiencing an incredible range expansion in the Northeast during the past few decades (Gochfeld and Burger 1997). The two European species recorded for the first time raise interesting problems. In recent years, a number of other European species have been recorded in the Northeast (Glassberg 1992). Whether these individuals represent deliberate releases by a misguided breeder, accidental escapes from an amateur breeder or stowaways transported by ship or airplane from Europe cannot be ascertained. An even more intriguing question is whether there are now small breeding populations of one or more of these species in the area, regardless of how the species arrived.

Species Confined to Specialized Habitats

The Shapiros listed 21 species "likely to become extinct on Staten Island within five years" (that is, by 1978). They are *Satyrodes appalachia, S. eurydice, Speyeria idalia, S. aphrodite, Boloria selene, B. bellona, Euphydryas phaeton, Chlosyne nycteis, Polygonia progne, Satyrium acadica, S. liparops, S. edwardsii,*

Callophrys irus, Hesperia leonardus, Polites mystic, Poanes massasoit, Atrytone arogos, Anatrytone logan, Euphyes dion, E. conspicua and *E. bimacula*. Of these, only three—*S. appalachia, S. liparops and A. logan*—persist to the point where they are likely to be recorded each season. A few others may still persist in small numbers or could conceivably turn up as strays, but, in large measure, their prediction was borne out.

The species which have suffered the most on Staten Island, and in the Northeast in general, over the last 40 years or so are those requiring open meadows with native grasses and other plants. Five of the violet-feeding fritillaries—*Speyeria idalia, S. cybele, S. aphrodite, Boloria selene* and *B. bellona*—are either gone completely or greatly reduced in numbers. The precise reasons for these declines are never certain, but butterflies in the genus *Speyeria* and their close relatives are apparently among the most sensitive to habitat disturbance (Hammod & McCorkle 1983). Other species which have suffered decline on the island are those associated with serpentine and acid habitats as well as those requiring freshwater wetlands to survive. Serpentine and acid habitats have generally undergone extensive development on Staten Island. The remaining wetlands are often the target of spraying with insecticides, ostensibly to control mosquito populations.

Table 2. List of dates and number of species recorded for Staten Island (4JBC).

22 June 1991	36 species
21 June 1992	16 species
18 July 1993	24 species
26 June 1994	26 species
22 July 1995	27 species
22 June 1996	28 species
21 June 1997	30 species
20 June 1998	26 species
19 June 1999	25 species
17 June 2000	28 species
30 June 2001	29 species
29 June 2002	26 species
28 June 2003	22 species
26 June 2004	29 species

Acknowledgments

No survey of this type can be carried out without the help of many individuals. The Fourth of July Butterfly Counts depend on volunteers, and I thank all of those who organized, participated in, and recorded the data for each of the counts referred to here. For providing me with their personal records from Staten Island, I thank Rick Cech, Robert Dirig, John Flynn, Edward Johnson, Cliff Hagen, Jeff Ingraham, Guy Tudor, Nick Wagerik, Steve Walter, and Tom Fiore. For providing the acreage data for park sites, I thank Theodore Boretti of the New York City Parks Department.

References

Cech, R., ed. 1993. *A Distributional Checklist of the Butterflies and Skippers of the New York City Area (50 mile radius) and Long Island, New York City Butterfly Club, N.Y.*

Davis, W.T. 1910 [1909]. A list of the macrolepidoptera of Staten Island, New York. *Proc. Staten Island Assoc. Arts and Sci.* 3: 1-30.

Glassberg, J. 1992. *Aglais urticae*: A nascent population in North America. *J Lepid. Soc.* 46: 302-304.

Gochfeld, M. and J. Burger. 1997. *Butterflies of New Jersey.* Rutgers University Press, New Brunswick, NJ.

Hammond, P.C., and D.V. McCorkle. 1983. The decline and extinction of *Speyeria* populations resulting from human environmental disturbances. *J Res. Lepid.* 22: 217-224.

NABA Revised Checklist, 2001.

Shapiro, A.M. and A.R. Shapiro. 1973. The ecological associations of the butterflies of Staten Island. *J Res. Lepid.* 12: 65-126.

Fort Tilden Dragonfly Migration Watch, 1993-1995

Steve Walter
6921 Springfield Blvd
Flushing NY 11364
SWalter@nyc.rr.com

Fort Tilden, a part of the Gateway National Recreation Area, is located in New York City's borough of Queens, on the Rockaway peninsula. From 1990 through 1995, it was the site of a formal hawk watch. For this reason and because of Fort Tilden's position along the coast, in early September 1992, I was invited to participate in the dragonfly migration data-gathering project conducted under the auspices of the Cape May Bird Observatory. The recording of data began in mid-September.

For me, that season had significant results: it introduced me to dragonfly identification and served to light a spark within me. The following summer I began studying dragonflies in the field in preparation for observing the year's coming migration, a project I believed needed to be started earlier in the season than the effort in 1992. The present summary was written following the 1995 dragonfly migration season and updated to include data from 1996 as well as records from more sporadic observations through 2000.

Study Area and Methods

Fort Tilden is on the Rockaway peninsula, the westernmost extension of the Atlantic shore of Long Island, a long-known flyway for migratory birds. Rockaway Inlet borders its north side. The width of the peninsula where observations were made is about 550 meters. Fort Tilden itself extends from about five to six kilometers east of Breezy Point, the western tip of land. The imminent water barrier prevents any milling about or congregating of dragonflies. Migrants tend to continue moving to the west-southwest, the direction of migration, only slowing for feeding activity or because of weather changes.

Observations focused solely on dragonflies were conducted from ground level. Those made in conjunction with or incidental to the hawk watch were done from a 15-meter-high former gun battery, or bunker, and generally took place beginning in mid-September with the advent of significant hawk flights. The ground-level observations of the early season proved important, as a number of species were low fliers, and ground level was more productive than the bunker for spotting low-flying individuals. It was also possible to spot the approach of small dragonflies a bit sooner from the ground, providing a better chance for identification. Observers watched at times from the Fort Tilden parking lot; at times from the roadway leading to the parking lot; and at times from the beach. The observation point chosen depended on where the flight appeared most active and also on the amount of human and vehicular activity on a particular day.

Identification was done by sight and with binoculars. Most species were captured at some point to confirm the observers' identification of in-flight dragonflies. Random capturing of reddish-looking immatures of Green Darner (*Anax junius*) also took place in an effort to determine if Comet Darner (*Anax longipes*) appeared in migration situations. All individuals were released. Observers also frequently checked a small freshwater pond, about a kilometer east of the observation site.

Data recording followed the method used for the hawk watch, with readings taken at the start of each hour of coverage. The data gathered included wind direction and speed, temperature and percentage of cloud cover. Dragonflies were counted individually when possible, i.e., when they passed close enough for identification and when spotting hawks did not take priority. Unidentified dragonflies were not recorded. The hordes of Green Darners and Black Saddlebags (*Tramea lacerata*) flying simultaneously with significant hawk flights were not counted, just labeled "abundant," "common," etc.

It should be noted that the numbers given as maximums represent a cross section of the flight. Because of their small size, dragonflies must pass close to the observer to be visible and identifiable. Moreover, there is a bias toward the larger or more distinctive species such as Swamp Darner (*Epiaeschna heros*) or Twelve-spotted Skimmer (*Libellula pulchella*). The actual numbers migrating through Fort Tilden would be significantly higher, as the flight often occurred over the width of the peninsula.

Observations began with the first available cold front in August— 15 August in 1993, 6 August in 1994. The success of both these outings confirmed the necessity to continue pushing the early starting date. In 1995, a significant cold front passed through the northeastern United States on 30 July. Observations on this date showed southbound dragonfly migration could occur as early as the month of July; in fact, it was the most spectacular flight observed, excluding those dominated by Green Darners. There was some indication of movement prior to this date, a question that needs to be explored in the future. Because of the hawk watch operation at Fort Tilden, the dragonfly watch season had no "official" end—dragonflies were recorded as long as temperatures allowed them to stay active.

Results

The greatest species diversity occurred in August, with twelve species recorded. In September eleven species were recorded, though many in reduced numbers. In fact, only Green Darner increased in numbers in September. Autumn Meadowhawk (*Sympetrum vicinum*) was the only species not recorded before September. Seven species were recorded in October, six of these regularly. Green Darner was always the last species recorded—to 14 November in 1993, 13 November in 1994, and 26 October in 1995.

Migration was most often associated with the passage of a cold front and winds from the north, the most common after a front. However, favorable winds may at times be long in coming. In fact, the peak flight (excluding those dominated by Green Darner) of 1994, on 27 August and 28 August, occurred on a southwest wind. Many of the species peaking with this flight were scarce after August in all three years, suggesting the lateness of the date provided an urgency to move on. Interestingly, a substantial movement of birds, most notably Eastern Kingbird (*Tyrannus tyrannus*) and Bobolink (*Dolichonyx oryzivorus*), also occurred on these two days.

Light to moderate wind speeds appeared to be preferable to strong winds, but this finding is not conclusive. Certainly the dragonflies responded to lighter winds than would be necessary to trigger hawk movements (on the coast). One situation that was definitely and without exception unfavorable was the onset of onshore winds. With the onset of the sea breeze, migration activity came to a screeching halt. As would be expected, the best migration days were those with an abundance of sunshine. In fact, migration was seen to slow when clouds obscured the sun and improve with the return of sunshine. However, a substantial flight (of mostly Green Darner) occurred on 8 September 1995, under mostly overcast conditions.

The temperature required to allow migration activity was a factor I constantly tried to determine. This was difficult for the early migrating species, as temperatures in August seldom dropped below their tolerance level. One such occurrence came on 6 August 1994, when morning temperatures dropped to about 13° C. With an active wind from the north to northeast, few dragonflies were seen—until midday, when the temperature rose above 15.5° C. Recall that this was the first cold front of the season.

Did the day have to warm up to trigger the flight or did the dragonflies need time to reach the coast for the first time? This question may have been answered with the flight of 30 July 1995. Despite the so-called "cold" front and an active wind from the northwest, temperatures lowered only to 28.8° C (and rose to 34.4° C). Even though few dragonflies had been noted on the coast prior to this day, the flight was already in high gear by 8:00 a.m. After August, of course, more opportunities offered themselves for measuring the effect of temperature on dragonfly migration. Unfortunately, only Green Darner and Black Saddlebags appeared in a significant enough sample. The temperature required to trigger significant migration among these species appeared to be about 16° C. Green Darner, however, was occasionally spotted at temperatures below 10° C.

Two types of migration flight were observed. One, a direct, purposeful flight to the west-southwest, was the type normally exhibited by Swamp Darner, skimmers (*Libellula* sp.), and Eastern Pondhawk (*Erythemis simplicicollis*). The second type of behavior was swarming, the flight mannerism usually, though not always, seen in Green Darner, gliders (*Pantala* sp.), and saddlebags (*Tramea* sp.). Numbers of these migrating dragonflies could be seen feeding in swarms and every few minutes advancing in waves. This is one reason I advise against extrapolating counts on a per-minute or per-hour basis. Blue Dasher (*Pachydiplax longipennis*) distinguished itself from other species by landing frequently and by often appearing to avoid flying over paved areas. Green Darner, Swamp Darner, Blue Dasher, both gliders, and Black Saddlebags were observed flying in from the ocean, probably having been steered there by strong winds.

As noted above, identification was made mostly by sight. In the species accounts, I detail how each species was identified. Both mature and immature patterns are described, as all species with recognizable age (or sex) variations did, in fact, appear in those variations. Tandem flight was observed occasionally for Green Darner through the three years and for about 75 pairs of Wandering Glider (*Pantala flavescens*) on 30 July 1995. Green Darner and Twelve-spotted Skimmer were occasionally observed egg-laying at the pond. On one occasion, a Green Darner was observed eating a Blue Dasher at the pond.

Species Accounts

GREEN DARNER (*Anax junius*), although the best-known migrant, proved to be atypical of migrant dragonflies. Some of the ways in which it differed from other species have been noted above. The highest recorded daily total was 1055 on 25 August 1995, however, this species was often much more numerous, appearing into the thousands. No attempt was made to count these larger flights as they occurred during September, coinciding with significant hawk flights. During these flights, American Kestrels (*Falco sparverius*) and Merlins (*F. columbarius*) heavily preyed on the dragonflies. This species was recorded as early as 30 July (1995) and as late as 14 November (1993). Green Darner was easily identified, even at a distance or altitude, by its large size and moderately slender build. At close range, its green thorax coupled with the bluish or reddish-brown abdomen added to the distinguishing characteristics.

SWAMP DARNER (*Epiaeschna heros*) was identified by its slender and dark appearance, very large size, and often drooped abdomen. This species was recorded as early as 21 July (1996) and as late as 24 September (1993). The maximum count of 754 was on 10 August 1996. This occurred in a year in which the species had been locally scarce prior to migration. Conversely, in 1995 the species had been very common in the New York region, but after a count of 125 on 30 July, numbers dropped to 14 on 13 August, to single digits thereafter and completely disappeared after 1 September. It seems likely the drought that affected the northeastern United States during August was responsible for this quick downward spiral. In suitable habitat away from Fort Tilden, I observed a good amount of egg laying into August, with one individual laying eggs as late as 28 August. This was done in the muddy edges of vernal ponds whose water was only receding, no doubt reducing the availability of juveniles of this and other vernal pond breeders to the fall migration. Consequently, the fall 1995 migration of the spring's invaders failed to live up to expectations.

PAINTED SKIMMER (*Libellula semifasciata*) was identified by its medium size, stout build, and reddish-brown body and wing patches. Although never common, its flight in its few appearances was direct and unquestionably that of a migrant. The daily high count reached 35 on 29 July 1997. This species was an early migrant, recorded as early as 27 July (1996) and only as late as 30 August (1994). Harder to quantify at Fort Tilden is this species' status as a spring migrant. In May 1993 it became numerous in the New York area, even appearing on Manhattan streets. It might have been expected that a notable southbound migration would follow, but only one was recorded that fall. There may have been several reasons for this. With this study in its infancy, this was not a species I was on the lookout for nor did I realize that its flight could bypass me on a southwest wind. In addition, its flight, direct and low to the ground, did not make it conspicuous.

TWELVE-SPOTTED SKIMMER (*Libellula pulchella*) was the only member of its genus to appear with any frequency. The high count was 990 on 10 August in the good year of 1996. More typical were peaks such as 155 on 27 August 1994, and 112 on 13 August 1995. In all years, numbers dropped off sharply after August. Migration dates ranged from 27 July (1996) to 28 September (1995). This species typically exhibited a direct flight. Twelve-spotted Skipper was readily identified by its distinctive wing pattern consisting of three large dark spots on each wing and, in mature males, alternating white spots.

GREAT BLUE SKIMMER (*Libellula vibrans*) was first recorded 6 August 1994, and recorded six times that season through 14 September. The maximum count was 29 on 10 August 1996, with peak numbers relegated to single digits in most years. In the wake of a large northward eruption in the spring and summer of 1995, I looked forward to a more significant flight. However, only two of this species were observed migrating. My hope to further substantiate the species as a fall migrant may well have been dashed by the drought in the Northeast. So far, this has been the only species found migrating that exhibits dark wing tips and otherwise inconspicuous wing markings when in flight. At least two of the 1994 individuals were mature males, lending their color to the identification process.

COMMON WHITETAIL (*Libellula lydia*) is another common dragonfly in eastern North America with limited appearances along the migratory route. Two individuals were recorded with certainty on 10 August 1996.

AUTUMN MEADOWHAWK (*Sympetrum vicinum*) remains an enigma. A high count of seven on 22 October 1994, were moving in the direction indicative of migration. But such movements were too sporadic to be conclusive. In 1995 none were noted migrating. Only one individual appeared at the hawk watch on 28 September and provided the earliest sighting for Fort Tilden. In the New York area this species is notable for its lateness, breeding in October and continuing to mid-November in mild years. Nonetheless, it appears no more active in cold weather than other species. Fall 1995 featured cold weather setting in and becoming entrenched earlier than normal, a possible contributor to the species' near absence at Fort Tilden. The species was distinguished by its small size and bright red body.

CALICO PENNANT (*Celithemis elisa*)—a single mature male was captured on 23 August 1995. It wasn't until 2000, particularly 19 - 22 August, that I saw additional evidence of migration. During those four days I found two individuals at Fort Tilden, three at Floyd Bennett Field, in Brooklyn, and two at Jones Beach, Nassau County. All these sites lie a good distance from the nearest breeding site. However, the arrival of these individuals at these sites could be just a dispersal rather than true southward migration. None was actually observed in a directional movement.

BLUE DASHER (*Pachydiplax longipennis*) was distinguishable by its small size and, in the case of closely seen mature individuals, black-tipped blue abdomen. Also helping with identification was the tendency of this species to land quite often, a stark contrast to other species' behavior. It was also usually, though not exclusively, observed close to the ground. Interestingly, this species, more than any other, seemed to avoid flying over paved areas. Nonetheless, movement was too consistently to the south and represented by too many individuals to doubt its migratory flight. The high count of 207, observed on 1 August 1998, is a relatively low total for a species considered by many as the most abundant dragonfly in the northeastern United States. Two causes may be responsible. First, its small size required close passage to the observer for detection. Second, it is possible the species may be only a partial migrant, evacuating only the more northern portions of its range where it may be less able to overwinter. A similar situation appears to exist for the Mourning Cloak (*Nymphalis antiopa*) butterfly; although well known in the New York area for appearing on the wing with the first mild spell of the spring or even winter, it may not be able to survive winters in areas to the north. It has also been suggested for spring migration (Soltesz, Barber, Carpenter, *Argia* Dec. 1995) that this species is more of a habitat general-ist than other migrants and it is the populations using vernal ponds that undertake movements due to drought conditions. This species appeared at the freshwater pond in greater numbers than any other species. Following the flight of 7 August 1994, about 50 were found where only a very few had been before. The presence of so many, mostly mature individuals, provided additional evidence this species was migratory. Blue Dasher was recorded as early as 27 July (1996) and as late as 8 October (1995).

EASTERN PONDHAWK (*Erythemis simplicicollis*) was almost always seen close to the ground and, due to its relatively small size, within six meters of the observer. At this distance the distinctive green coloration of immatures and females could be seen. Blue males were also identified, fitting in between Blue Dasher and Great Blue Skimmer in size. This species was seen as early as 13 August (1995) and as late as 2 September (1994). The maximum count was nine on 28 August 1994, rather low considering the species' general abundance. The same reasons cited for the Blue Dasher's rate of occurrence apply here.

WANDERING GLIDER (*Pantala flavescens*) was identified by its medium size and stout build and by its yellow to orange abdomen and clear wings. The species was not particularly common in 1993 and 1994, with no daily counts reaching 20. However, on 30 July 1995 a total of 2420 individuals were recorded. Thereafter, the highest count for 1995 was 56 on 13 August, with much lower numbers the rest of the season. Migration dates ranged from 21 July (1996) to 13 October (1995).

SPOT-WINGED GLIDER (*Pantala hymenaea*) was identified by its darker coloration compared to Wandering Glider and by the diagnostic spot at the base of the hind wing. With practice, the spot proved to be more detectable than expected and quite apparent in individuals directly overhead. This species was quite common in the New York area in the summer of 1994, and the abundance translated into a strong migration showing. It was less abundant, though still common, in 1995, peaking at 62 on 30 July. There was another strong flight in 1996 with a maximum count of 512 on 27 July. The species was seen in migration as early as 21 July (1996) and as late as 29 October (1994), although numbers dropped off sharply after the first week of September.

BLACK SADDLEBAGS (*Tramea lacerata*) was readily identified by its mostly black abdomen and the large black patches at the base of the hind wings. This species was observed as early as 27 July (1996) and as late as 25 October (1995). The highest count was 251 on 28 August 1994. In 1993, the high was 103 on 29 August and, in 1995, 195 on 25 August. My notes show it to be common to abundant as late as 24 September, but (because of having to deal with hawks) I had no numbers to compare it to the early season flights.

CAROLINA SADDLEBAGS (*Tramea carolina*) was identified by its red abdomen and wing patches. It is likely this species was undercounted since the brown-winged immatures were difficult to distinguish from Black Saddlebags except upon close passage. Nonetheless, this was a relatively uncommon species, as it is near the northern limit of its range. The maximum count was only 24 on 29 July 1997. Still, it appeared consistently on days when other species were moving. Migration dates were as early as 27 July (1996) and as late as 22 October (1994).

Addendum

The early migration dates cited above are probably typical of most years, with activity of most species beginning in late July. However, in the summer of 2000, which featured a number of strong cold fronts, I observed a convincing movement on 5 July at Point Lookout, Nassau County. Species recorded that day in low numbers were Green Darner, Swamp Darner, Painted Skimmer, Twelve-spotted Skimmer, Great Blue Skimmer, Blue Dasher, Wandering Glider, Spot-winged Glider, Black Saddlebags and Carolina Saddlebags. In another good year for Spot-winged Glider, a major flight took place this day. Hundreds were observed, with many pairs in tandem.

Future Efforts

In addition to continuing fall migration efforts, I would like to see similar methods employed for spring migration. The best locations to check would be north-pointing peninsulas and barrier islands, as well as water barriers to the north or east. Sandy Hook, New Jersey, should receive attention. The western shore of Chesapeake Bay may be worth a look, as would the southern shores of the eastern Great Lakes. Cape Cod and Plum Island, Massachusetts, are properly oriented but may be too far north for some of the species of interest. Subsequently, we could attempt to correlate spring and fall movements, as well as summer abundances of migratory species. The fall of 1995 proved a disappointment in this respect, most likely because of the drought in the northeastern United States. I had hoped to prove Bar-winged Skimmer (*Libellula axilena*) a migrant—in addition to the circumstantial evidence from appearances north of its normal range—but was unable to do so. Perhaps in a future year that opportunity will present itself. Certainly, every year is different, as the years 1993, 1994 and 1995 have shown. Future observations may yield more knowledge regarding fluctuations from year to year as well as the dynamics of daily flights.

Salamander Diversity and Distribution in New York City, 1820 to the Present

Ellen Pehek
Natural Resources Group
City of New York Parks & Recreation
1234 Fifth Avenue
New York NY 10029
Ellen.Pehek@parks.nyc.gov

Background

NATURAL RESOURCES GROUP (NRG) HAS KEPT RECORDS on sightings of wildlife since its formation in 1984. In 1993, we began intensive inventory and monitoring of amphibians. We have focused much of our efforts on salamanders because 1) salamanders may be good bio-indicators, helping us make decisions on land acquisition, protection, and management of parklands; 2) they can be a good educational tool, as some species are abundant, easy to monitor, and illustrate urban conservation problems; and 3) several species have been extirpated and others may be in imminent danger.

In the 1980s and '90s, scientists noticed sharp declines globally in formerly stable amphibian populations, some even in seemingly pristine wilderness. Many studies followed, attempting to establish the causes of this "global amphibian decline" (Wake 1991, Petit 1992, Stebbins and Cohen 1995, Yoon 1997, SSAR 1998). The results of these studies indicate that no one factor can be implicated in the global decline; rather, multiple changes to the environment, many caused by human activities, combine and interact to degrade habitat and/or directly affect health of amphibian individuals and populations. Surviving salamander populations in cities are subjected to a greater variety and amount of anthropogenic impacts than are their rural and suburban neighbors (Orser and Shure 1972, Campbell 1974, Windmiller 1996, Rocco et al. 1999, Mierzwa et al. 2002, Pember et al. 2002). The long history of European settlement and high population density in New

York have had a profound impact on its salamanders, but no comprehensive assessment of salamander diversity and status has been completed.

As suburban sprawl accelerates in the northeastern states, lessons taken from studies of wildlife in our most developed cities may help planners, wildlife managers, land trusts, and others involved in nature conservation to avoid the pitfalls and build on the successes of urban conservation. Amphibians are good early indicators of habitat degradation (Vitt et al. 1991, Stebbins and Cohen 1995, Davic 2002, Smithsonian Environmental Research Center 2004, Pehek and Mazor 2003). They live in some of the most vulnerable habitats, such as vernal ponds, streams, and the forest floor. Because their skin is permeable, they are more strongly affected by chemical changes than reptiles, birds, or mammals (Stebbins and Cohen 1995, McAlpine et al. 1998, Marco et al. 1999). They are less mobile than many insects, birds, and mammals and are often killed when attempting to cross roads and other developed land. NRG uses its studies of amphibians, especially salamanders, to identify and evaluate human activities that threaten the city's natural areas.

Amphibians are also good subjects for research on urban conservation because of their popularity with the public, especially children. Many amphibian monitoring programs have taken advantage of this popularity to recruit volunteers (Gosselin and Johnson 1995, Droege et al. 1997, Griffin 1998, North American Amphibian Monitoring Program 2003, Frogwatch USA 2003, New York State Department of Environmental Conservation 2003, The Nature Conservancy 2004). In addition to providing data that aid amphibian conservation efforts, these programs educate the volunteer monitors and participating school groups about conservation, stewardship, and the wonders that exist literally underneath their feet. NRG has begun recruiting and training volunteers to monitor terrestrial salamanders and hopes to expand these efforts to include stream and pond-breeding salamanders and other amphibians (Cox et al. 2000, Cox and Pehek 2000).

Our goals in this study were to 1) inventory New York's parks and natural areas for salamander diversity; 2) compare historical and recent salamander distributions; 3) investigate the causes of extirpations and population reductions; 4) assess the status of each salamander species in each borough and citywide; 5) compare the status of salamanders in New York City to that of New York State and adjacent states; and 6) propose actions to increase population sizes and stability for species of conservation concern.

Methods

We consulted literature records, museum collections, and local biologists and naturalists for historical records of salamander distributions in New York (Appendix A, Davis 1884, Sherwood 1895, Paulmier 1902, Wilmott 1931, Wilmott 1933, Bishop 1941, Mathewson 1955, Ricciuti 1984, Yeaton 1988, Klemens 1993, Tanacredi 1995, DeCandido 1999, Johnson pers. comm.). From 1993 to 2003, NRG conducted moderate to intensive field surveys for salamanders and other amphibians (Berkeley 1993, Miller 1995, Cox 1999, Pehek and Mazor 2003). Our methods included: searches under cover objects and artificial coverboards for terrestrial salamanders; informal and transect-based cover object searches in streams; and informal and transect-based searches in potential breeding ponds for adults, eggs, and juveniles of pond-breeding salamanders (Heyer et al. 1994, Olson et al. 1977, Welsh et al. 1997, Pauley 1999, Monti et al. 2000, NEARMI 2003A). We supplemented these searches with informal targeted dipnetting in ponds and streams and records incidental to invertebrate collection in Hess and drop-box samplers (Heyer et al. 1994, Pehek and Mazor 2003).

We divided salamander records into "present" and "historical" groups. The present encompasses the years 1980 to 2006, the period during which Parks collected the majority of their salamander records. All historical records but one (from 1820) were collected during the 100-year period from 1880 to 1979. To bring out changes within the historical period, we divided it into two 50-year spans, 1880-1929 and 1930-1979. We calculated the following measures of salamander distribution and abundance for each of New York's five boroughs and each time period: number of locations/species; number of records/species; number of individuals/species; and number of clutches of eggs/species. A record is defined as a sighting or collection of one species at one location on one occasion. We collected geographic/demographic data for each county consisting of: area in hectares, population density (persons/hectare), percent parkland, and percent vacant land (New York City Department of City Planning 2003). We looked at relationships between the number of recent salamander records and demographic/geographic data using Pearson correlation coefficients. We considered results significant that had an alpha <.10.

We identified current threats to salamander populations through observations during field surveys, unpublished reports by the New York City Parks Department, consultation with local experts, and the literature. We also searched internet sources and the literature for data on amphibian diversity and distribution in surrounding states for comparison.

Results

CHRONOLOGICAL PATTERNS: These are the eleven species of salamanders that historically occupied the five boroughs of New York City:

Ambystoma laterale	Blue-spotted Salamander
Ambystoma maculatum	Spotted Salamander
Ambystoma opacum	Marbled Salamander
Ambystoma tigrinum	Tiger Salamander
Desmognathus fuscus	Northern Dusky Salamander
Eurycea bislineata	Northern Two-lined Salamander
Hemidactylium scutatum	Four-toed Salamander
Plethodon cinereus	Red-backed Salamander
Plethodon glutinosus	Northern Slimy Salamander
Pseudotriton ruber	Red Salamander
Notophthalmus viridescens	Eastern Newt

Of the eleven species of salamanders, four have disappeared from the city (Tables 1 and 2). Another species, the Four-toed Salamander, is probably extirpated, but the secretive nature of this species makes such a determination difficult (Rumph 1979, Hunter et al. 1999). This leaves us with six (possibly seven) surviving species, only 54% (or 64%) of the original fauna. Four of the five species extirpated from all boroughs disappeared well before 1980. *Ambystoma laterale*, known only from one record in one borough, has not been found since 1880. This was the earliest species to disappear from the city. Thirty-five years later, we find the last record of *A. tigrinum*. Another 16 years passed before the probable disappearance of *A. opacum*. The last confirmed natural population, sighted in 1931, consisted of a large number of larvae (Wilmott 1931). *Plethodon glutinosus* was last reported the same year (1931). The last species to disappear was *Hemidactylium scutatum*. Twice it has been reported extirpated (Wilmott 1931, Mathewson 1955), only to be "rediscovered" in 1979 (Rumph 1979). Although we have searched many mossy, boggy wetlands near historical locations, we have not been able to find this species.

We found 361 records of salamander sightings and/or specimens from 67 locations between 1820 and 2006 (Tables 1 and 2). The combined data consisted of a minimum of 3289 individuals (adult/juvenile/larvae) and 94 clutches of eggs. In historical records, number of individuals was not always available and we had to use "1" in our tally as the minimum sighted in a record. If multiple life stages were noted, we recorded "1" for each life

Table 1. Number of locations for each salamander species native to New York City for all years and for the periods from 1820-1929, 1930-1979, and 1980-present. Reintroduction sites are not included in the chronological tally.

	All years	1820-1929	1930-1979	1980-present
AMBYSTOMATIDAE				
Ambystoma laterale	1	1	0	0
Ambystoma maculatum	11	4	2	5
Ambystoma opacum	2	2	1	0
Ambystoma tigrinum	2	2	0	0
PLETHODONTIDAE				
Desmognathus fuscus	11	4	4	8
Eurycea bislineata	21	4	7	16
Hemidactylium scutatum	4	3	1	0
Plethodon cinereus	47	8	6	41
Plethodon glutinosus	3	3	1	0
Pseudotriton ruber	7	1	5	4
SALAMANDRIDAE				
Notophthalmus viridescens	16	7	2	6
TOTAL NUMBER OF LOCATIONS	67	25	17	49

stage. This tactic, of course, biases the data toward more detailed records and recent records but is unavoidable. Fifty-seven (15.8%) records were from 1820-1929, 38 (10.5%) from 1930-1979, and 260 (72%) from 1980 to the present. Observers reported a minimum of 251 individuals (7.6%) from 1820-1929, 1396 (42.4%) from 1930-1979, and 1632 (49.6%) from 1981 to the present. Eighty-two of the clutches of eggs were recorded from 1980 to the present, with the other two clutches from 1930-1979. Because of the disparity in number and detail of records, we could use the pre-1980 data only to indicate presence and probable time of extinction, and even that has to be interpreted carefully. Most of the data after 1979 came from NRG inventory and monitoring and can be used to assess patterns of distribution, relative number of populations and, in some cases, relative population sizes.

Two of New York's six remaining salamander species dominate recent records (Table 2). From 1980 to the present, *Plethodon cinereus* was recorded 101 times, and *Eurycea bislineata* 103 times. *P. cinereus* is widespread in the city and often abundant where it occurs (mean individuals/record = 4.7).

Table 2. Number of records / total number of individuals (minimum) / number of clutches of eggs sighted since 1820 for New York City salamanders, by species and time period. For records that did not list numbers (1) was used as number of individuals. Reintroductions are not included. Totals for all years and all species include several pre-1980 records of uncertain vintage.

	1820-1929	1930-1979	1980-present	All years
AMBYSTOMATIDAE				
Ambystoma laterale	1/4/0	--	--	1/4/0
Ambystoma maculatum	6/6/0	4/28/1	14/18/88	25/53/89
Ambystoma opacum	2/2/0	1/1/0	--	3/3/0
Ambystoma tigrinum	2/4/0	--	--	2/4/0
PLETHODONTIDAE				
Desmognathus fuscus	6/45/0	4/21/0	30/115/1	41/184/1
Eurycea bislineata	5/134/0	10/1271/1	103/1011/2	118/2416/3
Hemidactylium scutatum	5/6/0	2/4/0	--	7/10/0
Plethodon cinereus	11/17/0	6/21/0	101/470/1	119/510/1
Plethodon glutinosus	3/3/0	1/1/0	--	4/4/0
Pseudotriton ruber	5/7/0	8/12/0	6/8/0	19/27/0
SALAMANDRIDAE				
Notophthalmus viridescens	11/23/0	2/37/0	6/10/0	22/74/0
ALL SPECIES	57/251/0	38/1396/2	260/1632/92	361/3289/94

E. bislineata consists of dense populations at fewer locations (mean individuals/record = 9.8). *Desmognathus fuscus*, with 30 records and 3.8 individuals per record, is the third most abundant species in the City. *Pseudotriton ruber*, the city's rarest extant species, had only six records of eight individuals since 1980, the most recent being three larvae found in 2004. *Ambystoma maculatum* has been a subject of concern for NRG and others for many years. Although it occurs in several protected ponds and woodlands, we have only 14 recent records of 18 individuals and five records of 88 egg clutches since 1980. *Notophthalmus viridescens* has been the target of moderate inventory efforts, but we found only six records of ten individuals from 1980 to the present. Species that have always been rare within the city are more vulnerable to extirpation and endangerment; those with five or fewer records from 1820 to 1979 have all been extirpated from the City.

GEOGRAPHICAL PATTERNS: Staten Island has, at present and historically, the highest diversity of salamanders, with six of nine (67%) original species still present (Table 3). Queens also has historical records of nine species (Table 3). Between 1880 and 1929 Queens lost four (44%) of its original species, and another two (22%) have their last records in the early 1930s. *P. cinereus*, *E. bislineata* and *A. maculatum* have persisted until the present. The other three boroughs had low diversity in historical records (1-5 species). The Bronx lost one species, *P. glutinosus*, before 1929, and *D. fuscus* has not been reported since 1944. *E. bislineata*, *P. cinereus*, and *N. viridescens* had only one historical record each from the Bronx, but have all been reported again since 1980 (Table 3). Reintroduction attempts for *N. viridescens* in the Bronx do not appear to have been successful. Only two species (*D. fuscus and P. cinereus*) were reported from Manhattan prior to 1979, but *E. bislineata* has been reported in recent years (Table 3). At present, we are aware of sizable populations of *P. cinereus* and *D. fuscus* in Manhattan, but have not been able to re-locate *E. bislineata*.

Brooklyn had the lowest reported species diversity, with only one species, *N. viridescens*, which has not been seen since 1918 (Table 3).

Four salamander species (*P. cinereus, D. fuscus, E. bislineata*, and *N. viridescens*) were fairly widespread in the city historically (Table 3). Records

Table 3. Number of locations for each salamander species native to New York City by species and borough, 1820 to 1929. Reintroduction sites are not included in the tally.

Time Period: 1820-1929	Bronx	Brooklyn	Manhattan	Queens	Staten Island	Citywide
AMBYSTOMATIDAE						
Ambystoma laterale	--	--	--	1	--	1
Ambystoma maculatum	--	--	--	1	3	4
Ambystoma opacum	--	--	--	1	1	2
Ambystoma tigrinum	--	--	--	2	--	2
PLETHODONTIDAE						
Desmognathus fuscus	1	--	1	1	1	4
Eurycea bislineata	--	--	--	2	2	4
Hemidactylium scutatum	--	--	--	1	2	3
Plethodon cinereus	--	--	1	2	5	8
Plethodon glutinosus	2	--	--	--	1	3
Pseudotriton ruber	--	--	--	--	1	1
SALAMANDRIDAE						
Notophthalmus viridescens	--	1	--	3	3	7
TOTAL NUMBER OF LOCATIONS	2	1	2	6	14	25

Table 3 (continued). Number of locations for each salamander species native to New York City by species and borough, 1820-present. Reintroduction sites are not included in the tally.

Time Period: 1930-1979	Bronx	Brooklyn	Manhattan	Queens	Staten Island	Citywide
AMBYSTOMATIDAE						
Ambystoma laterale	--	--	--	--	--	--
Ambystoma maculatum	--	--	--	1	1	2
Ambystoma opacum	--	--	--	--	1	1
Ambystoma tigrinum	--	--	--	--	--	--
PLETHODONTIDAE						
Desmognathus fuscus	1	--	1	1	1	4
Eurycea bislineata	1	--	--	2	4	7
Hemidactylium scutatum	--	--	--	--	1	1
Plethodon cinereus	1	--	--	1	4	6
Plethodon glutinosus	--	--	--	--	1	1
Pseudotriton ruber	--	--	--	--	5	5
SALAMANDRIDAE						
Notophthalmus viridescens	--	--	--	1	1	2
TOTAL NUMBER OF LOCATIONS	2	--	1	3	11	17

Time Period: 1980 to present	Bronx	Brooklyn	Manhattan	Queens	Staten Island	Citywide
AMBYSTOMATIDAE						
Ambystoma laterale	--	--	--	--	--	--
Ambystoma maculatum	--	--	--	3	2	5
Ambystoma opacum	--	--	--	--	--	--
Ambystoma tigrinum	--	--	--	--	--	--
PLETHODONTIDAE						
Desmognathus fuscus	--	--	1	--	7	8
Eurycea bislineata	2	--	2	2	11	17
Hemidactylium scutatum	--	--	--	--	--	--
Plethodon cinereus	9	--	2	3	28	52
Plethodon glutinosus	--	--	--	--	--	--
Pseudotriton ruber	--	--	--	--	4	4
SALAMANDRIDAE						
Notophthalmus viridescens	1	--	--	--	5	6
TOTAL NUMBER OF LOCATIONS	10	--	3	5	31	49

of the first three species were found for all boroughs except Brooklyn and of *N. viridescens* from all except Manhattan. *P. cinereus* and *E. bislineata* are still found in four boroughs. *N. viridescens* is gone from two of four boroughs, with only one recent record from the Bronx, and five from Staten Island. *D. fuscus* remains in one park in Manhattan and in several on Staten Island. Records from Queens are probably errors, as this species does not occur on the coastal plain south of the glacial moraine. We re-located the last known population in Manhattan (Gans 1945) in 2005, and also found another population. *D. fuscus* remains at seven locations on Staten Island, but they are reliably found only at the headwaters of one stream. We found records of *A. maculatum, A. opacum, H. scutatum,* and *P. glutinosus* from two boroughs each. *Ambystoma maculatum, A. opacum,* and *H. scutatum* were originally found in Queens and Staten Island and *P. glutinosus* in the Bronx and Staten Island. *A. maculatum* is still present at two locations in Queens, but two recent records from Staten Island are probably releases (R. Mattarazzo, pers. comm). *P. glutinosus* has not been reported from either borough since 1931, but *H. scutatum* was still present on Staten Island at least until 1979. The remaining three species have been reported only from one borough. *A. laterale* and *A. tigrinum* both disappeared from Queens before 1930, and *P. ruber* survives at only a few locations on Staten Island.

We compared the number of locations, records, and individuals of each species in the five boroughs from 1880 to the present (Tables 3 and 4). The number of locations citywide where an individual species has been found varied from one (*A. laterale*) to 47 (*P. cinereus*). *E. bislineata,* although recorded only one time less than *P. cinereus,* was found at far fewer locations (21). *N. viridescens* was found at 16 locations. *A. maculatum* and *D. fuscus,* have been found at 11 locations each since 1880. *P. ruber,* originally found at five locations, has been relocated at four sites, but in very small numbers, since 1980. The five species considered extirpated have been found at only one to four locations throughout the entire period examined.

The vast majority of locations where salamanders have been reported are in Staten Island, even in the period from 1820 to 1929 (Table 3). Of 25 locations during that period, 14 (56%) were on Staten Island. Queens had 24% of locations before 1930, the Bronx and Manhattan each had two locations, and Brooklyn only one. Salamanders were reported from 17 locations from 1930 to 1979, 11 of these on Staten Island, three in Queens, two in the Bronx, and one in Manhattan. Locations where salamanders have been found in the recent period (1980 to present) are 63% on Staten Island, 20% in the Bronx, 10% in Queens, and 6% in Manhattan. An even higher

Table 4. Number of records / total number of individuals (minimum) / number of clutches eggs sighted since 1820 for New York City salamanders, by species and borough. For records that did not list numbers (1) was used as number of individuals. Reintroductions are not included. Totals for all years and all species include several pre-1980 records of uncertain vintage.

	Bronx	Brooklyn	Manhattan	Queens	Staten Island	Citywide
AMBYSTOMATIDAE	--	--				
Ambystoma laterale	--	--	--	1/4/0	--	1/4/0
Ambystoma maculatum	--	--	--	15/44/88	10/9/1	25/53/89
Ambystoma opacum	--	--	--	1/1/0	2/2/0	3/3/0
Ambystoma tigrinum	--	--	--	2/4/0	--	2/4/0
PLETHODONTIDAE						
Desmognathus fuscus	2/22/0	--	3/49/1	2/2/0	34/111/0	41/184/1
Eurycea bislineata	4/7/0	--	2/2/0	11/1385/0	101/1022/3	118/2416/3
Hemidactylium scutatum	--	--	--	1/2/0	6/8/0	7/10/0
Plethodon cinereus	13/71/0	--	5/121/0	15/34/0	86/284/1	119/510/1
Plethodon glutinosus	2/2/0	--	--	--	2/2/0	4/4/0
Pseudotriton ruber	--	--	--	--	19/27/0	19/27/0
SALAMANDRIDAE						
Notophthalmus viridescens	2/2/0	3/3/0	--	5/17/0	12/52/0	22/74/0
TOTALS	23/104/0	3/3/0	10/172/1	53/1493/88	272/1517/5	361/3289/94

percentage of records (75%) come from Staten Island (Table 4). Queens had 15% of records, the Bronx 6%, Manhattan 3%, and Brooklyn less than 1%.

The number of salamander records collected from 1980 to the present was significantly correlated with the percent vacant land (-0.629; p=0.078), but not with the percent parkland (-0.371; p=1.000) or the population density (0.922; p=0.766). The boroughs with more vacant land had greater numbers of records.

Regional distributions and habitat preferences provide us with clues to the origin of present distributions and patterns of extirpation of New York salamanders (Tables 5 and 6) (Klemens 1993, Amphibian Research and Monitoring Initiative 2003, Johnson et al. 2003). As expected, none of the species that have widespread distributions (*A. maculatum*, *P. cinereus*, and *N. viridescens*) have been extirpated from the city. Both species that are found mostly on the coastal plain, *A. opacum* and *A. tigrinum*, have been extirpated. Species found mostly upland and inland have fared somewhat better, with two of four species extant (*D. fuscus* and *E. bislineata*). One species, *H. scutatum*, has always had a spotty range in the northeast due to its specialization on bogs, and it has most likely been extirpated from New York City. Two of the three salamander species that are at the edges of their ranges in the city have been extirpated. *P. ruber* and *A. tigrinum* are at the northern edges of their ranges in southeastern New York but are common in much of the southeastern United States. *A. laterale* ranges primarily north of the City.

We compared salamander diversity and status in the city with that in the surrounding states of Connecticut, New Jersey, and New York (Table 5) (Klemens 1993, Northeast Amphibian Research and Monitoring Initiative 2003B, New Jersey Division of Fish and Wildlife 2003, New York State Department of Environmental Conservation 2003, Connecticut Department of Environmental Protection 2004). As expected, diversity increases with increasing area. The number and identity of salamander species native to New York City (11) is very similar to that in the smallest state, Connecticut (12 species). But in contrast to the city's loss of five species, no species have been extirpated from Connecticut or from the other two states studied. Two species extirpated from New York City, *A. laterale* and *P. glutinosus*, are listed as species of special concern or threatened in Connecticut. The others are either not native to Connecticut (*A. tigrinum* and *H. scutatum*), or are not considered in danger at present (*A. opacum*). New Jersey contains all of New York City's native species, plus five additional species. Four of these (*Ambystoma jeffersonianum*, *Eurycea longicauda*, *D. ocrophaeus*, and *Gyrinophilus porphyriticus*) historically have ranged only inland of the city. The other species, *Pseudotriton montanus*, has never been found north of southern New Jersey. Four of the five species extirpated from New York City are considered decreasing (D) or endangered (E) in New Jersey. Only one (*P. glutinosus*) is stable in New Jersey. New York State has seven species in addition to New York City's 11. Again, these all have ranges inland of the city. Three of the city's five extirpated species are considered species of special concern (SC) or endangered in the state, while two apparently are stable.

Six of the city's native salamanders are considered pond breeders (Table 6). These species cannot exist without breeding ponds surrounded by a woodland, grassy, or coastal buffer. They have suffered the most from human activities in the city, with 67% extirpated. The city has three stream salamanders, and none have been extirpated. The city has only two totally

Table 5. Status of salamander species in the states surrounding New York City (New Jersey, New York, and Connecticut. P = present, S = stable, E = endangered, T = threatened, SC = special concern with legal protection, D = decreasing, ? = uncertain status, O = other protection such as game bag limits, PU = present with no legal protection. Blank cells indicate no historical records.

	Connecticut	New Jersey	New York
CRYPTOBRANCHIDAE			
Cryptobranchus alleganiensis			SC
PROTEIDAE			
Necturus maculosus	P		?
AMBYSTOMADIDAE			
Ambystoma jeffersonianum	SC	DO	SC
Ambystoma laterale	SC/T	E	SC
Ambystoma maculatum	PO	DO	PU
Ambystoma opacum	PO	DO	SC
Ambystoma tigrinum		E	E
PLETHODONTIDAE			
Desmognathus fuscus	P	SO	PU
Desmognathus ocrophaeus		?O	PU
Eurycea bislineata	P	SO	PU
Eurycea l. longicauda		T	SC
Hemidactylium scutatum	P	DO	PU
Gyrinophilus porphyriticus	T	DO	PU
Plethodon cinereus	P	SO	PU
Plethodon glutinosus	T	SO	PU
Plethodon wehrlei			PU
Pseudotriton m. montanus		T	
Pseudotriton r. ruber		DO	PU
SALAMANDRIDAE			
Notophthalmus viridescens	P	SO	PU
Number of native salamander species	12	16	18
Number of extant native species	12	16	18
Percent of extant species that are D, SC, T, or E	33	63	33
Percent of native species extirpated	0	0	0

Table 6. Status of New York City salamander species categorized by breeding habitat and primary distribution.

	Habitat		
	Pond	**Stream**	**Terrestrial**
Extant species	A. maculatum N. viridescens	E. bislineata D. fuscus P. ruber	P. cinereus
Extirpated species	A. laterale A. opacum A. tigrinum H. scutatum	None	P. glutinosus
% of species extirpated	67	0	50

	Original Distribution				Edge of Range
	Widespread	**Coastal**	**Upland**	**Spotty**	
Extant species	A. maculatum P. cinereus N. viridescens	None	D. fuscus E. bislineata	None	P. ruber (South)
Extirpated species	None	A. opacum A. tigrinum	A. laterale P. glutinosus	H. scutatum	A. laterale (North) A. tigrinum (South)
% of species extirpated	0	100	50	100	67

terrestrial native salamanders, one extirpated (*P. glutinosus*), and one the most common extant species (*P. cinereus*).

Threats to Salamanders of New York City: Amphibians face threats of population and species extinction in many parts of the world, ranging from densely populated cities to seemingly pristine wilderness areas (Wake 1991, Petit 1992, Yoon 1997, SSAR 1998). In cities, however, the number and intensity of threats are greater than in suburban and rural areas (Orser and Shure 1972, Campbell 1974, Windmiller 1996, Mierzwa et al. 2002, Pember et al. 2002). The greatest threat to salamanders in New York City is development of natural areas, both within parks and on private lands (Gibbs 1993, Richter and Azous 1995, Cox 1999, Rendon 1999). Elimination of wetlands during construction of buildings for residential and commercial use is one of the greatest threats to urban amphibians (Barnes and Halliday 1997).

Replacement of mature forest or wetlands with lawn or other cultivated plants for residences or recreational facilities may eliminate amphibians from large swaths of landscape (Rendon 1999). Development also causes fragmentation by construction of roads, installation of dams or impoundments in stream corridors, and conversion of migration corridors to lawn or asphalt (Lind 1996, Barnes and Halliday 1997, Pember et al. 2002).

Manhattan, the Bronx, and Brooklyn were the first boroughs to be developed, and we see the results of this early and intensive residential/ commercial development in the low number of species and records for those boroughs. Much of the parkland in these boroughs is used for recreation and horticulture and does not provide salamander habitat. Natural areas are separated from each other by dense urban development that does not allow movement of amphibians among habitat areas. Queens was considered a rural borough during Manhattan's early development and today it is still less densely populated than all boroughs except Staten Island (14.7 persons/ acre [36.3 persons/hectare]). Because most salamander habitat in Queens is already protected as parkland, development within natural areas is the greatest threat to Queens salamanders. Staten Island is the only borough with substantial acreage of natural areas in private ownership. These are the most threatened wildlife habitat in the city. Residential and commercial development has removed large blocks of natural areas on Staten Island in recent years, and construction projects are planned for several others. Much of this natural land contains woodlands and freshwater wetlands that are excellent salamander habitat.

Even in Parks-owned natural areas, habitat degradation is threatening the city's salamanders. The increase in impermeable land cover in the City increases stormwater volume and velocity. Resulting flash floods can directly eliminate amphibian larvae (Petranka and Sih 1986), or degrade habitat by altering water levels and hydroperiods (Richter and Azous 1995). Increased stormflow also increases erosion and sedimentation. Smothering of stream beds with sediment is one of the greatest threats to salamander habitat (Kerby and Kats 1998, Welsh and Ollivier 1998, Lowe and Bolger 2002, Pehek and Mazor 2003). One of the last remaining populations of *P. ruber* is threatened by sediment runoff from construction on adjacent private land and erosion from high velocity and volume street runoff. Huge gorges have developed in this area, and streams and swamps are filling in with sediment. Illegal use and overuse of natural areas also contribute to erosion and sedimentation. Erosion from dirt bikes, all-terrain vehicles, mountain bikes, and heavy foot traffic removes the litter layer, effectively destroying large areas of terrestrial salamander habitat and allowing bare soil to wash into the habitat of *A. maculatum*, *D. fuscus*, *E. bislineata*, and *P. ruber*. Foot traffic in springs and streams degrades water quality, disturbs the substrate, and may directly kill salamanders (Haney and Kostalos 2004).

Urban development often increases the input of pollutants into ponds, streams, and forest areas (Stebbins and Cohen 1995). Urban areas add large amounts of stormwater contaminated with hydrocarbons, metals, salts, fertilizers, and pesticides to ponds and streams. These substances are toxic to a wide range of aquatic life, including salamanders (Hellawell 1988, Reardon 1995, McAlpine et al. 1998, Marco et al. 1999, Sparling et al. 2000, Pehek and Mazor 2003). Sewage and graywater is dumped directly into streams and ponds, often through unmapped, illegal connections. Urban residences, businesses, and recreational areas increase the amount of pesticides and fertilizers added to forests and wetlands. Atmospheric deposition from urban traffic and energy generation acidifies soils and waters and contaminates them with heavy metals and hydrocarbons, affecting both terrestrial and aquatic salamanders (Pough 1976, Freda and Dunson 1986, Wyman 1988, Wyman and Jancola 1992). Gasoline and other chemicals from dumped cars and construction debris seeping into streams and ponds threaten populations of pond-breeding salamanders in Queens and terrestrial salamanders throughout the city. NRG has found potential evidence of the effects of pollutants on salamanders. After pesticide spraying and runoff from a recent rain, we found a dead adult *P. ruber* at one of its two recent locations on Staten Island. At this same location we have found spinal deformities in up to 60% of larval *E. bislineata*. Streams with greater amounts of paved and horticultural surfaces in their watersheds have fewer larval *E. bislineata* and often no *D. fuscus*. Of three *A. maculatum* breeding ponds within one Queens park, more egg masses have been found in the pond at the highest elevation, which receives the least sediment and pollutants from runoff.

Invasive species have degraded wetlands and woodlands throughout the city. In a city with as many people as New York, native and exotic animals are released into natural areas daily, and others spread from surrounding states. NRG projects currently underway seek to evaluate the impact of invasion by exotic shrubs, trees, and earthworms on woodland salamander populations. Plants such as Norway Maple (*Acer platanoides*) and Tartarian Honeysuckle (*Lonicera tartarica*) change the vegetation diversity and structure in all forest layers. Invasive earthworms consume leaf litter and disrupt soil structure, changing vital refuge and foraging habitat for *P. cinereus* and *A. maculatum* (Blossey et al. 2002, Maerz et al. 2004).

Wetlands in the city have been invaded by emergent and submergent plants. One large population of Purple Loosestrife (*Lythrum salicaria*) exists within the city and is increasingly found in small amounts around wetlands throughout the five boroughs. The monocultures of this species that often develop reduce diversity of structure that may be essential to pond-breeding salamanders. *Phragmites australis* also simplifies wetland plant communities, increases stagnation and sediment retention, and shades formerly open water. Submergents such as Eurasian Water-milfoil (*Myriophyllum spicatum*), Curly-leaved Pondweed (*Potamogeton crispus*) and Fanwort (*Cabomba caroliniana*) choke many of the city's ponds and streams, causing stagnation and low oxygen and altering foraging and breeding structure (Hellquist and Straub 2002, Pehek and Anzelone 2003, Invasive Plant Council of New York State 2003). Exotic plants such as Japanese Knotweed (*Polygonatum cuspidatum*) and European Black Alder (*Alnus glutinosus*) change the amount of shading over stream corridors and may alter stream morphology if their root systems are more or less stable than native riparian plants (Murphy et al. 1981, Invasive Plant Council of New York State 2003). The impact of invasive freshwater species of fish, turtles, snails, and crayfish on native salamanders is poorly known but could be considerable because these animals may prey on salamanders or compete with them for food (Gamradt and Kats 1996, Earth Crash 2001, Hellquist and Straub 2002, Smithsonian Environmental Research Center 2004, United States Geological Survey 2004).

Discussion

The present distribution of salamanders in New York City results from an interaction of range, habitat preferences, and the effects of urbanization. The data we have collected reflect these factors but also suffer from the biases of the individuals who collected them. Common species, such as *P. cinereus*, appear to have been neglected prior to the recent period. Rare and endangered species have always held more interest for naturalists and thus are probably overrepresented in the data. Naturalists also tend to concentrate their work in more pleasant locations or locations more likely to yield results. Because of this bias, data from more rural areas, such as Queens and Staten Island, may overstate the diversity and abundance of salamanders. Despite these biases, we believe that the data in this paper reflect true chronological and geographical patterns of diversity, population reduction, and extirpation.

Island biogeographic theory postulates that the most basic determinant of how many species can exist in one location is the size of the area (MacArthur and Wilson 1967). Data from Chicago conform to this theory, with more native species and fewer extirpated species in larger counties. New York does not show this pattern, perhaps because it was already obscured by urbanization in 1880, when our data begin (Mierzwa et al. 2002). As we look at larger areas in the Northeast, increasing from city to state to region, we do see the expected increase in salamander diversity and decrease in numbers of endangered salamander species. How widely a species ranges and where within its range New York lies also affect vulnerability to extinction. Species that have a spotty range, such as *H. scutatum*, are more likely to disappear under the pressures of urbanization than those that are widespread, such as *P. cinereus*. Species that are at the edge of their range in the city, such as *A. tigrinum*, appear to be eliminated before species that have New York closer to the center of their range (Table 6). Urbanization, by eliminating some salamander populations, increases the distance between surviving populations and thus decreases the chance of genetic exchange and recolonization of vacant habitat. Species that already have decreased access to sources of recolonization, such as spotty or edge-of-range species, will be the first to suffer from urban development.

What characteristics of urban environments have the greatest effects on salamander diversity and abundance? The number of times we found salamanders was correlated with the percent of vacant land in each borough, but not with the percent of parkland. In New York City, parks are not necessarily good salamander habitat. A large percent of city parks is composed of lawn, eutrophic urban ponds, paved playgrounds, buildings, and other environments hostile to salamanders. In Queens and Brooklyn, the boroughs with the greatest number of hectares of parkland, much of this area is comprised by the Gateway National Recreation Area, primarily salt marsh and associated maritime uplands, which are not suitable habitat for most salamander species.

Counties with higher population densities may have large amounts of parkland, but they have smaller acreage of natural area. The percent of land cover left in natural vegetation is a better determinant of salamander diversity than the percent of parkland. Much natural area in New York's least developed borough is on private land, or land owned by agencies other than Parks. This land contains some of the best wetlands and woodlands in the city. Parks instituted the "Forever Wild" program to identify natural areas in need of protection, but without sufficient support for acquisition, management and restoration activities, these areas will continue to degrade and be developed.

Not all natural areas are equally critical for maintaining salamander diversity (Gibbs 1993). Wetlands such as vernal ponds, kettle ponds, marshes, and shrub swamps, have been reduced to a fraction of their original acreage in New York. Many, especially the vernal ponds, are unmapped and unprotected. Even protected wetlands are deluged with sediment and pollutant-laden stormwater and vulnerable to invasive species. Salamanders that rely on ponds for breeding have suffered the most from urbanization (Table 6). Even *N. viridescens*, a species that can utilize a wider variety of ponds for breeding, including disturbed, eutrophic ponds, has been eliminated from most of the city (Gates and Thompson 1982). Stream salamanders have fared slightly better than pond-breeders, perhaps due to their ability to disperse through stream corridors without having to traverse the hostile urban land cover. Streams and springs have, however, been damaged by being culverted or channelized and are subject to the sediment and other contaminents brought in by urban stormwater. New York had only two entirely terrestrial salamander species in 1820. Although one species has been extirpated, the remaining species is the most stable in the city, probably because woodland, although often degraded, is one of the largest categories of natural areas remaining in the city.

Nearly half the city's species have been lost due to urbanization. If we want to maintain the diversity and abundance of salamanders that we have at present, action must be taken swiftly. We recommend a program combining inventory, acquisition, protection, habitat restoration, reintroduction, and monitoring. Although extensive herpetological inventories have been completed, we should now focus our efforts on the most endangered parcels of land and endangered wildlife species in the city. Steps should be taken to inventory land thought to contain most important salamander habitats, such as vernal ponds, marshes, and stream corridors. Privately owned lands in this category include Arlington Marsh and the Cable Avenue Woods, both on Staten Island. We should also inventory undeveloped parcels owned by NYC Parks & Recreation. The results of inventory should be used to rate each parcel's value as salamander habitat. Privately owned lands with the most valuable habitat should be targeted for acquisition. Wetlands and woodlands on Staten Island are under imminent threat of development, and inventory and acquisition priorities should focus on this borough's remaining natural areas.

When lands are already owned by the city, either Parks or another agency, protection, restoration, and reintroduction become the solutions to habitat degradation. Construction and stormwater control projects have destroyed and degraded salamander habitat in many city-owned parcels. Inter- and intra-agency negotiations have been successful in the past in reducing the impact of development within city-owned natural areas. Only when construction cannot be moved from critical habitat to another location should mitigation be considered. This could include migration tunnels around newly installed obstacles, such as roads and impoundments, restoration of degraded wetlands and forests, and creation of new wetlands. (Biebighauser undated, Donahue undated). The Forever Wild initiative will give Parks a greater chance of protecting the most critical salamander habitat. Studies of salamander populations before and after disturbance will provide evidence of impacts that can be used in future bargaining for reducing or mitigating disturbances. NRG is presently evaluating the effect of construction of a stormwater impoundment within a stream channel on populations of *E. bislineata* and *D. fuscus*.

In natural areas owned by Parks, illegal or excessive use must be controlled. Arden Heights and Long Pond parks are heavily used by all-terrain vehicles (ATV) drivers and dirt bikers. Alley Pond Park (Queens) and Arden Heights (Staten Island) have suffered from dumping of cars and other debris within wetlands and streams. Installing guardrails around natural areas will reduce these illegal activities. Increased presence of Parks' personnel will also help curtail illegal vehicle traffic and dumping. Even legal foot traffic can harm salamander habitat if excessive (Haney and Kostalos 2004). Signs that educate the public about trampling vegetation and wetlands may help reduce some overuse, although vandalism and theft of signs have been a problem in the past for the Parks Department. Signs may also be used to warn motorists about salamander, frog, and turtle migration routes over roads (Associated Press 2003).

Nearly every natural area in New York City could benefit from restoration. NRG has improved salamander habitat in woodlands by removing invasive plant species, installing erosion control fabric and cribbing, and planting native species (Wenskus 2003). These activities improve the terrestrial environment and reduce sedimentation of wetland habitats. NRG has also restored wetlands by removing invasive plants at Flushing Meadows and Seton Falls Park and by excavating and replanting previously filled ponds as at Forest Park. More wetlands, and a greater variety, need to be restored and created in the city. Vernal ponds and streams, in particular, need to be evaluated and, where they have been degraded or eliminated, restored (Whissel and Wissinger 1999, Biebighauser undated, Donahue undated).

The utility of restored and created wetlands for frogs has been shown, but salamander use of these habitats has not been as well established (Peyton 2004). Fowler's toads (*Bufo fowleri*) have bred in created wetlands at Idlewild

Preserve and Forest Park for several years. We know of no salamander populations that have returned to restored wetlands in New York without human
assistance. We need to understand what characteristics of restored and created
wetlands are critical to the colonization and persistence of native salamanders. We also need to know if present methods of forest restoration improve
habitat for foraging and refuge for *P. cinereus* and *A. maculatum* (Harper and
Guynn 1999). This information can only come from monitoring of restored
sites over several years. Monitoring of restored forests and wetlands and their
salamander populations will help improve future restoration designs.

If natural areas are so fragmented that natural colonization is not
likely, introductions of native salamanders should be attempted (Marsh and
Trenham 2001). The National Park Service documented reproduction of
salamanders introduced into ponds created at the Jamaica Bay National
Wildlife Refuge (Cook 1989). The results of other introductions in the city
are not as certain (NRG 2001 unpublished data, Künstler 1998, pers. comm.,
Johnson 1993 pers. comm.). By monitoring introduced salamander populations we can learn which reintroduction methods will provide best results
and which wetlands will have the best chances of success.

Although salamanders have suffered greatly from urbanization in
New York, the recent increase in interest in habitat protection and restoration
gives us hope that the remaining species diversity can be maintained and
perhaps even increased. Funding for restoration has been plentiful in recent
years, but Parks should seek financial support for acquisition, protection
activities such as guardrail installation and migration tunnels under roads,
and monitoring.

References

Amphibian Research and Monitoring Initiative. 2003. ARMI national atlas for
     amphibian distributions. http://www.mp2-pwrc.usgs.gov/armiatlas/.
Associated Press. 2003. Town orders "salamander crossing" signs. *Duluth Superior*,
     March 26, 2003. http://www.duluthsuperior.com/mld/duluthsuperior/news/
     weird_news/5470569/5470569.html.
Barnes, N. and T. Halliday. 1997. Loss of amphibian breeding sites in Milton Keynes,
     Central England, 1984-94. *Urban Nature Mag* 3: 56-61.
Berkeley, B. 1993. Staten Island amphibian survey. Unpublished report. New York
     City Department of Parks & Recreation, Natural Resources Group: New
     York, NY.
Biebighauser, T. R. Undated. A guide to creating vernal ponds. USDA Forest Service,
     Morehead, KY. 33 pp.
Bishop, S. C. 1941. The salamanders of New York. *New York State Museum Bulletin*

324. New York State Museum: Albany, NY. 365 pp.

Blossey, B., J. C. Maerz, J. K. Liebherr, and V. Nuzzo. 2002 progress report: Impact of invasive plants on abundance of salamanders. US Environmental Protection Agency Grant No. R828902. http://cfpub.epa.gov/ncer_abstracts/.

Campbell, C. A. 1974. Survival of reptiles and amphibians in urban environments. In: Noyes, J.A. And D.R. Progulske (eds.), Wildlife in an Urbanizing Environment. University of Massachusetts Cooperative Extension Service: Springfield, MA.

Connecticut Department of Environmental Protection. 2004. Endangered, Threatened, and Special Concern Amphibians. http://dep.state.ct.us/cgnhs/nddb/amphib.htm

Cook, R. P. 1989. And the voice of the grey tree frog was heard again in the land. In: *Park Science Spring* 6-7.

Cox, S. and E. Pehek. 2000. Terrestrial salamander monitoring program. Grant application submitted to New York City Environmental Fund, April: New York, NY. 7 pp.

Cox, S., R. Mazor, P. Katzer, and E. Pehek. 2000. Salamander monitoring in New York City Parks. *Abstracts NY Nat Hist Conf VI. NY State Mus. Circ.* 62:58. 2000.

Cox, S. 1999. Salamanders of New York City: Evidence of Local Extinctions Due to Urbanization. Unpublished BS thesis, Barnard College: New York, NY. 31 pp.

Davic, R.D., editor. 2002. Field evaluation manual for Ohio's primary headwater habitat streams. Final version 1.0. Ohio Environmental Protection Agency, Division of Surface Water, Twinsburg, Ohio. 60 pp.

Davis, W. T. 1884. The reptiles and batrachians of Staten Island. *Proc Natural Sci Assoc Staten Island, Extra* No. 1:1.

DeCandido, R. 1999. Species distribution chart: herptiles. Unpublished report. New York City Department of Parks & Recreation, Urban Park Service: New York, NY.

Donahue, D. F. Undated. A Guide to the Identification and Protection of Vernal Pool Wetlands of Connecticut. University of Connecticut Cooperative Extension System: Union, CT. 18 pp.

Droege, S., L. Monti and D. Lanz. 1997. The terrestrial salamander monitoring program. http://www.mp1-pwrc.usgs.gov/sally/.

Earth Crash. 2001. Scientists warn anglers' illegal introduction of non-native pickerel into at least 72 Nova Scotia lakes is devastating native trout, salmon, minnows, frogs and salamanders. http://eces.org/archive/ec/bioinvasion/fish.shtml.

Freda, J. And W. A. Dunson. 1986. Effects of low pH and other chemical variables on the local distribution of amphibians. *Copeia* 1986:454-466.

Gamradt, S. C. And L. B. Kats. 1996. Effect of introduced crayfish and mosquitofish on California newts. *Conserv Biol* 10:1155-1162.

Gans, C. 1945. Occurrence of the dusky salamander on Manhattan. *Copeia* 1945:118.

Gates, J. E. and E. L. Thompson. 1982. Small pool habitat selection by red-spotted newts in Western Maryland. *J Herpetol.* 16:7-15.

Gibbs, J. P. 1993. Importance of small wetlands for the persistence of local populations of wetland-associated animals. *Wetlands* 13:25-31.

Gosselin, H. M., and B. R. Johnson. 1995. The urban outback—wetlands for wildlife: a guide to wetland restoration and frog-friendly backyards. Metro Toronto Zoo: Toronto, Ont. 89 pp. http://www.torontozoo.com/adoptapond/ UrbanOutback/intro.html.

Griffin, J. 1998. Amphibian decline:Monitors search for answers. *The Volunteer Monitor* 10:1-4.

Haney, J. D. And M. S. Kostalos. 2004. A study of the *Plethodontid* salamander populations at Raccoon Creek State Park, Pennsylvania. *Froglog* 61:2-3.

Harper, C. A. and D. C. Guynn, Jr. 1999. Factors affecting salamander density and distribution within four forest types in the Southern Appalachian Mountains. *Forest Ecol Management* 114:245-252.

Hellawell, J. M. 1988. Toxic substances in rivers and streams. *Environ Pollution* 50:61-85.

Hellquist, C. B. And J. Straub. 2002. A guide to selected invasive non-native aquatic species in Massachusetts. Massachusetts Department of Environmental Management, Lakes and Ponds Program: Devens, MA. http://www.state. ma.us/dem.

Heyer, W. R., M. A. Donnelly, R. W. McDiarmid, L. C. Hayek and M. S. Foster, eds. 1994. Measuring and Monitoring Biological Diversity: Standard Methods for Amphibians. Smithsonian Institution Press: Washington, DC. 364 pp.

Hunter, M. L., Jr., A. J. K. Calhoun, and M. McCollough, eds. 1999. Maine Amphibians and Reptiles. The University of Maine Press: Orono, ME. 252 pp.

Invasive Plant Council of New York State. 2003. Primary list of invasive plants in NYS. http://www.ipcnys.org/.

Johnson, G., A. R. Breisch, J. W. Ozard, P. K. Ducey, M. E. Richmond, and C. R. Smith. 2003. Assessment of reptile and amphibian species richness and distribution in New York. NYSDEC. http://www.dec.state.ny.us/website/ dfwmr/wildlife/herp/publications/specrich.html.

Kerby, J. L. And L. B. Kats. 1998. Modified interactions between salamander life stages caused by wildfire-induced sedimentation. *Ecology* 79:740-745.

Klemens, M. W. 1993. Amphibians and reptiles of Connecticut and adjacent regions. State Geological and Natural History Survey of Connecticut, Bull 112. 318 pp.

Lind, A. J. 1996. Amphibians and reptiles in urban streams: their role and habitat needs. Presented at Western Regional Urban Streams Conference, Arcata, CA, Nov. 15-17.

Lowe, W. H., and D. T. Bolger. 2002. Local and landscape-scale predictors of salamander abundance in New Hampshire headwater streams. *Conserv Biol* 16:183-193.

MacArthur, R. H. and E. O. Wilson. 1967. The Theory of Island Biogeography. Princeton University Press: Princeton, NJ. 224 pp.

Maerz, J. C., B. Blossey, J. K. Liebherr, and V. Nuzzo. 2004. The impact of non-indigenous plant invasions on woodland salamander fitness and abundance. EPA STAR Program Grant R828902. http://www.invasiveplants.net/impsal.htm.

Marco, A., C. Quilchano, and A. R. Blaustein. 1999. Sensitivity to nitrate and nitrite in pond- breeding amphibians from the Pacific Northwest, USA. *Env Toxicol Chem* 18:2836-2839.

Marsh, D. M., and P. C. Trenham. 2001. Metapopulaion dynamics and amphibian conservation. *Conserv Biol* 15:40-49.

Mathewson, R. F. 1955. Amphibians and reptiles of Staten Island. *Proc Staten Island Inst Arts Sci* 17:29-48.

McAlpine, D. F., N. M. Burgess, and D. G. Busby. 1998. Densities of mink frogs, *Rana septentrionalis*, in New Brunswick forest ponds sprayed with the insecticide Fenitrothion. *Bull Environ Contam Toxicol* 60:30-36.

Mierzwa, K. S., V. Nuzzo, R. Hendricks III, and J. Schlosser. 2002. Impact of urban fragmentation on Chicago region amphibian assemblages. http://www.kmier.net/ecology/scb00.html.

Miller, T. 1995. Herptile Survey. Unpublished report. New York City Department of Parks & Recreation, Natural Resources Group: New York, NY. 3 pp.

Monti, L., M. Hunter, Jr., and J. Witham. 2000. An evaluation of the artificial cover object (ACO) method for monitoring populations of the redback salamander, *Plethodon cinereus. J Herpetol* 34:624-629.

Murphy, M. L., C. P. Hawkins, and N. H. Anderson. 1981. Effects of canopy modification and accumulated sediment on stream communities. *Trans Am Fisheries Soc* 110:469-478.

New Jersey Division of Fish and Wildlife. 2003. Amphibians of New Jersey. http://www.state.nj.us/dep/fgw/chkamph.htm.

New York City Department of City Planning. 2003. Land Use Facts. http://www.nyc.gov/html/dcp/html/landusefacts/landusefactshome.shtml

New York State Department of Environmental Conservation. 2003. New York State Amphibian and Reptile Atlas Project: salamanders – Order *Caudata*. NYS DEC. http://www.dec.state.ny.us/website/dfwmr/wildlife/herp/salam.html.

North American Amphibian Monitoring Program. 2003. http://www.mp2-pwrc.usgs.gov/naamp.

Northeast Amphibian Research and Monitoring Initiative. 2003B. Table of Northeast amphibian species. http://www.mp2-pwrc.usgs.gov/nearmi/species.

Olson, D. H., W. P. Leonard and R. B. Bury, eds. 1977. Sampling Amphibians in Lentic Habitats: Methods and Approaches for the Pacific Northwest. Society for Northwestern Vertebrate Biology: Olympia, WA. 134 pp.

Orser, P. N. And D. J. Shure. 1972. Effects of urbanization on the salamander *Desmognathus fuscus fuscus. Ecology* 53:1148-1154.

Pauley, T. K. 1999. Protocols for Long-Term Monitoring Projects. Marshall University: WV. 11 pp.

Paulmier, F. C. 1902. Lizards, tortoises and batrachians of New York. *NY State Mus Bull*

5I:389-414.

Pehek, E., and M. Anzelone. 2003. Beetles reduce purple loosestrife in a restored wetland, but will other weeds move in? *Ecol Restoration* 21:55-56.

Pehek, E., and R. Mazor. 2003. Sediment, salamanders, and streams: a study of four streams on Staten Island, New York. Unpublished report to the EPA. 23 pp.

Pember, B. C., B. C. Knights, M. G. Knutson, and S. E. Weick. 2002. Effects of agricultural and urban land use on movement and habitat selection by northern leopard frogs (*Rana pipiens*). USGS Upper Midwest Environmental Sciences Center. http://www.umesc.usgs.gov/terrestrial/amphibians/chapter4.html.

Petit, C. 1992. Disappearance of toads, frogs has some scientists worried. *San Francisco Chronicle* April 20, 1992.

Petranka, J. W. And A. Sih. 1986. Environmental instability, competition, and density-dependent growth and survivorship of a stream-dwelling salamander. *Ecology* 67:729-736.

Peyton, M. M. 2004. Amphibian colonization of mitigation wetlands in Nebraska. *Froglog* 61:1.

Pough, F. H. 1976. Acid precipitation and embryonic mortality of spotted salamanders, *Ambystoma maculatum. Science* 192:68-70.

Reardon, R. C., ed. 1995. Effects of Diflubenzuron on non-target organisms in broadleaf forested watersheds in the Northeast. USDA Forest Service, National Center of Forest Management. Report FHM-NC-05-95. 174 pp.

Rendon, J. 1999. Golf courses displace the once-thriving California tiger salamander. *Metro, Silicon Valley's Weekly Newspaper*, Nov. 24-Dec. 1.

Ricciuti, E. R. 1984. The New York City Wildlife Guide. Schocken Books: New York. 216 pp.

Richter, K. O. And A. L. Azous. 1995. Amphibian occurrence and wetland characteristics in the Puget Sound basin. *Wetlands* 15:305-312.

Rocco, G. L., R. P. Brooks, and C. J. Condliff. 1999. Stream salamander assemblage responses to acidified and degraded streams in the central Appalachians of Pennsylvania. Fourth Conference of the North American Amphibian Monitoring Program, Eastern Streamside Salamander Meeting: State College, PA. http://www.mp1-pwrc.usgs.gov/amphib/naamp4/papers/ROCCO. htm. 13 pp.

Rumph, W. T. 1979. The rediscovery of a Plethodontid salamander on Staten Island. *Proc Staten Island Inst Arts Sci* 1979:2-3.

Sherwood, W. L. 1895. The salamanders found in the vicinity of New York City, with notes upon extra-limital or allied species. *Abstract Proc Linnaean Soc NY* 7:21-37.

Smithsonian Environmental Research Center. 2004. Salamanders: Sensitive indicators of environmental quality. http://www.serc.si.edu/watershed/ august2001/salamanders.htm.

Society for the Study of Amphibians and Reptiles. 1998. Conserving amphibians and reptiles. Pamphlet.

Sparling, D. W., G. Linder and C. A. Bishop (eds.). 2000. Ecotoxicology of amphibians and reptiles. Society of Environmental Toxicology and Chemistry. 904 pp.

Stebbins, R. C. And N. W. Cohen. 1995. A Natural History of Amphibians. Princeton University Press: Princeton, NJ. 316 pp.

Tanacredi, J. T. 1995. Gateway: A Visitor's Companion. Stackpole Books: Mechanicsburg, PA. 166 pp.

The Nature Conservancy. 2004. Berkshire Taconic Landscape. http://www.lastgreatplaces.org/ berkshire/diversity/spc065.html.

United States Geological Survey. 2004. Nonindigenous Aquatic Species. http://nas.er.usgs.gov/.

Vitt, L. J., J. P. Caldwell, H. M. Wilbur, and D. C. Smith. 1991. Amphibians as harbingers of decay. *Bioscience* 40:418.

Wake, D. B. 1991. Declining amphibian populations. *Science* 253:860.

Welsh, H. H., Jr., and L. M. Ollivier. 1998. Stream amphibians as indicators of ecosystem stress: A case study from California's redwoods. *Ecol Applications* 8:1118-1132.

Welsh, H. H., Jr., L. M. Ollivier, and D. G. Hankin. 1997. A habitat-based design for sampling and monitoring stream amphibians with an illustration from Redwood National Park. *Northwestern Naturalist* 78:1-16.

Wenskus, T. 2003. Natural Resources Group – Forest Restoration Team Fall 2003 Summary. Unpublished report. New York City Department of Parks & Recreation, Natural Resources Group: New York, NY. 5 pp.

Whissel, J. C. and S. A. Wissinger. 1999. The effects of forest corridor width on streamside salamander communities. Fourth Conference of the North American Amphibian Monitoring Program, Eastern Streamside Salamander Meeting: State College, PA. http://www.mp1-pwrc.usgs.gov/amphib/naamp4/papers/whissel.html.

Wilmott, G. B. 1931. The salamanders of Staten Island, NY, in 1931. *Proc Staten Island Inst Arts Sci* 6:61-164.

Wilmott, G. B. 1933. Salamanders of Staten Island. *Am Field Naturalist* 1.

Windmiller, B. S. 1996. The pond, the forest, and the city: spotted salamander ecology and conservation in a human-dominated landscape. Ph.D. dissertation, Tufts University. UMI Dissertation Services: Ann Arbor, MI. 184 pp.

Wyman, R. L. And J. Jancola. 1992. Degree and scale of terrestrial acidification and amphibian community structure. *J Herpetol* 26:392-401.

Wyman, R. L. 1988. Soil acidity and the distribution of amphibians in five forests of southcentral New York. *Copeia* 1988:394-399.

Yeaton, S. 1988. Unpublished letter to New York City Department of Parks & Recreation, Natural Resources Group: New York, NY. 4 pp.

Yoon, C. K. 1997. Eerie quiet of frogs and toads isn't part of a normal cycle, study says. *Endangered: American Museum of Natural History* 1:1.

Appendix Specimen records used in analysis

American Museum of Natural History		Cornell University Museum of Vertebrates
A 467	A40175-A40186	Amphibian 1152
A1490	A40481-A40486	Amphibian 1657
A2176-A2178	A41368-A41373	Amphibian 11383
A2246-A2269	A41482	
A2323-A2326	A44332-A44333	
A2505-A2506	A44335	**Kansas University Natural History Museum**
A2577-A2579	A50809	
A2639	A51544	KU175634
A2696	A51575	KU175823
A3023-A3025	A52317-A52321	
A3636	A52333	
A3638-A3640	A78264-A78268	
A3734-A3738	A103509	**Museum of Comparative Zoology**
A6403	A127985	
A6491-A6494	A130202-A130215	MCZ 230
A13088	A145229-145248	
A16581-A16597	A146374-A146393	
A32789	A146834	
A32794-A32795	A149086-A149106	
A33271-A33398	A149107	
A33946-A33948	A150144-150154	
A35127-A35128	A151769-A152235	
A35531-A35545	A152236-987	
A37314-A37316		
A37591		
A37649		
A38103		
A38140-A38143		
A38185-A38189		
A38234		

Migratory Bird Mortality at the World Trade Center and World Financial Center, 1997-2001: A Deadly Mix of Lights and Glass

Allison Sloan
3227 Pennington Lane
Winston-Salem NC 27106
allisonlynnsloan@yahoo.com

Background

PUBLISHED SCIENTIFIC ACCOUNTS OF BIRDS colliding with tall, lighted structures during night migration date back to the 1880s, when flocks of migrants were observed crashing into lighthouses (Avery et al. 1980). Most songbirds migrate at night and can become disoriented by bright lights near their flight altitude. This is especially the case when low clouds or fog obscure such navigational cues as the stars and moon and force migrants closer to the ground. In these conditions, bright light emitted from manmade structures—lighthouses, communications towers, floodlit structures, skyscrapers, bridges, smokestacks and, in the past, airport ceilometers—reflects off water particles in the air, forming an illuminated area that passing birds are reluctant to leave (Avery et al. 1976). Trapped in the lighted space, they tend to circle the light source (Larkin et al. 1988), where collisions with the structure, one another or the ground may result in mass mortality (Avery et al. 1976). On multiple occasions over the past century in which night migrants encountered worst-case weather conditions, the death toll at individual structures has numbered in the thousands (Avery et al. 1980).

The urban landscape presents a second potentially deadly hazard in the form of glass windows. Besides letting light escape at night, glass causes daytime collisions, either by being invisible to birds or by reflecting nearby trees and sky. Glass may in fact be one of the largest anthropogenic killers of birds, claiming from 100 million to a billion birds a year in the United States alone (Klem 1990, Dunn 1993), an average of one to 10 birds for every

183

building in the nation. At and before sunrise, night migrants that land in cities find themselves in a maze of deceptive glass, where they are vulnerable to colliding with windows throughout the day. For birds unable to find an escape route, collisions are often fatal: in downtown Toronto, the Fatal Light Awareness Program (FLAP) has documented some 35,000 birds killed or injured since 1993. While FLAP was able to rehabilitate about 11,000 of the survivors, approximately half of the casualties died from their impacts. Of the 4,738 birds found in 2005, about 65% struck glass during the day (FLAP director Michael Mesure, pers. comm.).

New York City's glistening skyline has its own history of migration disasters, dating back to at least 1890. As recorded in the pages of this very journal, at the Linnaean Society of New York meeting of October 3, 1890, member Jonathan Dwight reported observing several hundred migrating birds attracted to rays of light from the Statue of Liberty, then brilliantly illuminated (Linnaean Society of New York 1891). On November 18, 1891, ornithologist Frank Chapman related similar observations of night migrants fluttering around the statue's lights (Linnaean Society of New York 1892). In 1904, naturalist William Beebe spent a foggy May night inside the statue's torch. He reported masses of confused birds swarming around and striking the statue, even landing on Beebe himself, until the fog lifted (Beebe 1953). The next morning, he picked up 271 dead birds at the statue's base. Beebe mentions an anecdotal report of 1,400 birds found dead there after an earlier foggy night. He concludes this account on a brighter note, however: "Thanks to the protests of bird lovers and especially half-dazzled pilots of passing vessels, the light of the statue was diminished and rendered indirect, so that, in more recent years, there have been very few avian casualties."

The Empire State Building (ESB) has also taken a toll on migratory birds through the years. On September 12, 1948, the front page of *The New York Times* described "hundreds" of birds dropping from the sky around the famous skyscraper on the foggy night of September 10; the article mentions that similar incidents had occurred there "every year when the birds migrate." On the night of October 5, 1954, a cold front which had brought migrants aloft converged with warm, moist air over New York City, forming a low ceiling of turbulent rain clouds. By morning, "hundreds" of birds had died at the ESB, along with "several thousand" more at two military airfield ceilometers in Long Island. Over the following two nights, this same weather front proved to be one of the greatest migration tragedies in recorded history, ultimately killing 100,000 birds at 24 lighted locations as it moved south across the eastern seaboard (Johnston et al. 1957, Audubon

Society 1965). Another massive collision involving "hundreds of migrating warblers, thrushes, vireos and tanagers" at the ESB was reported in the *Times* in September 1970 (Carmody 1970).

Starting in April 1997, a volunteer effort documented migratory bird mortality at New York City's tallest structures, the two 110-story towers of the World Trade Center (WTC). The study also included the other four buildings of the WTC complex and the adjacent World Financial Center (WFC). We were not aware of a single-night migration disaster like those described in earlier reports. However, our steady findings of casualties nearly every day during migration indicate that, in the aggregate, buildings are taking a significant toll on birds passing over Manhattan. This report describes these findings and offers possible solutions for preventing or reducing further bird mortality at buildings.

Purpose
Inspired by FLAP's work in Toronto, in 1997 birder Rebekah Creshkoff began monitoring the WTC and the WFC in an effort to assess mortality rates of migrating birds and rescue survivors. Other volunteers gradually joined in her effort, which in 2000 was adopted by New York City Audubon and is now called "Project Safe Flight." The growing size of the group permitted much more thorough coverage of the structures during early-morning monitoring. It also increased the time and resources available to develop strategies to mitigate the structures and forge partnerships with building managers.

The Study Sites
The 6.5-hectare WTC complex comprised six buildings that featured vast expanses of plate glass that was either transparent, mirrored, or black-tinted. (The building known as 7 World Trade Center was actually outside of the complex and was not monitored on a consistent basis.) These buildings were set around a large paved plaza. Given the buildings' vast scale and the relatively narrow passageways between them, the overall effect was one of a courtyard with a significant opening on only one side (the east). The plaza included a number of small planters with flowers, shrubs or small trees. Two larger planters (about 12 meters by 6 meters) held sizable London plane trees. It was to these scraps of habitat that disoriented birds trapped on the plaza retreated to rest and forage. Immediately west of the WTC complex, along the Hudson River, sit the five buildings of the 5.7-hectare WFC. Four of these structures range in height from 34 to 44 stories. Three are adjoined by

the fifth structure, a three-story glass atrium known as the Winter Garden, which has palm trees growing inside. The WFC features great quantities of transparent glass, which can appear to be anywhere from invisible to highly reflective, depending on the time of day, the light and weather conditions.

In general, more than half the office windows in both complexes were illuminated for most or all of the night. Additional light came from a communications tower atop the northern twin tower, which was lit with floodlights until fall 2000, when WTC staff began dousing this nonessential lighting during migration per our request (Port Authority 2000). However, the antenna retained its red warning lights, as required by law for aircraft safety. Since this type of lighting has proved disorienting to birds at ground-level communications towers, it was likely doing so here as well. At the WFC, decorative lighting at the top of the four towers sometimes remained lit throughout the night, forming a brilliant crown on each building. Harsh white floodlights kept on for the palm trees also radiate from inside the Winter Garden each night.

Method

Each morning during migration seasons, from about late March to early June, and again from early September through early December, volunteers arrived early in the morning and searched the WTC and WFC grounds for dead or injured birds. Actual arrival times varied considerably: In 1997, Rebekah generally arrived at 6:30 a.m. Later, most volunteers made a concerted effort to be on site much earlier—preferably a half-hour before sunrise. It took at least an hour to check all the buildings, even without finding anything; rescuing and releasing stunned birds took considerably longer. Volunteers generally continued to circle the buildings at least until 7:30 a.m. and often later on heavy mornings. While many bird strikes seemed to occur before or around sunrise, disoriented migrants that took refuge in flowerbeds and other bits of habitat around the buildings were vulnerable to collisions throughout the day. We often had the experience of finding birds on our second or third go-round, or even at a window checked just five minutes earlier.

When we located a dead or injured bird, we recorded its species, status (dead, rescued, or injured but not capturable), gender (for sexually dimorphic species), and precisely where and when it was found. Subsequently, we also began to note factors which might have contributed to the crash. These included reflections of the surrounding landscape, potted trees inside the window or exterior habitat visible through the building (e.g. through paired windows on opposite sides of the building, or a corner formed entirely of glass). Data gathering actually began the night before, when volunteers recorded the overnight weather forecast, wind direction, NEXRAD radar images and BirdCast predictions at www.birdsource.org/birdcast. (A radar ornithology project operated by the Clemson University Radar Ornithology Laboratory, the Cornell Lab of Ornithology and other organizations, BirdCast provided NEXRAD-based migration forecasts every night during migration season from April 2000 to June 2001.) The phase of the moon was also logged.

Injured birds were captured if possible and placed in brown paper lunch bags, as prescribed by wildlife rehabilitators (FLAP Web site; Tesa Sallenave, pers. comm.) Invalids can breathe through the unwaxed paper, and the soft walls prevent restless birds from further injuring themselves. Most stunned birds perked up by the end of our rounds and were released in parks according to the direction of their migration. In fall, birds were released in Robert F. Wagner Park, immediately south of Battery Park City. Spring birds were freed in Nelson A. Rockefeller Park north of the WFC, in Central Park, or in Inwood Hill Park, far north of Manhattan's skyscrapers. Although we counted these apparently recovered birds as successful rescues, in reality we had no way of knowing their actual survival rates. Birds still lethargic or displaying other signs of injury were delivered to a wildlife rehabilitator.

Dead birds were collected under Rebekah's New York State and federal salvage permits and frozen, photographed for documentation, and shipped to the Patuxent Wildlife Research Center in Laurel, Maryland.

Numbers and Species Affected

Over the migration seasons from 1997 to spring 2001 that we monitored the WTC and WFC, we found a total of 2,352 casualties representing at least 83 species (see Table 1). Of these, 68% (1,604 birds) were dead. Of the 748 injured, 60% (447 individuals) were rescued and released. Because the species of 87 casualties were unidentified, the true number of species affected may actually be higher. And because we undoubtedly missed many birds, the total number affected, too, was probably much greater. We know from maintenance, security and office workers that birds continued to collide throughout the day. An additional unknown number were swept up or scavenged before we reached them. This was evidenced by reports from sweepers, dead birds found in garbage cans, severed wings or heads near the buildings and occasional sightings of injured birds being picked off by gulls or Peregrine Falcons. Also missed were birds that may have fallen onto rooftops, ledges, or other inaccessible areas.

Table 1. List of birds found dead and injured at selected buildings in New York City, 1997-2001.

Species	Scientific Name	Dead	Injured	Total
Yellow Rail	*Coturnicops noveboracensis*	0	1	1
Virginia Rail	*Rallus limicola*	1	5	6
Sora	*Porzana carolina*	1	0	1
American Woodcock	*Scolopax minor*	50	16	66
Rock Pigeon	*Columba livia*	3	2	5
Mourning Dove	*Zenaida macroura*	4	1	5
Black-billed Cuckoo	*Coccyzus erythropthalmus*	1	0	1
Ruby-throated Hummingbird	*Archilochus colubris*	4	0	4
Red-bellied Woodpecker	*Melanerpes carolinus*	1	0	1
Yellow-bellied Sapsucker	*Sphyrapicus varius*	13	2	15
Northern Flicker	*Colaptes auratus*	19	6	25
Eastern Wood-Pewee	*Contopus virens*	2	1	3
Eastern Phoebe	*Sayornis phoebe*	1	2	3
Great Crested Flycatcher	*Myiarchus crinitus*	1	0	1
Flycatcher, species?	*Family: Tyrannidae*	1	3	4
Yellow-throated Vireo	*Vireo flavifrons*	0	1	1
Red-eyed Vireo	*Vireo olivaceus*	3	0	3
Blue Jay	*Cyanocitta cristata*	2	0	2
Black-capped Chickadee	*Poecile atricapillus*	2	0	2
White-breasted Nuthatch	*Sitta carolinensis*	3	0	3
Brown Creeper	*Certhia americana*	10	12	22
House Wren	*Troglodytes aedon*	4	6	10
Winter Wren	*Troglodytes troglodytes*	5	9	14
Marsh Wren	*Cistothorus palustris*	2	2	4
Wren, species?	*Family: Troglodytidae*	1	1	2
Golden-crowned Kinglet	*Regulus satrapa*	7	5	12
Ruby-crowned Kinglet	*Regulus calendula*	16	11	27
Veery	*Catharus fuscescens*	2	1	3
Gray-cheeked Thrush	*Catharus minimus*	1	1	2
Swainson's Thrush	*Catharus ustulatus*	7	2	9
Hermit Thrush	*Catharus guttatus*	34	32	66
Wood Thrush	*Hylocichla mustelina*	13	4	17

Table 1 continued.

Species	Scientific Name	Dead	Injured	Total
Thrush, species?	Family: Turdidae	5	4	9
American Robin	Turdus migratorius	2	1	3
Gray Catbird	Dumetella carolinensis	26	24	50
Brown Thrasher	Toxostoma rufum	2	2	4
Cedar Waxwing	Bombycilla cedrorum	2	1	3
Blue-winged Warbler	Vermivora pinus	1	1	2
Tennessee Warbler	Vermivora peregrina	3	2	5
Nashville Warbler	Vermivora ruficapilla	11	3	14
Northern Parula	Parula americana	10	3	13
Chestnut-sided Warbler	Dendroica pensylvanica	6	4	10
Magnolia Warbler	Dendroica magnolia	23	9	32
Cape May Warbler	Dendroica tigrina	1	0	1
Black-throated Blue Warbler	Dendroica caerulescens	42	10	52
Yellow-rumped Warbler	Dendroica coronata	20	6	26
Black-throated Green Warbler	Dendroica virens	9	3	12
Blackburnian Warbler	Dendroica fusca	2	0	2
Pine Warbler	Dendroica pinus	2	0	2
Prairie Warbler	Dendroica discolor	2	1	3
Palm Warbler	Dendroica palmarum	8	4	12
Bay-breasted Warbler	Dendroica castanea	2	0	2
Blackpoll Warbler	Dendroica striata	27	8	35
Black-and-white Warbler	Mniotilta varia	34	18	52
American Redstart	Setophaga ruticilla	24	10	34
Worm-eating Warbler	Helmitheros vermivorus	3	1	4
Ovenbird	Seiurus aurocapillus	134	70	204
Northern Waterthrush	Seiurus noveboracensis	27	7	34
Kentucky Warbler	Oporornis formosus	2	2	4
Connecticut Warbler	Oporornis agilis	5	0	5
Mourning Warbler	Oporornis philadelphia	2	0	2
Common Yellowthroat	Geothlypis trichas	183	126	309
Hooded Warbler	Wilsonia citrina	0	2	2
Wilson's Warbler	Wilsonia pusilla	2	0	2
Canada Warbler	Wilsonia canadensis	10	2	12

Table I continued. List of birds found dead and injured at selected buildings in New York City, 1997-2001.

Species	Scientific Name	Dead	Injured	Total
Yellow-breasted Chat	*Icteria virens*	4	0	4
Warbler, species?	*Family: Parulidae*	36	25	61
Scarlet Tanager	*Piranga olivacea*	3	3	6
Eastern Towhee	*Pipilo erythrophthalmus*	6	3	9
Chipping Sparrow	*Spizella passerina*	4	1	5
Field Sparrow	*Spizella pusilla*	1	0	1
Savannah Sparrow	*Passerculus sandwichensis*	2	0	2
Fox Sparrow	*Passerella iliaca*	10	6	16
Song Sparrow	*Melospiza melodia*	67	20	87
Lincoln's Sparrow	*Melospiza lincolnii*	20	2	22
Swamp Sparrow	*Melospiza georgiana*	56	10	66
White-throated Sparrow	*Zonotrichia albicollis*	369	149	518
White-crowned Sparrow	*Zonotrichia leucophrys*	1	0	1
Sparrow, species?	*Family: Emberizidae*	17	11	28
Dark-eyed Junco	*Junco hyemalis*	73	45	118
Rose-breasted Grosbeak	*Pheucticus ludovicianus*	1	0	1
Indigo Bunting	*Passerina cyanea*	6	1	7
Common Grackle	*Quiscalus quiscula*	1	0	1
Orchard Oriole	*Icterus spurius*	1	1	2
Purple Finch	*Carpodacus purpureus*	1	0	1
House Finch	*Carpodacus mexicanus*	2	2	4
American Goldfinch	*Carduelis tristis*	1	0	1
House Sparrow	*Passer domesticus*	6	2	8
Unidentified bird, reported		70	17	87
Grand Totals		1604	748	2352

Ninety-three percent of the dead and injured birds (2,265 individuals) were identified as to species (the remaining 7% could not be identified because they were reported by secondhand sources such as sweepers and security guards, or by monitors inexperienced in bird identification). Of these, 94% were songbirds (order Passeriformes). Among the passerines, warblers (Family Parulidae) constituted 42% of the total, with 952 individuals representing at least 30 species killed or injured. Sparrows (Family Emberizidae) placed a close second, with 873 dead and injured sparrows of 12 species making up 38.5% of the total. Combined, these two families represented more than 80% of all casualties. The third hardest hit was the thrush family (Turdidae), with 109 individuals of six species making up 5% of the total. Other songbird families rounding out the top ten list included mimids, kinglets, wrens, creepers, and flycatchers (Table 2).

Table 2. Top ten bird families found at selected New York City buildings, 1997-2001.

	Family	Scientific Name	Number of Individuals	Number of Species	Percent of Total*
1	Warbler	(Parulidae)	952	30+	42%
2	Sparrow	(Emberizidae)	873	12	38.5%
3	Thrush	(Turdidae)	109	6	5%
4	Woodcock	(Scolopacidae)	66	1	3%
5	Mimid	(Mimidae)	54	2	2.4%
6	Woodpecker	(Picidae)	41	3	1.8%
7	Kinglet	(Regulidae)	39	2	1.7%
8	Wren	(Troglodytidae)	30	3	1.3%
9	Creeper	(Certhiidae)	22	1	1%
10	Flycatcher	(Tyrannidae)	11	3+	0.5%
*Total number of birds identified = 2265					

Only 130 casualties (6%) belonged to nonpasserine orders of bird families, but their diversity demonstrates that a wide variety of species, from rails to hummingbirds, are vulnerable to building collisions. These orders include Charadriiformes (Family Scolopacidae: 66 dead or injured American Woodcocks), Piciformes (Family Picidae: 25 Northern Flickers, 15 Yellow-bellied Sapsuckers, 1 Red-bellied Woodpecker), Columbiformes (Family Columbidae: 5 Rock Pigeons, 5 Mourning Doves), Gruiformes (Family Rallidae: 1 Yellow Rail, 6 Virginia Rails, 1 Sora), Apodiformes (Family Trochilidae: 4 Ruby-throated Hummingbirds), and Cuculiformes (Family Cuculidae: 1 Black-billed Cuckoo). Of the bird families comprising the highest portions of the total casualty number (Table 2), the American Woodcock and the woodpecker family rank fourth and sixth respectively.

Four species accounted for more than half the casualties: White-throated Sparrow (*Zonotrichia albicollis*), with 518 dead and injured, or 23% of the total identified as to species; Common Yellowthroat (*Geothlypis trichas*) at 14% (309 birds); Ovenbird (*Seiurus aurocapillus*) at 9% (204 casualties), and Dark-eyed Junco (*Junco hyemalis*) at 5% (118 individuals). The Song Sparrow (*Melospiza melodia*) ranked fifth in the total casualty list, with 87 killed and injured, or 4% of the total identified. Tied at 66 casualties (3%) each were Swamp Sparrow (*Melospiza georgiana*), American Woodcock (*Scolopax minor*), and Hermit Thrush (*Catharus guttatus*), followed by the Black-throated Blue Warbler (*Dendroica caerulescens*) and Black-and-white Warbler (*Mniotilta varia*), with 52 each (2%). For a ranking in casualties of the top 15 birds found, see Table 3.

Although the WTC and WFC hosted resident populations of House Sparrows, Rock Pigeons and House Finches, these species are scarcely represented among our casualties. We found only 17 individuals of these three species, or less than 1% of the total.

Table 3. Top 15 birds found dead or injured at New York City buildings, 1997-2001.

Species	Scientific Name	Total	Percent of Total*
White-throated Sparrow	*Zonotrichia albicollis*	518	23%
Common Yellowthroat	*Geothlypis trichas*	309	14%
Ovenbird	*Seiurus aurocapilla*	204	9%
Dark-eyed Junco	*Junco hyemalis*	118	5%
Song Sparrow	*Melospiza melodia*	87	4%
Swamp Sparrow	*Melospiza georgiana*	66	3%
American Woodcock	*Scolopax minor*	66	3%
Hermit Thrush	*Catharus guttatus*	66	3%
Black-throated Blue Warbler	*Dendroica caerulescens*	52	2.3%
Black-and-white Warbler	*Mniotilta varia*	52	2.3%
Gray Catbird	*Dumetella carolinensis*	50	2.2%
Blackpoll Warbler	*Dendroica striata*	35	1.5%
Northern Waterthrush	*Seiurus noveboracensis*	34	1.5%
American Redstart	*Setophaga ruticilla*	34	1.5%
Magnolia Warbler	*Dendroica magnolia*	32	1.4%
*Total number of birds identified = 2265			

Why songbirds, and certain species in particular, appear most vulnerable to collisions is uncertain. While flight altitude between species is highly variable, songbirds as a group migrate at lower altitudes than other birds (Cooper and Ritchie 1995, Able 1970). This pattern may increase their susceptibility to crashes from light disorientation or inability to perceive glass. The difference in casualty rates among songbird species seems more complex, however. For many of the highest-collision species, such as White-throated Sparrows, Ovenbirds, Common Yellow-throats, Dark-eyed Juncos and Hermit Thrushes, the high rates may simply reflect their abundance. However, we found very few of certain other plentiful night-migrating songbirds, such as American Robins, Red-eyed Vireos, and Yellow-rumped Warblers. This discrepancy suggests that some aspect of physiology or behavior may be at work. Possible factors may include stronger phototactic responses, differences in eye structure and perception of color or light, flight altitude and ground-foraging tendencies. More study is needed in these areas.

Collision Factors: Weather and Seasonal Variations

Upon arriving at the study site, the density of the previous night's migration was often immediately apparent by the volume and variety of bird vocalizations echoing from the planters. Our daily findings varied tremendously, from zero to 65 casualties on a single morning. Several factors seemed to generally affect the magnitude of daily collisions, although none was without exception:

1. Wind direction and resulting migration density: Birds are most likely to migrate with a tail wind, or when the wind is light and variable, and we found that south or southwest winds in the spring and northwest winds in fall typically generated the most collisions. This was especially the case when weather abruptly shifted to favorable migration conditions following a period of opposing winds or inclement weather. However, exceptions abound. On one May night, although we had opposing winds locally, a warm front passed through immediately southwest of New York. The following morning brought our highest number of collisions in the spring of 2001. Opposing winds also spawned high casualty rates when following in the wake of a favorable weather front and when accompanied by clouds or rain.

2. Moon phase: In general, bird crashes tend to be more frequent when there is little or no moon, and they subside considerably

when the moon is near full and is visible for most of the night, providing this phase coincides with clear weather.

3. Clouds and precipitation: Our findings show that while clouds and fog can result in large kills, overcast skies are not required for birds to be disoriented by lights and collide with buildings. In spring, our highest-collision mornings followed nights of fog, rain, dense cloud cover or haze, which typically accompany the south winds ideal for spring migration. In fall, however, we found more birds after clear nights with northwest winds, the conditions that attract the largest fall migrations. Inclement weather may play a larger role in spring collisions because the weather is generally more un-settled than in fall, and birds taking off in clear skies may be more likely to encounter bad weather along the way.

Although the highest daily casualty totals occurred in the spring, our overall totals were much higher in fall, probably because the young of the year swell the autumn population. Despite nearly equal coverage both seasons, the fall of 2000 yielded nearly twice as many dead (478) as the following spring (256), although numbers of injured were inexplicably comparable (188 and 175, respectively). Casualty rates varied greatly each year (Table 4), partly reflecting fluctuations in coverage, which depended on volunteer availability. Arriving before sunrise and spending more time on site yielded more collision reports in later seasons. Variations in weather conditions from year to year and search efficiency may have also played a role in these differences.

Anatomy of the Collisions

Because monitors were never on site throughout the night, we did not observe the majority of the collisions. By the time we arrived, most of the victims we

Table 4. Bird casualties found at selected New York City buildings each year, 1997-2001.

Year	Number of Days Monitored	Dead	Injured	Total	Daily Average (# of casualties)
1997	144	331	121	452	3.1
1998	32	81	15	96	3
1999	51 (fall only)	224	120	344	6.7
2000	124	711	317	1028	8.3
2001	69 (spring only)	257	175	432	6.3

would eventually find had already been killed or injured; therefore, we do not know whether these birds collided high up on the buildings and fell to the ground, or crashed into bright lower-level windows after being grounded by light disorientation. Of the 2,352 total casualties, a significant number did collide while monitors were present. Both before and after sunrise, we observed many birds strike the bottom two stories when flying toward windows from nearby planters or from the ground. Michael Mesure theorizes that some birds initially collide up high (primary collision) and survive the impact, but become increasingly disoriented and descend to the ground, where secondary collisions occur with lobby-level windows (Michael Mesure, pers. comm.). In many cases, injured birds were found fluttering against the glass near the ground, as if trying to get inside the buildings, particularly when it was brighter indoors than outside. Because our inspections focused on the ground, only rarely did we directly observe birds falling from high up on the glass walls. However, it is likely that this event occurs more frequently; a small portion of the dead were found as far as 12 meters from buildings, and birds were seen fluttering upward against higher windows as they attempted to fly over buildings. We presumably missed an additional number of casualties that collided up high but fell onto the roofs of the shorter WTC buildings or the numerous ledges at the WFC which were inaccessible to volunteers.

As further evidence that many fatal strikes probably do not occur immediately when birds encounter the buildings, there appears to be no correlation between migration direction and location of casualties, with windows facing north and south yielding no more hits than those facing east and west.

Although collisions with glass can occur wherever birds and glass coexist (Klem 1989), windows at the WTC and WFC seemed to invite the most collisions when they provided misleading cues—specifically, when they:

1. Reflected surrounding trees or planters in the daytime.
2. Showed plants or trees inside buildings.
3. Reflected the sky in the daytime.
4. Paired with another window to provide a clear line of sight through buildings in the daytime.
5. Were brighter than the predawn sky.

Each complex contained several areas where collisions were consistently most frequent. At the WTC, the two sections of windows that yielded the most casualties reflected the only large trees on the plaza, at the east side of the south tower and the north side of the north tower. At the WFC, the most victims were claimed by the immense glass Winter Garden, which shows palm trees inside and reflects sky at certain times of day, as well as by a corner of windows adjacent to a tree-filled garden. Over the course of the study, we documented about twice as many bird victims at the WTC as at the WFC (Table 5). However, the WFC sweeping crews start work at 6:00 a.m., a full hour before the WTC staff.

Our total casualty number also includes 95 dead and 10 injured birds that collided with other buildings in the city. These birds either were found at several other large glass structures in downtown Manhattan that we occasionally monitored in fall 2000 or were reported to us by secondhand sources.

Table 5. Total bird casualties found at selected New York City buildings, 1997-2001, grouped by location.

Location	Dead	Injured	Total	Percent of Total*
World Trade Center	1008	519	1527	65%
World Financial Center	501	219	720	30.6%
Other buildings	95	10	105	4.4%
*Total			2352	

Preventive Steps and Successes

After learning of the bird collisions in Spring 2000, the Port Authority of New York and New Jersey, which owns and manages the WTC site, agreed to place nets over the windows at the worst collision spot, near a large tree and flowerbed on the east side of the south tower. Nearly invisible from just a few feet away, this fine-mesh garden netting was stretched taut and anchored to the tower's steel outer frame. As the windows were set back an additional three feet, the netting served as a trampoline for any birds that flew toward it. This measure, implemented in fall 2000, resulted in reducing the collisions there by about 65% from the previous spring's levels. Extending this net higher to cover the building's second story (including the top of the tree's reflection) and lengthwise to cover the remainder of first-story windows would probably have made it even more effective.

Upon our request, the Port Authority extended the netting to cover the bottom story of windows on two sides of each of the two towers in May 2001. Although the nets somewhat reduced collisions at those locations, again they were not high enough to be fully effective. How high they would have had to reach to prevent all collisions is not known.

At the urging of an employee there who consulted us about bird collisions, higher-grade netting was professionally installed over a hazardous section of windows at 26 Federal Plaza in downtown Manhattan. We discovered that bright floodlights shine from the roof of this building; these may play a role in drawing birds to the site.

It remains uncertain how effective netting can be if it is not accompanied by a reduction in light at night. Although the WTC netting was diminishing collisions at those particular windows, birds saved by the netting could still crash elsewhere on the plaza. Port Authority requested that tenants douse lighting or close blinds at night, but their request seemed to have had little immediate impact on tenant behavior. PSF volunteer Patrick Harty began viewing the WTC at night via an online web camera, enabling us to determine exactly which tenants frequently left lights on overnight. This strategy proved effective in darkening or dimming six brilliantly lit floors near the top of the north tower, after we requested lighting changes from the resident company, Marsh & McLennan. The strategy of approaching specific tenants, in addition to expanding educational efforts to office workers, holds promise for reducing light emitted from downtown office towers.

In a promising step toward citywide light reductions, in fall 2005 New York City Audubon, in partnership with the Building Owners and Managers Association, the New York Department of Parks and Recreation and other organizations, launched Lights Out NY. Modeled after the Lights Out Chicago program enacted in 2001, which extinguishes the decorative lighting at some 20 skyscrapers every migration season, Lights Out NY encourages building owners to save birds and reduce energy costs by voluntarily turning off lights at midnight during migration season.

Conclusions and Recommendations

Given our findings of more than 2,300 bird collisions at only a few of Manhattan's buildings over a 4.5-year period, the actual number of bird strikes in the city is likely to be many times greater. Considering that populations of neotropical migrants are declining due to a variety of factors, and that windowed structures are multiplying as urban and suburban areas continue to invade natural habitat, the impact of building collisions on birds is alarming in its potential magnitude. Nevertheless, it remains largely overlooked as a conservation issue.

With respect to tall buildings, one obvious solution to reducing bird mortality is to turn off lights at night during migration season. In 1958,

Cochran and Graber observed that birds clustering around a communications tower dispersed within minutes after the tower was darkened (Cochran et al. 1958). Thanks to light reductions in decades past, reports of massive bird kills at the Empire State Building (ESB) and Statue of Liberty no longer make newspaper headlines. By implementing the following changes, building managers and tenants can minimize bird hazards locally:

1. Extinguish nonessential, decorative lighting during spring and fall migration, especially on foggy or overcast nights.
2. Shut off office lights at the end of the day. If working at night, close blinds or curtains. These steps can be included in the job descriptions of overnight security or cleaning staff, as they were at Marsh & McLennan's offices in the WTC north tower.
3. Install motion-detector lighting in offices that automatically shuts off when employees leave at night.
4. Where these exist, adjust lighting timers to turn off more frequently throughout the night.
5. Create smaller lighting zones by reducing the number of lights controlled by each individual switch.

Daytime window strikes can be mitigated at skyscrapers and low-level windows alike if building managers and homeowners take steps either to make glass visible to birds or to cushion its impact, as follows:

1. Install fine-mesh netting tautly stretched several inches away from glass outside windows. Suitable netting is available at most garden-supply stores.
2. Enable birds to perceive glass as a barrier. This can be achieved through a variety of methods, including applying window frosting, positioning vertical strips of ribbon or tape at 10-centimeter intervals or affixing decorative decals on the exterior of the glass. Closing drapes and blinds helps somewhat. A clear adhesive film that eliminates reflections when applied to the outside of windows exists, but covering large areas with it might prove prohibitively expensive (FLAP web site). For homes, suspending potted plants, wind chimes or fabric strips under the eaves directly in front of glass will reduce habitat reflections.
3. Outdoors, position bird baths, feeders and bird-attractive vegetation less than one meter away from windows.

4. In office building lobbies, move potted trees and shrubs away from windows and out of view of birds outside.

But these are only short-term fixes. In the long run, glass manufacturers should be able to develop glass that is transparent from inside, but incorporates patterns visible to birds outside. Architects should resist the urge to incorporate nonessential lighting and large expanses of glass in their designs. And legislators could pass legally enforceable lighting ordinances to replace the voluntary light-reduction programs now in place in New York and Chicago. The alternative is to continue contributing to the decline of bird species on a massive scale.

Update: Project Safe Flight (PSF) Findings Since 2001
This report was originally drafted in the summer of 2001 and had already been submitted for review on September 11, 2001. On that crystalline day, I arrived at the World Trade Center at 6:00 a.m. Finding no casualties, I left the complex at 7:20, never imagining it was for the last time. Among those that perished in the attacks were Ed Strauss, the Port Authority manager who had supervised the installation of bird-protective netting over windows at the twin towers, and several security guards with whom we had formed relationships over the years. Marsh & McLennan, the insurance company which had adopted a lights-out policy to protect birds migrating past its offices near the top of the north tower, lost 295 employees.

Since that time, PSF's volunteer base has grown to over fifty, and monitors have identified numerous other structures in Manhattan that produce bird collisions throughout migration season. As of September 12, 2006, PSF has documented 2,482 additional casualties (1,848 dead and 634 injured), for a total of 4,834 birds found killed (3,452) or hurt (1,382) by window strikes in New York City since 1997.

The number of species found also climbed from 83 to 102, and now includes Sharp-shinned Hawk (1), American Kestrel (1), Peregrine Falcon (2), American Coot (1), Yellow-billed Cuckoo (4), Chuck-Will's-Widow (1), Yellow-bellied Flycatcher (3), Least Flycatcher (1), Blue-headed Vireo (2), Tufted Titmouse (3), Red-breasted Nuthatch (14), Eastern Bluebird (1), Yellow Warbler (3), Louisiana Waterthrush (2), Seaside Sparrow (1), Eastern Meadowlark (1), Common Grackle (3), Brown-headed Cowbird (1), and Baltimore Oriole (4). A complete list of collision reports, including species, outcome (dead, rescued, rehabilitated, etc.), date, and location, may be viewed online in PSF's database at www.nycaudubon.org. (Members of the public may also report collisions on this site.)

Although differences in monitoring time and building size make it difficult to compare collision rates, we have identified a number of buildings that consistently cause bird strikes.

In lower Manhattan, we continue to regularly find casualties at the World Financial Center, as well as a handful of other office towers in the financial district. Chief among these is 1 Chase Manhattan Plaza, a 60-story high-rise with a transparent glass lobby that shows exterior trees on opposite sides of the building. Across the street, the black-tinted windows at 140 Broadway, which are not transparent but reflective, also draw casualties. Although we located several other consistent collision sites in this area, we often found individual birds at random locations, seemingly trapped in the mazelike canyons between the buildings. On at least three separate occasions, I found over 40 birds scattered throughout the financial district.

We also studied several stretches of tall office towers in midtown, on Sixth Avenue from 47th to 50th Street and on Park Avenue from 47th to 53rd Streets. Most have glass lobbies, with planters outside or inside lobby windows. Although we located a few structures that drew a modest amount of bird strikes—the Chase Bank offices at 270 Park Avenue, and 1251 Sixth Avenue across from the floodlit Rockefeller Center, for example—we overall found few casualties in this area. A number of these locations were regularly swept prior to our arrival, however.

I also checked the grounds around the Empire State Building on about a dozen mornings. These visits were motivated by historical reports of migration disasters around the bright, decorative crown lights (see Background), as well as by a fall 2000 posting on the eBirds listserv by bird enthusiast Angus Wilson, who reported several hundred to a thousand migrants swirling around the ESB at 10:30 pm on the previous foggy night. On one fall 2001 visit, I too observed a fair amount of bird disorientation. Although the crown lighting is ordinarily extinguished every night at midnight, in fall 2001 it shone red, white and blue all night to inspire rescue workers downtown. On October 23rd, 2001, following a night with clear skies and northeast winds, I arrived in darkness at 5:15 am to witness roughly six dozen birds flying chaotically near street lights at the base of the building, and near lighted windows up to approximately the 20th floor. I found only five dead on the ground: three Yellow-rumped Warblers, an Eastern Towhee, and a White-throated Sparrow. Another White-throated Sparrow swarmed with several other birds around a street light, then dropped to the ground, panting; however, it took off down Fifth Avenue before I could grasp it. I watched for about 20 minutes, as individual birds fluttered around bright windows and street lights, disappearing down the streets, around corners, and behind the skyscraper. I saw only a few regain altitude and disappear skyward, and was not able to remain on-site to observe whether the disoriented birds dispersed at daybreak. On subsequent visits, I found nothing. However, later that fall one monitor learned that a roving crew of sweepers from the 34th Street Partnership Business Improvement District cleans around the ESB each night at approximately 3:30 am. The sweepers told her that they sometimes found dead birds there.

According to the Empire State Building's website, it is ESB policy to extinguish the lights before the usual midnight shut-off time to protect birds:

> During spring and fall bird migration seasons and particularly on cloudy, humid and/or foggy nights, when large numbers of birds are seen flying near the building, the tower lights are turned off. Observatory personnel on the 86th floor outdoor deck notify the engineers. The birds are attracted by the lights and there is a danger they will fly into the building and be killed. (Empire State Building Official Internet Site)

While our studies initially focused on other tall, brightly lit structures that we suspected could disorient birds at night, we discovered that shorter structures also could cause numerous strikes on a daily basis if they reflect habitat in daytime (even though lights may still play a role in drawing birds to the area at night). At the U.S. Postal Service's 6-story Morgan Processing and Distribution Center, on Ninth Avenue at 29th Street, monitors have found over 500 casualties since fall 2002, about 92% of which were dead. All of the collisions occurred at the south side of this sprawling structure. The windows here emit no light, since they are a façade for a brick wall, but instead mirror treetops from a park across the street. Another daytime hazard is the Metropolitan Museum of Art, where monitors have found at least 150 casualties (97% dead) in the past year at the museum's glass west wall, which reflects Central Park. Significant daytime collisions have also been documented at the glass-covered Jacob Javits Convention Center and the World Financial Center.

Although we found higher concentrations of collisions at the aforementioned locations—structures with abundant glass, lighting, height, and/or surrounding habitat—there were also numerous occasions when a single bird was found at a building that posed no hazard beyond standard-size residential windows or storefronts reflecting trees on the sidewalk. These events support the findings of Dr. Daniel Klem, Jr., Professor of Ornithology and

Conservation Biology at Muhlenberg College in Allentown, Pennsylvania, and a leading authority on building collisions. He concludes that ultimately, birds can collide with windows "wherever they mutually occur" (Klem 1989).

PSF representatives have also observed the Tribute in Light memorial at the former World Trade Center site each September 11th, fearing that the two brilliant columns of light, each consisting of 44 7,000-watt bulbs, would affect migrants much like ceilometers. These tall floodlights, formerly used at airports to gauge the height of clouds above the ground, occasionally led to massive bird mortality in inclement weather. In by far the worst recorded event, approximately 50,000 birds perished at a ceilometer near Macon, Georgia during an infamously disastrous weather front in October 1954 (see Background; Johnston 1957).

At the Tribute, most birds had been observed flying through the beams without being thrown off course. However, in 2004, the Tribute coincided with a new moon and dense migration, and thousands of birds were seen swirling in the lights (NYC Audubon 2005; includes photo). No birds were observed falling or colliding, though. (In the event that observers see five or more birds killed, the lighting engineers will extinguish the beams for twenty minutes to allow the birds to disperse.) In 2005, NYC Audubon enlisted ornithologist Andrew Farnsworth to observe the Tribute from a 38th-floor rooftop nearby. Despite clear skies and sparse migration, Farnsworth still observed up to 50 birds at a time hovering in and near the beams, with some individuals remaining in the lights for up to 15 minutes (Farnsworth, unpublished data). He saw none collide. The 2006 Tribute produced similar results, with up to 50 birds seen in the beams and no casualties observed (Rebekah Creshkoff, pers. comm.).

In addition to continuing to document bird strikes in the city and return survivors back to the wild, NYC Audubon is taking a number of steps to reduce the city skyline's impact on migrating birds. It is enlisting new participants in the Lights Out NY program, and has convened a Bird-Safe Glass Working Group, a multi-city task force aiming to design a new form of glass that is visible to birds. NYC Audubon will also continue consulting with designers of the Freedom Tower to implement bird-friendly measures into their building plans, as well as with U.S. Postal Service managers to reduce window strikes at the Morgan Processing and Distribution Center. With funding from the U.S. Fish and Wildlife Service (USFWS), NYC Audubon is conducting a comprehensive study to quantify the magnitude of the bird collision problem in New York City and to evaluate the importance of the various factors involved in collisions. The study is being led by Dr. Daniel Klem, and will run from fall 2006 to spring 2007. The USFWS grant will also fund the creation of pamphlets for architects and for building owners and managers that will explain how to reduce bird kills.

Acknowledgments

I am infinitely grateful to Rebekah Creshkoff for her hours of careful reviews, edits, and research assistance, and to William R. Evans and Michael Mesure for their reviews and suggestions. Many thanks to Patrick Harty for his dedication in constructing a database for PSF to record and easily tabulate collision data online, and to current PSF coordinators Yigal Gelb and Nicole Delacretaz for their leadership and information provided for the update. And I thank the other building monitors who collected bird collision data for this study: Marge Alston, Ned Boyajian, Rhoda Chaloff, Angela Cichoski, Richard Doll, Meryl Greenblatt, Patrick Harty, Nancy Heidel, Amy Kaup, Linda Lange, MaryBeth LaReau, Sara Lundberg, Pat O'Malley, Mona Payton, and Larry Yates.

Scientific names and taxonomic order of species in all tables follows the seventh edition of The American Ornithologists' Union's Check-List of North American Birds.

Allison Sloan coordinated Project Safe Flight's monitoring and rescue efforts from 1999 to 2004.

References

Able, K.P. 1970. A radar study of the altitude of nocturnal passerine migration, *Bird Banding* 41:4, 282-290.

Audubon Society. 1965. *The Audubon Nature Encyclopedia*, 6, Curtis Publishing Co., N Y.

Avery, M.L., P.F. Springer, and J.F. Cassel. 1976. The effects of a tall tower on nocturnal bird migration - a portable ceilometer study, Auk 93, 281-291.

Avery, M.L., P.F. Springer, and N.S. Dailey. 1980. Avian mortality at man-made structures: an annotated bibliography (revised), U.S. Fish and Wildlife Service, FWS/OBS-80/54.

Beebe, William. 1953. *The Unseen Life of New York as a Naturalist Sees It*, Duell, Sloan & Pearce and Little, Brown & Co., N Y.

Carmody, Deirdre. September 29, 1970. *Confused birds die at Empire State, The New York Times.*

Cochran, William W. and Richard R.Graber.1958. Attraction of nocturnal migrants by lights on a television tower, *Wilson Bulletin* 70, 378-80.

Cooper, B.A. and R.J. Ritchie. 1995. The altitude of bird migration in east-central

Alaska: a radar and visual study, *J Field Ornithology* 66:4, 590-608.

Dunn, E.H. 1993. Bird mortality from striking residential windows in winter, *J Field Ornithology*, 61:3, 302-9.

Empire State Building Official Internet Site > Lighting Schedule, http://www.esbnyc.com/tourism/tourism_lightingschedule. cfm?CFID=12792298. Accessed 29-Aug-06.

Fatal Light Awareness Program web site, www.flap.org.

Johnston, D. W. and T.P. Haines.1957. Analysis of mass bird mortality in October, 1954, *Auk* 74:4, 447-58.

Klem, D., Jr. 1989. Bird-window collisions, *Wilson Bulletin*101:4, 606-20.

_____.1990. Collisions between birds and windows: mortality and prevention, *J Field Ornithology* 61:1, 120-8.

Linnaean Society of New York. 1891. *Abstract of the Proceedings of the Linnaean Society of New York, 3.*

_____.1892. *Abstract of the Proceedings of the Linnaean Society of New York, 4.*

Larkin, Ronald P. and Barbara A. Frase. 1988. Circular paths of birds flying near a broadcasting tower in cloud, *J Comparative Psychology* 102, 90-3.

New York City Audubon Press Release, September 2005. Tribute May Go Dark to Protect Migrating Birds. http://www.nycaudubon.org/projects/safeflight/ tributeLights.shtml. Accessed 16-Sept-06.

Ogden, Leslie J. E. 1996. *Collision Course: The Hazards of Lighted Structures and Windows to Migrating Birds*, World Wildlife Fund Canada and Fatal Light Awareness Program.

Port Authority of New York and New Jersey Press Release, November 8, 2000: Port Authority Takes Steps to Protect Migratory Birds Around World Trade Center. http://www.panynj.gov/pr/158-00.html. Accessed August 30, 2006.

Changes in Wildlife at Floyd Bennett Field over 20 Years with Emphasis on Birds

Jean Bourque
2250 Brigham St. Apt 3K
Brooklyn NY 11229
ron.jean1@verizon.net

FLOYD BENNETT FIELD, New York City's former municipal airport, became part of Gateway National Recreation Area in 1972. In the 30 odd years since then the Field has seen great changes, and not for the better, from the point of view of those who care about wildlife. Yet these changes reflect trends in our entire region.

In 1979, when I first came to know Floyd Bennett Field, it gave an impression of being a place which had been abandoned by people and where wildlife had taken over. The Field was not then open to the general public except for special use permits, mostly for model airplane flying and community gardening. People went directly to the place of their activities and remained there so that there was little traffic. Once in a great while a Park Service vehicle would go by. Finding a Northern Harrier (*Circus cyaneus*) nest was the reason for going there, and indeed the Northern Harrier nest was found, but there was also a Short-eared Owl (*Asio flammeus*) nest. Turning a corner one would see an owl teetering along far down a runway, hunting in daylight. One had an impression of tremendous open space, and overhead the weather systems could be seen marching across the sky from one horizon to the other. In those days practically the whole Field was grassland. It seemed there was always an Eastern Meadowlark (*Sturnella magna*) singing, and Grasshopper Sparrows (*Ammodramus savannarum*) were ticking and buzzing everywhere. Where there was bare ground and sparse weeds, Horned Larks (*Eremophila alpestris*) tinkled overhead. American Kestrels went by carrying food. Early in that spring, at places in the North 40, a sweet smell seemed to rise from the ground, vegetation of some sort, I suppose. I never found out what it was.

What has brought about the change to the drab aspect Floyd Bennett Field presents now, with its endlessly circling traffic and wildlife scarcely to be seen? Probably not even maintaining the entire field as airport habitat, which was once proposed, could have retained the grassland birds in the swelling sea of development which has overtaken New Jersey, where the migrants come from, as well as Long Island.

Vegetation

I believe no recent surveys have been done on the vegetation of Floyd Bennett Field. To casual observation it is obvious that a large part of the Field, which comprises 579 hectares, is now shrubland, with many trees. A comparatively small area, 52 hectares, has been maintained as grassland, in the hope of retaining grassland birds. Airports, where grassland conditions are maintained, are the last refuge of grassland birds as their habitat is eliminated elsewhere. Species present at Floyd Bennett Field in 1979 were Upland Sandpipers (*Bartramia longicauda*), Eastern Meadowlarks, Horned Larks, Grasshopper Sparrows, besides such open country birds as Barn Owls (*Tyto alba*), Short-eared Owls, American Kestrels (*Falco sparverius*), and Ring-necked Pheasants (*Phasianus colchicus*). These were breeding birds. Other species might be seen in migration.

In the 52 hectares reserved as grassland shrubs and woody vegetation were cleared during the winters from 1985 to 1990. The whole grassland area has been mowed at least once a year since then, and a few experimental burns were done. (It is worth mentioning that according to a study by Peter Vickery (Vickery et al. 1997), there is a 50% chance of finding Upland Sandpipers in grassland of 200 hectares,, a 50% chance of finding Grasshopper Sparrows in 100 hectares, and a 50% chance of finding Savannah Sparrows (*Passerculus sandwichensis*) in 10 hectares. Thus the grassland at Floyd Bennett Field is scarcely adequate, although the birds were there at one time.

Since the grassland was established, the vegetation has changed greatly, in particular in the density of growth. Litter from the yearly mowing has built up year after year. There is no longer the bare ground among the grass clumps which some grassland birds, particularly Grasshopper Sparrows, are attracted by. There are widely spreading areas of a South African lovegrass, (*Eragrostis curvula*), which is a species said to have little value for birds (Bock and Bock 1988). Species of grasses have changed as many grasses which normally flower in late summer are hindered from sending up inflorescences by the yearly mowing, which begins the first of August. This makes those species, particularly little bluestem, less conspicuous and probably less prevalent. Since experimental burns present great difficulties it is necessary to manage for species which tolerate, or prefer, dense vegetation, such as Savannah Sparrows, Meadowlarks, Bobolinks (*Dolichonyx orizivorus*), or perhaps even Dickcissels (*Spiza americana*). (The last two are not yet known as breeding birds).

In the North 40, an area where natural processes are left unchecked, a plague of Asian Bittersweet (*Celastrus orbiculatus*) covers every tree and shrub.

Lepidoptera

Again, there are no data allowing insect life 20 years ago to be compared with the present. Casual observation suggests that there has been a general decrease. Cecropia (*Hyalophora cecropia*) cocoons used to be seen often as well as Polyphemus (*Anthera polyphemus*) cocoons. Io moth (*Automeris io*) caterpillars were once commonly seen, and skippers were on every patch of thistles. Even American Copper butterflies (*Lycaena phlaeas*), once very abundant, have declined as has their host plant, Sheep Sorrel (*Rumex acetosella*), a plant which likes rather barren conditions. The yearly mowing must be harmful to insects, considering that most skippers use grasses as their host plants.

Of course in the case of the silk moths, Cecropia, Polyphemus, Io, it is known that from Massachusetts through New Jersey and Pennsylvania native silk moths have declined. The culprit assumed to be responsible for this decline is the parasitic fly *Compsilura concinnata* introduced from Europe to control gypsy moths. (Yoon 2001).

Reptiles and Amphibians

Robert P. Cook, Wildlife Biologist for the National Park Service at Gateway for years, took a special interest in amphibians and reptiles. When an area on Long Island was about to be developed, he rescued as many of the amphibians and reptiles as he could find and introduced them to favorable habitats at Gateway. According to his records, Eastern Garter Snake (*Thamnophis sirtalis*) and Diamondback Terrapin (*Malaclemys terrapin*) were originally at Floyd Bennett Field, before any introductions occurred. Fowler's Toad (*Bufo woodhousii fowleri*) was there but was wiped out when its habitat was altered. The following species were successfully introduced: Fowler's Toad, Spring Peeper (*Pseudacris crucifer*), Grey Treefrog (*Hyla versicolor*) and Northern Brown Snake (*Storeria dekayi dekayi*). Probable successful introductions included Eastern Milk Snake (*Lampropeltis triangulum*), Black Racer (*Coluber constrictor*), eastern Painted Turtle (*Chrysemys picta picta*) and Eastern Box

Turtle (*Terrapene carolina carolina*) (Cook, pers. comm.). In spring, Spring Peepers, Fowler's Toads and Grey Treefrogs may all be heard calling at Return-a-Gift Pond.

Mammals

There are no recent studies on mammals at Floyd Bennett Field. A summary of early studies compiled by Robert Cook (Cook 1987) listed the following species: Cottontail Rabbit (*Sylvilagus floridanus*), Eastern Gray Squirrel (*Sciurus carolinensis*), Meadow Vole (*Microtus pensylvanicus*), Muskrat (*Ondatra zibethicus*), House Mouse (*Mus musculus*), and Norway Rat (*Rattus norvegicus*), besides feral cats and dogs. Raccoons (*Procyon lotor*) were present but at that time were not thought to be established as a breeding species. White-footed Mice (*Peromyscus leucopus*) have appeared since then and have increased and multiplied as the woody habitat they prefer has increased.

Raccoons and Opossums (*Didelphis marsupialis*) are now plague species. These animals are repeatedly introduced by exterminators who trap them elsewhere and release them in parks in the city, including Floyd Bennett Field. (This practice is illegal, of course. Transporting such animals from one place to another creates the possibility of transporting rabies from one place to another.) The Raccoon population is thought to be many times that present in undisturbed natural areas and the effect of these predators on ground-nesting birds can be imagined.

Birds

Floyd Bennett Field was never a birding hot spot but was visited mainly for certain specialties, grassland birds in the summer and raptors in the winter. Our greatest defeat is that most of the grassland birds are gone.

Upland Sandpipers nested until 1978, then disappeared, except for one eccentric pair which nested in 1992. Formerly there was a thriving colony of nesting Upland Sandpipers at Kennedy Airport (just across Jamaica Bay), where Sam Chevalier banded the young every year. Having been sued for the loss of an airplane engine destroyed by Canada geese, Kennedy Airport has now taken stringent measures to eliminate bird populations, all bird populations. Gulls over the airport are shot if they are not frightened away by the birds which the falconers fly there. Vegetation is heavily doused with pesticides so that there will be no insects available to attract birds. The Upland Sandpipers are now gone.

Short-eared Owls have not nested since 1981 and they have also withdrawn from their breeding sites in New Jersey and Long Island. There is one isolated report of a pair with 4 juveniles on Tuckernuck Island, Massachusets, in 2005 (Petersen 2006), but Short-eared Owls have essentially disappeared from eastern North America (BBS trend Map 1966-2003). They are still doing well in some parts of the west.

The Northern Harrier, although a threatened species, maintains a slender presence at Floyd Bennett Field and last nested successfully in 2000. Why Northern Harriers should, as it seems, fare better than Short-eared Owls is a bit of a mystery. Northern Harriers hunt the same prey (mostly Meadow Voles) over the same terrain as Short-eared Owls, but by day, while the Short-earded Owls hunt by night.

Horned Larks are not recorded as nesting after 1992. There is usually a flock of 30 or so birds in the winter on the runways or short grass areas, but they are gone by the nesting season.

Eastern Meadowlarks bred at Floyd Bennett Field for the last time in 1988 but are usually still found on the Christmas Count. The habitat is still perfectly suitable for Meadowlarks, but this species, along with other grassland birds, has suffered a decline of 80%-90% or more because of changing agricultural practices (Smith 1991). For 40 years, farmers have been converting pastures into alfalfa fields with new, fast-growing varieties that can be cut early and often. The date of first mowing has moved from about July 1 to June 1, the height of the nesting season. The effect on the nests of grassland birds has been disastrous (Thompson 1992, Paxton et al. 1984)

Grasshopper Sparrows nested for the last time in Floyd Bennett Field in 1995. They do not care for dense vegetation nor for dense ground litter, both of which now prevail in the grassland because of repeated mowing and the absence of fire.

A new grassland bird, the Savannah Sparrow, made its appearance as a nester in 1989. Savannah Sparrows like denser vegetation than do Grasshopper Sparrows and are more likely to be found in comparatively small grassland areas. This sparrow increased and for some years maintained about 30 territories a season, but territories have recently declined to 10 or fewer. It may be thought of as a common bird, but it is now classified as a threatened species in New Jersey.

Other birds that breed in the grassland are Ring-necked Pheasants and American Black Ducks (*Anas rubripes*). In upstate New York, Ring-necked Pheasants are both stocked and hunted. When they have a Ring-necked Pheasant to report, editors of *The Kingbird* and also editors of *Records of New Jersey Birds* usually suggest that these are stocked birds. At Floyd Bennett Field, without stocking or hunting, Ring-necked Pheasants seemed to be doing well, but in the last five years have nearly disappeared. The species is not hunted here, nor is it in competition with wild turkeys, sometimes suggested as a cause of its decline. That leaves Raccoons as the prime suspects.

Other birds which formerly hunted in Floyd Bennett Field, particularly over the grassland, were Barn Owl and American Kestrel. Since Barn Owls are quite nocturnal, they were not often seen hunting by visitors. They roosted in abandoned buildings and in the Pine Grove, where they were unfortunately much harassed by birders. Perhaps for that reason the Barn Owls now prefer to nest on the islands in Jamaica Bay, where they have nest boxes and more privacy.

The American Kestrel presents a sad story. It last nested in Floyd Bennett Field in 1992 but was known to be declining long before that. It was on the National Audubon Society Blue List in 1981 (Tate 1981). Since then there has been a long litany of alarm and mourning in the pages of *American Birds* (covers the U.S.), *The Kingbird* (covers New York State), and *Records of New Jersey Birds* (covers New Jersey).

> American Kestrels posted their lowest total of the decade at some hawk watches and were mostly below last fall's already dismal totals (Paxton et al. 1984)

> American Kestrel continues to decline at most hawk watches, especially at Sandy Hook, where the 901 counted was the second lowest ever, and continues an almost unbroken downward trend from the high of 3138 in 1984 (Paxton et al. 1991)

> American Kestrel numbers continue to slide that steep slope into oblivion (Vernachio1998)

> Observers in every part of the Region and most CBC compilers commented on the continuing decline of American Kestrel (Paxton et al. 1998)

Nevertheless, in 2001 American Kestrels were reported breeding in all 5 counties of NYC, and in 2005 there were 7 breeding locations in Manhattan alone (Schiff and Wollin 2001, Mitra, et al. 2005). They did not nest at Floyd Bennett Field.

As with most declining birds, there has been more lamentation than study. Since the kestrel is largely insectivorous, pesticides may appear to be the most likely cause. The Avian Monitoring System lists a number of incidents of kestrel deaths caused by pesticides. Predation by Peregrine Falcons and Cooper's Hawks is possible, but Kestrels have always coexisted with these birds. And Kestrels are not declining everywhere. The American Kestrel BBS Trend Map (1966-2003) is a peculiar patchwork of areas where Kestrels are declining, juxtaposed with areas where they are increasing.

Visiting winter raptors at Floyd Bennett Field include (or included) Rough-legged (*Buteo lagopus*), Red-shouldered (*B. lineatus*), Red-tailed (*B. jamaicensis*), Cooper's (*Accipiter cooperii*), Sharp-shinned Hawks (*A. striatus*) and Merlins (*Falco columbarius*). Except for Rough-legged Hawks, which are a thing of the past, any of these birds might still be seen but are not as regular as they used to be.

Breeding Bird Atlas Comparisons

A comparison of breeding birds found at Floyd Bennett Field on the most recent Breeding Bird Atlas, 2000-2004 with birds breeding there during the first Atlas, 1980-1985, shows these changes:

Birds lost as breeders	Birds gained as breeders
American Kestrel	Willet
Spotted Sandpiper	Carolina Wren
Black-billed Cuckoo	Brown-headed Cowbird
Barn Owl	Savannah Sparrow
Short-eared Owl	
Chimney Swift	
Horned Lark	
Eastern Meadowlark	
House Finch	
Grasshopper Sparrow	
Sharp-tailed Sparrow	

The first column shows breeding birds present in 1980-1985, but not found in 2000-2004. The second column shows birds breeding in 2000-2004 which were not found in 1980-1985.

Natural changes at the shore have nearly obliterated the small patch of high marsh where the Sharp-tailed Sparrows used to be, and they are not to be expected now.

Besides loss of breeding birds some birds still present may be reduced in numbers. A walk along the trails in the North 40 in fall or winter will convince anyone who can make the comparison that there are fewer sparrows than there used to be. A hunting Sharp-shinned Hawk flying ahead down the trail, once a common sight, would be surprising now.

It is obvious that most of the changes which have taken place over the last 20 years have not been for the better. All birders know the expectation that at any moment something marvelous may step out of the woods or drop down from the sky. That is why they are birding. That expectation is less likely to arise these days, in Floyd Bennett Field as in many other places.

References

Avian Incident Monitoring System www.abcbirds.org/aims/action.cfm

BBS Trend Map. 1966-2003. Web site http://www.mbr-pwrc.usgs.gov/bbs/htm03/trn2003/tr3600.htm

Bock, C. E. and J. H. Bock. 1988. Grassland birds in Southeastern Arizona: Impacts of fire,grazing and alien vegetation. In P. D. Goriup (ed.) *Ecology and Conservation of Grassland Birds.* ICBP Tech. Pub. no. 7. International Council for Bird Preservation Cambridge, UK.

Cook, R. P., compiler. 1987. Preliminary distributional list of the mammals of Gateway National Recreation Area, New York-New Jersey. Office of Resource Management and Compliance, Gateway National Recreation Area.

Mitra, S.S. and Patricia J. Lindsay, regional editors. 2005. Region 10. *The Kingbird 55.*

Paxton, R. O., W. J. Boyle and D. A. Cutler, regional eds.1984. Hudson-Delaware region. *American Birds* 38:1004.

Paxton, R. O., W. J. Boyle and D. A. Cutler, regional eds.1991. Hudson-Delaware region. *American Birds* 45:422

Paxton, R. O., W. J. Boyle and D. A. Cutler, regional eds.1998. Hudson-Delaware Region. *American Birds* 52:175.

Petersen, Wayne R. 2006. *North American Birds* Vol. 59:572

Schiff, S. and A. Wollin eds. 2001. Region 10. *The Kingbird* 5:818.

Smith, C. R. 1991. Partners in conservation. *Living Bird Quarterly* 10(2):16-20.

Tate, J. Jr. 1981. The Blue List for 1981. *American Birds* 35:6

Thompson, C. D. 1992. SOS Saving our songbirds. *Wisconsin Natural Resources* 16(2).

Vernachio, Brian. 1998. Region 3. In *Records of New Jersey Birds*, XXIV.

Vickery, P. D., M. L. Hunter, Jr. and S. M. Melvin, 1997. Effect of habitat area on the distribution and abundance of grassland birds in Maine. In *Grasslands of Northeastern North America,* P. D. Vickery and P. W. Dunwiddie eds. Massachusetts Audubon Society.

Yoon, Carol K. 2001. *New York Times* March 6.

The Piping Plover (*Charadrius melodus*) Colony at Rockaway Beach within a Regional Context

Theodore Boretti[1], Evelyn Fetridge[2] and Alexander Brash[3]
Urban Park Rangers[1] and Natural Resource Group[2]
City of New York Parks & Recreation, 1234 Fifth Avenue,
New York, NY 10029
National Parks Conservation Association[3]
731 Lexington Ave.
New York, NY 10022
abrash@NPCA.org

Introduction

IN 1986 THE NORTH ATLANTIC PIPING PLOVER (*Charadrius melodus*) population was federally designated as threatened. Under federal aegis, intensive monitoring of population size and productivity trends began the following year, and by 1992 a comprehensive scheme was in place to track the health of local populations all along the North Atlantic coast. Under the U.S. Fish and Wildlife Service's (USFWS) Atlantic Coast Piping Plover Revised Recovery Plan prepared in 1996, goals were set for both population size and productivity in each of three Atlantic Coast regions and over the U.S. Atlantic Coast as a whole. In order to qualify for de-listing, the entire U.S. Atlantic Coast population must attain to 1600 pairs and the overall productivity must stabilize at, or above, 1.5 chicks per nesting pair. The population sub-goals set for the three U.S. Atlantic coast sub-regions of New England, New York-New Jersey (NY-NJ), and the South are 625, 575, and 400 pairs, respectively.

Since the initiation of monitoring and management, the populations in New England and NY-NJ have grown steadily (Figure 1 and Appendix).

[3] Formerly, Chief, Natural Resource Group, City of New York Parks & Recreation. 1234 Fifth Avenue, New York N.Y. 10029

Figure 1. Piping Plover population estimates (1987- 2001) for the entire East Coast population, and the three sub-populations (New England, New York /New Jersey, and Southern).

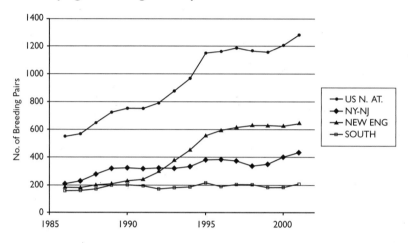

Even so, in NY-NJ significant increases are still needed to reach the population goals. NY-NJ has gone from 208 pairs in 1986 to 431 in 2001, a doubling in numbers; however, this still falls short of the requisite 575 pairs. The population size has remained fairly stable in the Southern Region, but it still remains 200 pairs short of its goal, while more positively, the New England population surpassed its 625 pair target by 15 pairs in 2001.

Productivity estimates during the period do not show as clear an upward trend as do the population estimates. For New England, the 1992-2001 productivity average slightly exceeded the goal of 1.5 chicks per pair; however, in recent years, productivity in this region appears to have been on a slight downward trajectory. The productivity averages over this period for NY-NJ and the Southern Region were 1.14 and 1.07, respectively, quite short of the USFWS goal (Figure 2).

The Rockaway Beach Colonial Seabird Site (RBCSS)

Possibly the most urban of the over hundred and seventy Piping Plover colonies along the metropolitan U.S. Atlantic coast is that found in the RBCSS. Situated on a barrier island in Queens County along the south shore of New York City, the seabird colony is flanked on the north by a highly

Figure 2. Piping Plover productivity estimates from 1987-2001 for the U.S. North Atlantic population, and the three sub-populations: New England (NE), New York-New Jersey (NY-NJ), and Southern (SOUTH).

Piping Plover Regional Productivity Estimates, 1988-2001

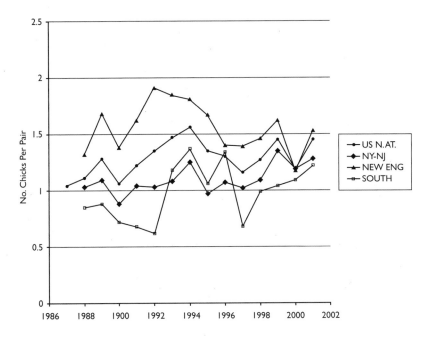

trafficked boardwalk, streets, a subway line, and low to medium-income housing, and on the south by the Atlantic Ocean. Prior to the 20th century the site was still fairly natural with sand dunes, native vegetation, and patches of Atlantic maritime forest on the lee side. In 1886 however, the dunes were leveled, low areas were filled in, and the streets were mapped out (Wall & Associates, 2003). Through the 1950s the area behind the beach, known as Arverne, was fully occupied with beach bungalows and small commercial establishments. In 1970 the area was then again cleared, this time for 'urban renewal'. However, development plans stagnated and the area remained a vast collection of vacant lots, thus the use of the beach fronting this site dropped off dramatically. Sporadic accounts of individual Piping Plover nests have been recorded since that era, but in 1996 nesting became more consistent as areas of Rockaway Beach were officially closed to public swimming.

In the mid-1990s the City of New York Parks & Recreation began experiencing a shortage of lifeguards, and in order to maximize swimming safety, in 1996 lifeguards were consolidated at those beach areas with the highest usage. At this time the Agency began staffing Park Rangers at closed beach areas to ensure compliance. As Piping Plovers increased their presence at the site, the Park Rangers soon began to actively manage the area for, and monitored the breeding success of, this threatened species. Since that time, the aim has been to maintain a balance between the avian and human interests in this beachfront property and to further the USFWS recovery goals for the piping plover.

Between 1996 and 2001, the Rockaway Beach Colonial Seabird Site encompassed the beach from 35th to 73rd Street. Most of the nesting occurred between 40th and 59th Street, though there were 'satellite' nests near 26th Street and also between 60th and 65th Street. As the site is but 400 meters west of the East Rockaway (or Atlantic Beach) Inlet with its westbound ebbing alongshore current of 2.3 knots, the width of the beach in the colony site varies significantly within the colony and over time. Prior to beach re-nourishment in 1995, when the Army Corps of Engineers (ACE) added over two million cubic meters of sand to Rockaway Beach, the width (mean high water line to Boardwalk) of the colony site ranged from 118 meters at 56th Street to 3.4 meters at 33rd Street (Ace, 1993). With re-nourishment, the beach width was re-established at 75 to 90 meters throughout the colony site. Beach width and profile will continue to change as the colony site is subject to periodic storms, including both 'nor'easters' and hurricanes. The average return period between substantive storms with a 2.0 meter elevation in sea level is 5 years, a 2.5 meter elevation occurs every 25 years, and a 3.0 meter elevation every 100 years. Luckily, while the storms will certainly affect the beach profile, none of the thirty-three documented significant storm events between 1635 and 1993 occurred during the plover nesting season (CZTF 1994).

As with most plover colonies, vegetation on the site is rather sparse, consisting predominantly of a 20% cover of American Beachgrass (*Ammophila breviligulata*) on 80% of the area. The beachgrass is interrupted occasionally by small clumps of Seaside Goldenrod (*Solidago sempervirens*), Salsola (*Salsola kali*), Seaside Spurge (*Chamaesyce polygonifolia*), American Searocket (*Cakile eduntula*), and Common Cocklebur (*Xanthium strumarium*). In addition, federally threatened and New York State "imperiled" Sea Beach Amaranth (*Amaranthus pumilus*) occurs in a broad swath close to the high tide line.

At this time, aside from the Piping Plover, several other bird species of interest use the RBCSS as a nesting site, including approximately 80-120 pairs of Least Terns (*Sterna antillarum*), 1-2 pairs of Common Terns (*Sterna hirundo*), and around 6 pairs of the American Oystercatchers (*Haematopus palliatus*). In addition the site is an important migratory bird staging area, and each year in late summer thousands of shorebirds gather there. For instance on 13 August 2003 more than 1600 Sanderlings (*Calidris alba*) and 800 Semipalmated Plovers (*Charadrius semipalmatus*) were observed; others species regularly include Least Sandpiper (*Calidris minutilla*) and Semipalmated Sandpiper (*Calidris pusilla*), Ruddy Turnstone (*Arenaria interpres*), Red Knot (*Calidris canutus*), Black-bellied Plover (*Pluvialis squatarola*), Short-billed Dowitcher (*Limnodromus griseus*), and Willet (*Catoptrophorus semiplamatus*) (Davis, pers obs.).

As RBCSS is located in a densely populated urban area with its unique faunal elements, a great number of pressures not experienced at more remote colonies affect breeding success at Rockaway. Predation by urban species such as American Crows (*Corvus brachyrhynchos*) and stray cats (*Felis silvestris*) are major threats to plover breeding and fledging. In addition, human vandalism and egg theft have occurred and will always be potential risks; and even innocent foot-traffic by beachcombers and dog walkers can disturb the colony.

Site Management

RBCSS was managed according to guidelines developed by the USFWS with the assistance of their U.S. Atlantic Coast Piping Plover Recovery Team. Standard USFWS management practices were followed and in time refined on an as-needed basis by NYC Park Rangers. Components of the management plan include:

- Symbolic Fencing. Symbolic fencing bounded the main portion of the site from 39th Street to 56th Street. Symbolic fencing consists of two lines of rope, one at knee and one at chest height, marked with neon-colored flagging. Symbolic fencing was also used to create a minimum 50 meter buffer zone around satellite nests lying outside of the main breeding area. The beach at the main breeding area is closed starting around 1 April each year.
- Snow fencing was additionally placed across the entire beach width at the two ends of the colony and in other sections of the perimeter that require a stronger demarcation. Unlike symbolic fencing, snow fencing functionally deters wandering patrons, and in addition is

more generally accepted as a boundary to a closed area.

- Signs designate the breeding area as restricted and post penalties for trespassing and vandalism. Both standard U.S.F.W.S. Piping Plover signs and Agency prepared educational signs were deployed along the boardwalk and on either end of the site.

- Park Rangers personally educated patrons about the importance of the Piping Plover colony, and their full-time presence deterred others from wandering into the colony site. In addition, when possible Rangers scared-off predators such as crows, feral cats, or dogs. These latter were also trapped or darted and transported to the City's Center for Animal Care and Control. Rangers were typically stationed at the colony site starting around 1 April and extending through Labor Day weekend.

- 24-hour surveillance. As necessary plainclothes Rangers were deployed in unmarked vehicles to patrol the boardwalk that runs the length of the site. Such surveillance was instituted after an incident (or attempt) of vandalism in which eggs are stolen or disturbed at any nest on the site. In addition, at night the Rangers often deployed Sentor 740 Portable Intruder Detectors. These large motion detectors, technology gleaned from NATO airfields, helped alert Rangers to any unseen movement in the colony.

- Predator exclosures were constructed around specified nests within the main breeding area. The exclosures were composed of standard 2" x 4" mesh garden wire supported by posts at the four corners. As consistent with USFWS guidelines, the exclosure walls are no closer than 1.5 meters from the nest, yielding at minimum a 3.0 meter diameter circle. The top of the exclosure consists of nylon mesh and stands 1.2 meters high. Because of the threat of vandalism, nests near the boardwalk and satellite nests did not receive predator exclosures.

- Dummy exclosures. To combat would-be vandals, dummy exclosures with quail eggs as bait, were erected in conspicuous locations each year. These exclosures serve as sacrificial lambs, and generally act as a barometer of human vandalism at the colony.

- Rodenticides were routinely placed under, and north of, the boardwalk bounding the site each year. The rodenticides are generally dispersed in March, timed so as to be available to rodents in late winter when food supplies are scarcest, and to also decrease the rat population just before the plovers' return. In some years, rats have

caused significant nest disturbance and egg predation in the Least
Tern colony.

- Escorts. The Agency uses several large tractors with beach-cleaning
attachments to prepare the beach for public use. These vehicles are
of course not allowed within the breeding area, but even when the
equipment must be moved past the colony to adjacent open areas, at
least one Park Ranger was present to escort the vehicles and ensure
the protection of the colony. This was particularly true when the
active swimming area between 57th and 61st street was cleaned.

- Litter removal was undertaken on an as needed basis by hand within
the colony. Some litter is certainly benign with respect to the colony, however litter associated with, or including food, attracts gulls.
Other litter, such as large pieces of Styrofoam, may blow down the
beach and physically harm nests or young.

- Vegetation management. In the winters of 1999 and 2000, mechanical scarification via bulldozer was used to control the density
and spread of American Beachgrass in a portion of the main nesting
area. These efforts met with only limited success as many of the fragmented roots re-sprouted. Efforts were continued on a more limited
basis with manual removal undertaken by Americorps staff.

Monitoring

Monitoring of Piping Plover population and productivity at RBCSS has
been conducted according to monitoring guidelines set by the USFWS
(1996), and has been independently undertaken by both the Park Rangers
and Donald Davis, a USFWS Monitor. The nesting area was monitored at
least three days a week to determine the total number of plovers present, the
number of nesting pairs, and the number of eggs in each clutch. During the
incubation period, the monitors approached the birds only if strictly necessary
so as to avoid disturbing them and causing nest abandonment. Observation
of behaviors were normally made through binoculars from outside the
fencing enclosing the breeding area, and calculations based on a twenty-
seven to thirty day incubation period were used to minimize the need for the
monitors to approach nests. The monitors entered the fenced area only to:

- To confirm the location of a nest once courtship behaviors and
other indicative behaviors have been observed.
- To determine clutch size and erect a predator exclosure once one to
two eggs had been laid.

- To remove an exclosure that was apparently deterring adult plovers from returning to their nest. The removal of such an exclosure was indicated when both adults have remained away from the nest for approximately an hour.
- To observe predator tracks and to look for other signs of disturbance or threats to the birds.

Once the eggs have hatched, the chicks were monitored and recorded three times a week from outside the main breeding area. The number of chicks reaching 30 days in age is the proxy for the number of chicks successfully fledged and was used to calculate productivity.

Data Analysis

We calculated mean population size (number of breeding pairs) and mean productivity (number of chicks fledged per pair) for the period between 1996 and 2001 (Davis 1996-2003). We also fitted linear regressions to the productivity and population size data and tested them for significance with a t-test against a null hypothesis that no increase in productivity or population size occurred during this period. We performed the same linear regression analysis on USFWS data of population estimates and productivity averages for the U.S. North Atlantic Piping Plover population and the NY-NJ population. To make this data set comparable to the RBCSS data, we conducted one set of tests using USFWS data for the years 1996-2001; we also conducted the same regression analysis on the full USFWS data set, which extends back to 1987.

Results

Foremost, the Piping Plover colony within the RBCSS grew from six to fifteen breeding pairs from 1996 to 2003. This represents a 250% increase in the breeding population at the site, and a 37% growth rate per year, (significance: $p=0.01$). The colony's productivity averaged 1.42 chicks per pair (SD=0.59), but did not increase significantly over time. Table 1 portrays the number of pairs of Piping Plovers breeding and their productivity by year at the RBCSS. Figures 3 and 4 show the colony's population size and productivity within a regional context, and respectively by year. The Appendix also provides additional graphs concerning the trends among the three population groups.

At the regional level, some changes were evident. For when the much greater time period of 1987 to 2001 is taken into account, both the NY-NJ and the U.S. North Atlantic populations did significantly increase in size,

Table 1. Breeding population size and productivity of Piping
Plovers at RBCSS.

Year	No. Pairs	Productivity (chicks per pair)
1996	6	0.50
1997	9	2.00
1998	11	1.55
1999	12	0.75
2000	11	1.64
2001	14	0.93
2002	14	2.21
2003	15	2.0

but without any real increases in productivity during the period. In 2001, population estimates for the NY-NJ region and Atlantic Coast populations were 431 and 1,525 pairs, respectively, and productivity averaged 1.28 in NY-NJ and 1.40 over the U.S. Atlantic coastline as a whole.

At the largest scale, the Atlantic Coastal population does show a substantive increase in population size during the period, with only a minor increase in productivity between 1996 and 2001. The average productivity for all the years was 1.34 chicks per pair, but for example, note that while in 2001—a good year—productivity averaged 1.40 chicks per pair, this was balanced by 2000 when the average was only 1.17 chicks. Most importantly, even with only 1.34 chicks per pair produced, the total population nearly doubled in the period, and between 1986 and 2001 the number of pairs on the Atlantic Coast grew from 790 to 1525.

The NY-NJ sub-region and New England have clearly contributed to the plover's recovery. The Appendix compares the population size and productivity trends among the RBCSS, NY-NJ, and U.S. North Atlantic populations for the six-year period during which the RBCSC population was managed.

Discussion

The marked increase in the size of the breeding population at RBCSS during the study period strongly suggests the management of the colony was very successful and the main proximate factor behind the colony's expanding size. The exclusion of pedestrian and pet traffic from the colony site prevented human disturbance from driving these birds away before they are able to lay eggs, and the control of cats, rats, vegetation, and human disturbance during nesting has then permitted the plovers to successfully raise their young. The

Figure 3. Piping Plover breeding pair estimates for 1986-2001:
North Atlantic (N.Atl.), New York-New Jersey (NY-NJ) region, and
the RBCSC site.

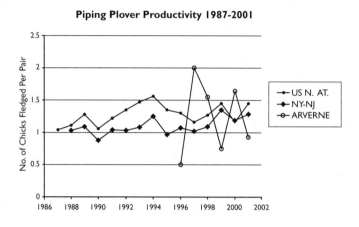

Figure 4. Piping Plover productivity, 1987-2001: North Atlantic
(N.Atl.), New York-New Jersey (NY-NJ) region, and the Rockaway
Beach area.

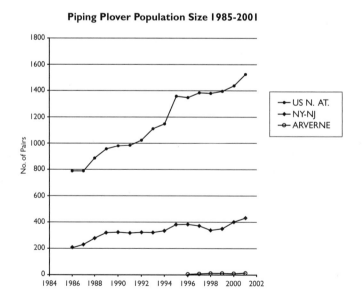

flat growth of the Piping Plover population on a regional scale during this same time period as compared to the high productivity at the Rockaway site adds further credence to this conclusion.

Our analysis suggests that Piping Plover populations in the local context (i.e., NY/NJ) have not significantly increased between 1996 through 2001, while the population at RBCSS more than doubled in size from 6 to 15 breeding pairs. Thus the RBCSC population was neither simply mirroring a regional rise in Piping Plover numbers, nor drawing surplus immigrants from it. Rather, it is probable that the rigorous management practices employed by the Agency at the Rockaway site with a resultant increase in returning young were the main factor that allowed this colony to outstrip regional growth. Unfortunately, after high productivity levels in the 1980s, productivity did not return to similar highs or even improve in a statistically significant way between 1996 and 2001 either at RBCSC, nor in NY-NJ, nor along the U.S. North Atlantic coastline as a whole. In fact, regional productivity remained stagnant when the longer period from 1988 until 2001 is considered. Such results suggest to us that once a colony site is established and essentially protected from human interference, natural large-scale factors are still dominant factors with respect to Piping Plover productivity. It would seem apparent that annual variations among abiotic factors such as rainfall, daily temperatures, and tidal flooding, and biotic factors such as predation or prey availability remain the key elements affecting productivity. At RBCSS, we believe that human disturbance and predation still remain the most critical factors at the site.

Productivity at RBCSS was sustained over the six-year period at levels a bit higher than plover productivity for the region. In NY-NJ pairs averaged 1.22 fledged chicks per nest, while at RBCSS nests averaged 1.42. Productivity for the entire North Atlantic population was lower at 1.30 chicks, and even this number includes a high yield from the New England region, with its greater number of isolated colonies. In New England alone, productivity matched Rockaway with an average of 1.43 chicks per nest. Unfortunately, none of these productivity levels reached the USFWS goal of 1.5 fledged chicks per nest, though this may be an unrealistic level to naturally sustain even at a highly successful colony. Luckily, lower goals may prove sufficient, as long as all current sites remain fully protected and additional ones can be made available.

As expected, productivity at RBCSS fluctuated more widely than did regional Piping Plover productivity during the same years. The Appendix shows productivity levels for Rockaway, NY-NJ, and the U.S. North Atlantic

Coast as a whole. The standard deviation at Rockaway is roughly five times that for NY-NJ and the entire U.S. North Atlantic Coast. Such variance is expected because local site conditions and biotic factors such as predation will widely fluctuate from year to year, while such amplitudes are naturally diminished in averages based on a large number of colonies. It is of interest however, and can be seen in the Appendix, that productivity at RBCSS appeared to react in a direction opposite regional trends. While we know of no explanation for this at this time, it certainly is worth pondering.

Future Management

One thing is very clear, and that is that while certain standards of protection and management are required by law for all Piping Plover breeding sites, the minimum legislative requirements would not have been sufficient at the RBCSS site. New York City's Department of Parks & Recreation was able to apply an intensive management regime at the site that was, and is, certainly not equaled at many, or perhaps any other, sites. Such a notion though should not overshadow the fact that we believe even more can be done.

We believe a number of factors have prevented RBCSS's Piping Plover productivity from consistently remaining in the higher parts of its range, and the additional refinement and application of various management techniques may still yield incremental productivity gains at the site. In addition to rat and cat predation, one such factor is the difficulty of access to foraging areas. During the first six years of management, pedestrians were still permitted to walk past the colony site along the waterfront in order to accommodate historic usage patterns at the beach. This is the prime foraging area for plovers, for they generally feed within five meters of the water's edge (Haig 1992). In fact, unimpeded foraging is critical to fledgling survival for those chicks that fail to double their weight within two weeks of birth are unlikely to survive (Cairns, 1977). In 2002, the symbolic fencing was extended down to the low tide line, allowing the plovers undisturbed access to foraging locations: the wrack line, inter-tidal zone, and the edge of vegetation above the high tide line. We believe that allowing pedestrian traffic in this area substantially decreased the quality of the RBCSS site as breeding habitat. Extending the symbolic fencing to the low tide line was probably critical to the high productivity achieved in 2002 and 2003.

A second factor affecting productivity and contributing to the fluctuations in this parameter is the plover's nesting chronology. In general, the earlier the plovers breed, the more chicks are likely to survive until fledging (Davis, pers obs.). Around Rockaway, Laughing Gulls (*Larus atricilla*) are the primary predator on plover chicks (Davis & Rangers, pers obs.), but they do not begin predating Piping Plover nests in full force until mid-June when their own nestlings' food demands are peaking. Thus the sooner plovers hatch and disperse before this date, the more of them are likely to survive to fledging. For instance, in 2002, 24 of 31 fledged chicks hatched on or before June 5th, which we believe was also a key factor in the year's high productivity.

Conclusion

The key to future management success at the RBCSS will lie in maintaining the current colony's boundaries, its breeding population size, and its recent productivity levels. Unfortunately, for reasons due to the inherent limitations associated with having a colony next to a beach that has several million visitors each year, the Piping Plover colony at Rockaway is not likely to expand in geographic scope. Indeed, it is probably now near its carrying capacity, though with some packing it may be possible for the colony to support a few additional pairs. Aside from geographic constraints, the Piping Plover colony at Rockaway will remain limited by several other factors. First, encroaching American Beachgrass threatens to reduce the amount of open sandy beach favored by the Piping Plovers for nesting. Managing beachgrass is costly and labor-intensive when done correctly, and debatable given that it may not benefit all beach-associated species equally. One reason this practice has been constrained to a manual approach is that by removing large amount of beachgrass one increasingly opens the colony up to another threat. This threat, and second population-limiting factor, is predation by Laughing Gulls. While a few pairs of cryptic Piping Plovers did not normally attract their attention, a large Least Tern colony certainly does. Management techniques that help the Least Terns expand their colony's size, will inherently also attract greater numbers of Laughing Gulls. These gulls then also prey on the Piping Plovers. Ultimately, future managers of the site will have to maintain a balance between Piping Plovers, Least Terns and beach grass. Finally, the width of the colony site has historically shrunk over time due to beach erosion. While obviously beach erosion is likely to continue, it is not given that the government will continue to step-in and periodically help with large scale beach re-nourishment projects.

In sum though, it is our hope that the recent productivity gains (near 1.5 young per pair per year) within the colony can be sustained, the beach will remain fairly stable, and that in the long run the colony, while forever limited in size itself, can become and remain a production center, or plover font, for the New York Bight.

Acknowledgements

Donald Davis, the volunteer Piping Plover Monitor for the U.S. Fish & Wildlife Service at Rockaway, is a pillar of plover support. Over the years Don has not only monitored the plovers but also monitored the monitors. In addition, he provided his data for this paper, and after reading an earlier draft he made extensive comments that were incorporated in this final version. Lastly, we thank Peter Stein whose indomitable spirit made the RBCSS possible.

References

Army Corps of Engineers. 1993. Environmental Assessment: East Rockaway Inlet, New York Federal Navigation Project Maintenance Dredging. New York District, 26 Federal Plaza, New York, N.Y.

Cairns, W.E. 1977. Breeding Biology and behavior of the piping plover *Charadrius melodus* in southern Nova Scotia. M.S. Thesis. Dalhousie University, Halifax. N.S. 115 pgs.

Coastal Zone Task Force. 1994. Final Report; New York Governor's Coastal Erosion Task Force. Albany, N.Y.

Davis, Donald. 1996-2003. U.S Fish & Wildlife Service Monitor's Annual Reports: Arverne Piping Plover Site.

Haig, S. M. 1992. Piping Plover. In The Birds of North America, No. 2 (A. Poole, P. Stettenheim, and F. Gill, Eds.). Philadelphia: The Academy of Natural Sciences; Washington, DC: The American Ornithologists' Union.

U.S. Fish and Wildlife Service. 1996. Piping plover (*Charadrius melodus*), Atlantic Coast population, revised recovery plan. Hadley, Massachusetts. 258pp.

Wall & Associates, Inc. 2003. Final Environmental Impact Statement for the Arverne Urban Renewal Area. CEQR#: 02 HPD 004 Q. Prepared fro the NYC Department of Housing Preservation and Development. 100 Gold Street, New York, N.Y.

Appendix

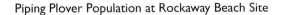

Piping Plover Population at Rockaway Beach Site

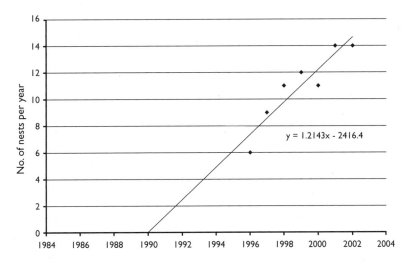

Appendix Graph 1. Piping Plover breeding population data with fitted regression line from the Rockaway colony. These data represent a significant increase (ts=5.67; p<0.01) in colony size in the years represented, 1996-2002.

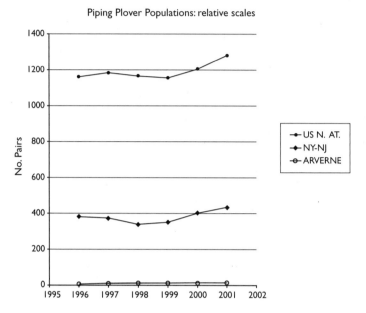

Appendix Graph 2. Piping Plover population (estimated by breeding pairs) among three populations: the U.S. North Atlantic population, the New York-New Jersey (NY-NJ) population, and the Rockaway colony (labeled "Arverne").

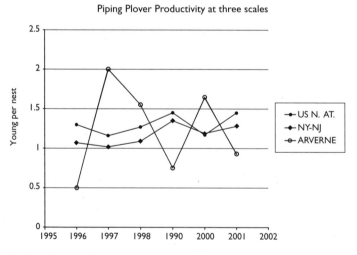

Appendix Graph 3. Comparison of Piping Plover productivity trends among the U.S. North Atlantic population, the New York-New Jersey (NY-NJ) population, and the Rockaway colony (labeled "Arverne").

The Colonial Waterbirds of Goose Island, Pelham Bay Park, Bronx, New York 1996-2006

David S. Künstler
Van Cortlandt and Pelham Bay Parks Administrators' Office
City of New York Parks & Recreation
1 Bronx River Parkway
Bronx NY 10462
david.kunstler@parks.nyc.gov

Introduction

THE COLONIAL BIRD ROOKERY ON GOOSE ISLAND, located in the lower Hutchinson River of Pelham Bay Park lies within the Thomas Pell Wildlife Refuge and Sanctuary (Fig. 1). The rookery was discovered on 1 May 1996 on a visit to the island by former Urban Park Rangers Mike Carmody, Jackie Broder, Walter Caballero and the author. It is located at 40°51'57"N, 73°49'6"W and is part of the Manhattan Hills Ecozone (Andrle and Carroll 1988). The nearest rookeries are on Huckleberry Island, about 3.5 mi (5.5 km) to the northeast and on the Brother islands, over 6 mi (10 km) to the southwest. The Van Cortlandt and Pelham Bay Parks Administration has monitored and surveyed the rookery's size and productivity since 1996. However, the survey has also been incorporated into New York City Audubon's Harbor Herons Project (Bernick 2005). There is no known biological description of Goose Island outside of the prior reports from this project, starting with Künstler (1997). No colonial waterbird nesting was included in Drennan (1981). Colonial waterbirds were not recorded nesting in this area (block 5952C) on the 1980-1985 New York State Breeding Bird Atlas (Andrle and Carroll 1988). Goose Island was also not included in the park's Natural Areas Management Plan (City of New York Parks & Recreation 1988), due to its relative inaccessibility. This was apparently because the colony was not initiated until later years.

The island comprises about 0.75 acre and reaches some 3 meters

Fig. 1. West side of Goose Island in the Hutchinson River, the mouth just beyond RR and Pelham Bridge on the right.

in elevation, with a rock outcrop on the east side. It was inhabited from 1843-1885 (Anonymous 1885) and the remnants of a more recent building foundation lie near its center. Goose Island has large, non-native Amur Honeysuckle (*Lonicera maackii*) growing densely over most of the upland with a small opening just north of the foundation. Three large Pin Oaks (*Quercus palustris*), a few somewhat smaller Sassafras (*Sassafras albidum*) and fewer White Mulberries (*Morus alba*) rise out of the honeysuckle in scattered locations. An additional small stand of Sassafras and White Snakeroot (*Eupatorium rugosum*) is next to the outcrop. Groundsel-bush (*Baccharis halimifolia*) and Poison Ivy (*Toxicodendron radicans*) dominate the south end. Thirty-one species of vascular plants, including about 13 non-native species, have been recorded since 1996 (Künstler, unpublished data). A strip of salt marsh, now only peat fringing the west side, appears to have been eliminated by the wakes of regularly passing barges in the nearby ship channel.

Survey Methods

The annual visit to monitor the wading birds of Goose Island took place on 25 May 2006 from 1100-1500 hrs. The temperature reached a high of roughly 78°F during the survey and it was mostly sunny during the visit. A party of three, including Nicole Delacrétaz of New York City Audubon, Tony Rho of Van Cortlandt & Pelham Bay Parks and the author, made a short trip up the Hutchinson River by canoe after launching southwest of the Pelham Bridge.

Goose Island surveys are generally begun near the south end of the island, then continued in a clockwise direction around it. All waterbird nests and their contents except some Great Egret nests (see below) and very few other nests difficult to access were examined. The number of active (with eggs or young) nests are counted whenever possible. However, when it is not possible to access or find every nest, adults are counted with one adult representing one pair, since one bird was assumed to be away foraging. This was also assumed for the night-herons, although they often feed at night, potentially giving daytime adult counts double the actual number of nests with both adults present.

The number of adults seen may sometimes be higher than that of breeding pairs or nests, despite Buckley and Buckley's (1980) heron, ibis and gull conversion factor of 1.0 for number of adults seen, thus equaling the number of presumed or estimated nests. Their aerial survey would occur briefly over a given colony. Since we were on the island for an extended period of time, an incoming bird might have stayed to defend its nest with its mate rather than the latter bird leaving to forage. Thus, the ratio of adults present to nests might increase with time during a survey. On the few occasions when both nest and adult counts were made (with the egrets), the higher of the two counts was recorded as the total (Table 1, Fig. 2).

In 2006, a telescoping pole mirror was used to observe nest contents, the majority of which were situated above eye level.

On 25 May 2006, residents of Co-op City, a high-rise apartment complex overlooking the island, provided two complimentary counts of readily visible adult Great Egrets roosting atop the vegetation. These counts took place at dusk when all Great Egrets were expected to be present for the night. A ground party cannot obtain a full view of undisturbed adult birds while on the island and our nest count of this species may not be complete.

Surveys were conducted annually using similar methods in 1996 through 2005.

Results and Discussion

GREAT EGRET (*Ardea alba*) – During the count, 20 nests and their contents were recorded (Table 2). Emily Yurlina counted 42 adult birds from her 24th floor apartment in Co-op City at 2015 hrs and volunteer Christina Aracil counted 43 adults at 2035 hrs from her nearby 22nd floor apartment. This was at dusk and it was assumed that virtually all adults were back at the rookery and that half the number of counted adults would equal the number

Table 1. Goose Island nesting population in number of pairs, 1996-2006. A – adults (= estimated no. pairs); N – nests; P – pairs. In case of dual numbers from different methods, such as egrets in 2006, the higher one is final.

	1996	1997	1998	1999	2000	2001	2002	2003	2004	2005	2006
Great Egret		5A	10P	10A	10A	AON	23A	24A	21A	30N	22P
Snowy Egret	2A	4A	10P	6A	7N	11N	28N	41N	43N	17N	21A
Little Blue Heron				1A	1N	1A				1N	
Black-crowned Night-Heron	27A	26N	21N	47N	48N	51N	60N	68N	57N	44N	61N
Yellow-crowned Night-Heron	1A	1A	1A	2A	2A	1A	3A	2A	8A	3A	4N
Glossy Ibis									1N		
Great Black-backed Gull	1A	1A	1A	2A	2A	1A	3A	2A		1N	
Total pairs	30	36	42	66	68	74	114	135	130	95	108

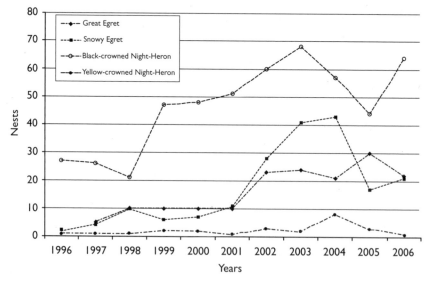

Fig. 2. Trends of regularly nesting waders of Goose Island according to the number of nests.

of nests. Thus, 43 birds would be the equivalent of 22 pairs (Table 1). This was our first dusk count and it should be continued in the future. The level of sustainability for the Great Egret is 2.9 young per nest (MANEM 2006). The production of young for the 2006 nesting season may not have been adequate with 2.12 young per nest, but neither is the cumulative >2.45 young per nest (Table 2). Therefore, this population may not be replacing itself.

Table 2. Great Egret productivity (# nests) 1997-2006

	1997	2001	2003	2004	2005	2006	Mean
Eggs/nest	2.00 (1)	3.50 (4)	2.86 (7)	4.00 (1)	4.00 (1)	3.00 (1)	3.13 (15)
Young/nest				2.67 (3)	>3.14 (7)	>2.12 (17)	>2.45 (27)
Eggs and Young/nest					3.00 (1)	4.00 (2)	3.67 (3)

SNOWY EGRET (*Egretta thula*) – Although there were 18 nests and their contents recorded, there were 21 adults observed. Thus the higher count was recorded as 21 pairs. Sustainable productivity for this species is 3.2 young fledged per female per year (MANEM 2006). In 2006 3.80 young per nest is substantially higher, but may reflect that nestlings were recorded rather than fledglings. The mean for all data collected thus far is 3.29 young per nest (Table 3), which means that the Snowy Egret appears to be producing enough young to maintain its population level or even increase it.

LITTLE BLUE HERON (*Egretta caerulea*) – None was detected on the island this year, but an adult was sighted on Twin Islands on the far opposite or east side of Pelham Bay Park from the heronry, or about 2.0 mi. (3.2 km) east, on 27 June. A nest of two eggs and a young were found in 2005. The Little Blue Heron should average 2.7 fledglings per successful nest (MANEM 2006).

BLACK-CROWNED NIGHT-HERON (*Nycticorax nycticorax*) – We recorded 61 Black-crowned Night-Heron nests, the most recorded since

Table 3. Snowy Egret productivity (# nests) 2000-2006

	2000	2001	2003	2004	2005	2006	Mean
Eggs/nest	3.20 (5)	~3.67(11)	3.49(39)	3.94 (32)	3.80 (10)	3.11 (9)	~3.63 (106)
Young/nest	3.00(2)			2.89 (9)	3.60 (5)	3.80 (5)	3.29 (21)
Eggs and Young/nest			4.00(1)	3.50(2)	2.50 (2)	4.00 (4)	3.56 (9)

2003. The nesting substrate was as follows: Amur Honeysuckle 60 and White Mulberry 1. An adult Black-crowned Night-Heron was seen hunting earthworms on a lawn elsewhere in Pelham Bay Park on 12 June 2006. This behavior has also been noted by DeGraaf and Rudis (1986) and observed in other parts of the Metropolitan region (A. Bernick, pers. comm.). The level of reproductive sustainability for the Black-crowned Night-Heron is 2.0-2.1 young per pair (MANEM 2006). This year's mean of 2.42 young per nest is well above that level. Since 1996 the mean has been 2.28 young/nest (Table 4), also more than adequate. The Black-crowned Night-Heron appears to have a healthy level of reproduction.

YELLOW-CROWNED NIGHT HERON (*Nyctanassa violacea*) – The first four definitive nests were found in a large Pin Oak. Extensive amounts of Mud Fiddler (*Uca pugnax*) and White-fingered Mud Crab (*Rithropanopeus harrisii*) shells were found under these nests. This was subtracted from the total night-heron nest count. The level of sustainability for the Yellow-crowned Night-Heron is 3.6 fledglings per nest (MANEM 2006). However, the reproductive output is not known for the Yellow-crowned Night-Heron on Goose Island.

GLOSSY IBIS (*Plegadis falcinellus*) – There has only been one nesting of Glossy Ibis on Goose Island. That was in 2004 when five eggs hatched into five young. However, despite their probably being successful, the birds did not return in 2005. This was similar to the only ibis nest on Huckleberry Island in 1989, which had two well-grown young. Five eggs or young are the maximum (Baicich and Harrison 2005), and well above 1.3 young per nest needed for sustainability (MANEM 2006).

Table 4. Night-heron productivity (# nests) 1997-2006

	1997	1998	1999	2000	2001
Eggs/nest	2.20 (5)	3.00 (7)	3.11 (19)	2.68 (25)	3.16 (50)
Young/nest	1.67 (12)	2.29 (7)	2.60 (10)	2.17 (24)	2.00 (1)
Eggs and Young/nest				3.00 (1)	3.00 (1)

	2003	2004	2005	2006	Mean
Eggs/nest	2.86 (56)	3.04 (54)	3.12 (34)	2.96 (26)	2.90 (276)
Young/nest	2.00 (1)	2.75 (4)	2.64 (11)	2.42 (26)	2.28 (96)
Eggs and Young/nest	3.00 (2)	3.14 (7)	3.00 (2)	1.78 (9)	2.55 (22)

Other Wildlife Observations

Several Great Black-backed Gulls (*Larus marinus*) were flying and calling in the vicinity of the island. This was only the second year that this species was not found nesting, the other being 2004. We counted 11 old or abandoned Canada Goose (*Branta canadensis*) nests and there were two carcasses of adult birds. A Spotted Sandpiper (*Actitis macularia*) sighting lent hope that there might be a nest in the vicinity. There was a flock of seven Least Sandpiper (*Calidris minutilla*) present upon our arrival. A crow (*Corvus* sp.) was observed flying around the island. We spotted a single Gray Catbird (*Dumetella carolinensis*) as well. A Common Grackle (*Quiscalus quiscula*) nest was found in an Amur Honeysuckle, but there was no sign of the birds. Crows and grackles are potential predators of nest contents (DeGraaf and Rudis 1986).

Management

Plantings from fall 2005 in the 15.2-meter diameter opening cleared of Porcelain-berry (*Ampelopsis brevipedunculata*) in the north central part of the island were briefly inspected. We did not stay long in order to keep disturbance of the birds to a minimum. A total of 109 small trees and shrubs of the following species had been planted as potential new nesting habitat (Künstler 2005). Gray Birch (*Betula populifolia*) appeared to be mostly doing well, as did the Groundsel-bush (*Baccharis halimifolia*) and one Spicebush (*Lindera benzoin*). The Witch-hazel (*Hamamelis virginiana*) did not seem to be quite as healthy. At least one Box-elder (*Acer negundo*) was also present. An Amur Honeysuckle toward the middle of the opening will be removed. Pokeweed (*Phytolacca americana*) has colonized much of the area from which Porcelain-berry was removed in 2004 and now dominates this area. This does not appear to be a serious problem for the plantings.

Conclusion

After a jump in population in 2005 (Künstler 2005), Great Egrets are back at the 2002-2004 level (Table 1 and Fig. 2). Production of young is below a suggested level of sustainability for this species. The Snowy Egret population appeared to rise slightly, but will need some time to attain 2002-2004 levels again. Enough young birds seem to be produced in order to maintain their numbers. The Black-crowned Night-Heron was probably the first to colonize Goose Island and perhaps the only wading bird nesting on the island prior to 1996. 2005 was a near record year for this species. Nestling production is and has been well above the level necessary for long term population maintenance. Yellow-crowned Night-Heron had four nests, the first recorded here. However, the colony may be remarkable in having had at least one apparent pair or nest each year since the heronry was discovered in 1996. The colony seems to have been climbing in numbers until 2002-2003 when the three common species more or less reached a plateau. They are now fluctuating in numbers. The absence of Double-crested Cormorants thus far has helped insure the long-term success of this colony, compared to Huckleberry Island (Künstler and Capainolo 1986; Künstler 2002; pers. obs.).

Although New York Harbor water quality has been steadily improving for many decades (NYCDEP 2005) and there may be some positive effects on wading birds, there are still significant levels of such pollutants as pesticides (Parsons 2003). More simultaneous daytime nest and adult counts of Great Egrets on Goose Island (and perhaps other colonies) should be conducted in which the results are compared with adult counts at dusk the same day. The aim would be to ascertain the accuracy of adult counts and any increase in the number of adults during a ground survey. It is thought that on Goose Island, the nest counts would generally be most accurate, but adult dusk counts would be the most accurate for the Great Egret. With the planting of various native shrub and tree species in a sizeable opening, there will hopefully be an increase in potential nesting sites over the next several years leading to an increase in nesting waterbirds.

Acknowledgements

Thanks to Peter Capainolo of the American Museum of Natural History for reviewing the manuscript, Jorge Santiago for the obscure literature and the Bronx River Alliance for the use of their canoe.

References

Anderle, R. F. and J. R. Carroll eds. 1988. *The Atlas of Breeding Birds in New York State*. Cornell University Press. 551 pp.

Anon. 1885. The owner of Goose Island, death of the odd old woman who presided over that desolate place. *New York Times* 28 March:8.

Baicich, P. J. and C. J. O. Harrison. 2005. *Nests, Eggs, and Nestlings of North American Birds*. 2nd ed. Princeton University Press. Princeton and Oxford. 347 pp.

Bernick, A. J. 2005. New York City Audubon Harbor Herons Project: 2005 interim nesting survey. 25 pp. Unpubl.

Buckley, P. A. and F. G. Buckley. 1980. Population and colony site trends of Long Island waterbirds for five years in the mid 1970s. *Transactions of the Linnaean Society of New York* 9:23-56.

City of New York Department of Environmental Protection. 2005. *2004 New York Harbor Water Quality Regional Summary*. NYCDEP. 22 pp.

City of New York Parks & Recreation, Natural Resources Group. 1988. *Natural areas management plan, Pelham Bay Park, Bronx, 1988*. NYCP&R, Natural Resources Group. 45 pp. + 8 apend.

DeGraaf, R. M. and D. D. Rudis. 1986. New England wildlife: Habitat, natural history and distribution. *General Technical Report NE-108*. U.S. Department of Agriculture, Forest Service. Northeastern Forest Experiment Station, Broomall, PA. 491 pp.

Drennan, S.R. 1981. Where to Find Birds in New York State, the Top 500 Sites. Syracuse University Press. 499 pp.

Künstler, D. S. 1997. A rookery on Goose Island, Hutchinson River, Pelham Bay Park, Bronx, New York. City of New York/Parks & Recreation, Van Cortlandt & Pelham Bay Parks Administrator's Office. Bronx. 3 pp. (unpublished).

————. 2002. The colonial waterbirds of Huckleberry Island, New Rochelle, Westchester County, New York, 2002. City of New York/Parks & Recreation, Van Cortlandt & Pelham Bay Parks Administrator's Office. Bronx. 3 pp.

————. 2005. The colonial waterbirds of Goose Island, Pelham Bay Park, Bronx, New York, 2004 & 2005. City of New York/Parks & Recreation, Pelham Bay Park Administrator's Office. Bronx. 7 pp. (unpublished).

————. and P. Capainolo. 1986. Huckleberry Island: Premier waterbird colony of western Long Island Sound. *Kingbird 37*(4):178-188.

Mid-Atlantic, New England, Maritimes Regional Working Group (MANEM). 2006. Mid-Atlantic, New England, Maritimes Regional Waterbird Plan. http://www.fws.gov/birds/waterbirds/manem/index.html

Parsons, K. C. 2003. Chemical residues in cormorants from New York Harbor and control location. Submitted to NYS Department of Environmental Conservation, Albany. 161 pp.

The Influence of Urbanization, Patch Size, and Habitat Type on Small Mammal Communities in the New York Metropolitan Region: A Preliminary Report

L. Stefan Ekernas and Katherine J. Mertes
WildMetro
PO Box 4220
Grand Central Station
New York NY 10163
resdir@wildmetro.org

Introduction

THE NEW YORK METROPOLITAN REGION, an area that includes parts of New Jersey, Connecticut, and New York State, is one of the most urbanized and densely populated areas in the world. Urban zones have traditionally been characterized as harsh, patchy, and biologically sparse, with little value to conservation or ecological research. The scientific community is increasingly altering this perception, however, and coming to view urban zones as biologically important and valuable for research (McDonnell et al. 1997; Pickett et al. 2001). The New York Metropolitan region includes natural areas that contain a variety of plants and animals that have adapted to urban ecosystems. These green areas are distributed in various patch sizes along an urban gradient extending from the city center to the surrounding suburban and rural landscape, which makes them excellent areas for pursuing ecological research (Kunick 1982; Cousins 1982; Goldstein-Golding 1991; Sauvajot et al. 1998).

Small mammal communities may be particularly important in elucidating the effects of urbanization on biological systems. Rodents and shrews can play a key role in influencing the biodiversity of urban green spaces by shaping successional dynamics and future composition of vegetative habitats (Pusenius et al. 2000; Hollander and Vander Wall 2004). They

239

can have a strong influence on the presence or absence of a wide array of wildlife either through competitive interactions (Morin 1999; Eccard and Ylönen 2003; Francl et al. 2004) or by serving as the prey base for carnivorous species, which are often of greater conservation concern. Furthermore, small mammals may be good indicators of habitat quality and landscape-level conservation threats, as high small mammal densities are often associated with superior habitat quality (Ostfeld et al. 1985; Krohne and Hoch 1999; Carey and Harrington 2001). Small mammals also have important implications for human health, since many diseases (including bubonic plague, hantavirus, and lyme disease) are strongly associated with them (Donahue et al. 1987; Mills and Childs 1998; Keeling and Gilligan 2000; Ostfeld and Keesing 2000).

Previous studies exploring the habitat preferences of small mammals provide us with general expectations of the species we are likely to find in habitats around New York City. White-footed mice (*Peromyscus leucopus*) are commonly considered habitat generalists, and are potential residents of shrubland, forest, and grassland habitat types (Dueser and Shugart 1978; Kaufman et al. 1983; Adler and Wilson 1987). Although generalists, white-footed mice are usually found at higher densities in hardwood forest habitat, areas with large volumes of stumps and logs, and areas with dense ground cover (Dueser and Shurgart 1978; Barnum et al. 1992; Flowerdew and Ellwood 2001; Brannon 2005). Barnum et al. (1992) tracked the path choice of adult *P. leucopus* using fluorescent powder, and found significant preferences for paths near logs greater than 5 cm in diameter, as well as significant decreases in travel as vegetative cover thinned. Among other species commonly found in the New York Metropolitan region, meadow voles (*Microtus pennsylvanicus*) tend to be restricted to grasslands, while short-tailed shrews (*Blarina brevicauda*) and masked shrews (*Sorex cinereus*) favor moist herbaceous and woody habitats (Getz 1961; Howell 1984).

In contrast to the small mammal communities of forests and grasslands, fewer data are available from salt marshes. Small mammals in tidal marshes are generally considered transients, or residents of only the high marsh vegetation, though *M. pennsylvanicus* may nest under salt marsh grasses year-round (Shure 1971; Shanholtzer 1974; Howell 1984). *P. leucopus* have also been recorded in wet areas (Kitchings and Levy 1981), but the extent to which these and other species are present in salt marshes in the New York Metropolitan region is unclear. Cook (1989) reported the presence of Norway rats (*Rattus norvegicus*) and possibly Black rats (*Rattus rattus*) in Jamaica Bay, but he did not identify population sizes or densities for either of these species.

General patterns of habitat preference observed in previous studies, however, may not correlate with sites in New York City, since urbanization might exercise a substantial influence on the composition of small mammal communities. Urban habitat patches are likely to be smaller in size, more exposed to invasive species, and surrounded by barriers to dispersal (Mahan and O'Connell 2005). Nonetheless, urban patches of native habitat may still contain the necessary microfeatures to support a robust small mammal community. Dickman and Doncaster (1987), for example, found that small mammal densities in urban areas were most strongly related to vegetation, with animals in urban areas exhibiting habitat preferences nearly identical to conspecifics in non-urban areas. Urban parks may therefore play an important role in preserving the microhabitat features necessary to maintain sizeable populations of native small mammal species with small home range requirements. If urban barriers suppress characteristic dispersal rates, however, densities in urban areas may grow atypically high (Mahan and O'Connell 2005).

This study was designed to obtain a clearer picture of how urbanization, patch size, habitat type, and other factors affect small mammal communities in the New York Metropolitan region. We used live-trapping surveys to describe and compare the structure of small mammal communities among and between a variety of native habitats such as tidal salt marsh, forest, shrublands, and grasslands; to compare the structure of small mammal communities in urban and rural sites and at different patch sizes; and to collect information that will be useful both for improving the quality of remaining urban habitat and for conserving urban biodiversity. As municipalities continue to expand, maintaining urban natural areas will be critical to ensuring resource sustainability in the future on both local and regional scales (Bengston et al. 2004). Gathering baseline data on these areas, and understanding the complex effects that urbanization has on ecological communities, is imperative for managing existing urban biodiversity and for managing biodiversity in ecosystems that may become subject to urban sprawl in the future.

Methods
STUDY SITES
From 2004 to 2005, WildMetro surveyed small mammal communities in a total of 24 trapping arrays at 12 different sites in the New York Metropolitan region (Table 1). Some sites and arrays were sampled multiple times over this 2-year period, while others were sampled once. We estimated patch size in hectares (ha) for each site from satellite photos provided by GoogleMaps

(Google 2005), and considered all paved roads visible from aerial photos and major bodies of water as barriers to dispersal (Oxley et al. 1974; Klee et al. 2004). All patches were therefore surrounded by paved roads and/or water bodies, though it is possible that thin strips of vegetation penetrated these boundaries and acted as dispersal corridors. Patch sizes for salt marshes, however, were calculated from only the area of the salt marsh, and adjacent non-marsh vegetation was excluded even if no roads or bodies of water were present. Following Marzluff et al. (2001), we classified each site as urban, suburban, or rural, and obtained deer densities from site managers.

Sampling Methods

Small mammal surveys were conducted using a capture-mark-recapture method. Our trapping protocol was designed to capture nocturnal and crepuscular, terrestrial (not diurnal, subterranean, or arboreal) species. All trapping periods occurred between May 2004 and November 2005.

We used Sherman live traps (aluminum, 3"x 3"x 9") in all our surveys. At most sites, arrays were composed of 49 traps placed 15m apart in a 7x7 grid (Burns 2005). This design allows a survey area of approximately 1 hectare, which is typically large enough to contain home ranges of multiple individuals of a variety of small mammal species, such as mice, shrews, and voles. In sites limited in area or with non-linear boundaries (such as salt marshes, which often have irregular borders and contain areas that are unsafe to directly sample) the trapping array was fitted to the area available. These design adaptations were determined on an individual-site basis, by changing the trap spacing distance from 15m to 10m and/or by designing irregularly-shaped trapping arrays.

Trapping took place over five-day sessions. During the first night, traps were positioned in the grid at the appropriate spacing distance, closed, and left with bait (birdseed and peanuts) scattered externally to allow animals to become familiar with the traps ("prebaiting"). Traps were covered with local vegetation or substrate to keep them inconspicuous. Over the following three nights, traps were internally baited approximately two hours before sunset and left open during the night, and checked and closed at dawn. In some cases, heavy rain or cold overnight temperatures (<40°F) made consecutive trapping nights unfeasible. When trapping was delayed mid-session for more than two days, we added an additional night of prebaiting to re-habituate animals to the traps and to maintain the presence of high-quality food near traps.

We used a modified trapping protocol at salt marsh sites that allowed us to compare salt marsh and upland habitat. At each marsh site, two separate

Table 1. Study sites for small mammal research in the New York Metropolitan region.

Site	Dates Surveyed	Patch Size (ha)	Urbanization class	Habitat type	Vegetation Description
Hunter's Island (Plot 204)	July 9-11, 2004	68	Urban	Forest	Old growth forest
Hunter's Island (Plot 207)	Oct. 23-26, 2004	68	Urban	Forest	Old growth forest
New York Botanical Garden	May 13-19, 2004	16	Urban	Forest	Old growth forest
New York Botanical Garden	Oct. 2-4, 2004	16	Urban	Forest	Old growth forest
New York Botanical Garden	July 16-19, 2005	16	Urban	Forest	Old growth forest
New York Botanical Garden	Sept. 12-17, 2005	16	Urban	Forest	Old growth forest
Pelham Bay Old Oak	June 9-13, 2004	43	Urban	Forest	Young (20 yrs) secondary forest
Spring Creek High Marsh	Oct. 10, 2005	130	Urban	Shrubland	Mix of *Phragmites* (10-15'), trees, and woody vegetation
Spring Creek Low Marsh	Oct. 16-17, 2005	0.35	Urban	Marsh	*Spartina alterniflora*
Van Cortlandt Park (Plot 310)	July 15-16, 2004	87	Urban	Forest	Old (~100 yr) secondary forest
Big Egg High Marsh	Oct. 10, 19, 21, 2005	2.1	Suburban	Shrubland	Shrubland/grassland with mix of *Phragmites*, bayberry shrubs, vines, and grasses
Big Egg Low Marsh	Oct. 16-20, 2005	2.8	Suburban	Marsh	Shrub forest; *Myrica cerifa* shrubs (5')
Floyd Bennett Field Area D	Oct. 27-29, 2005	3.4	Suburban	Grassland	Low (6") grass
Floyd Bennett Field Area G	Oct. 27-29, 2005	18	Suburban	Grassland	Low (6") grass
Fort Tilden Edge/Grassland	Nov. 13-15, 2005	90	Suburban	Grassland	Mosaic of beach grass (1') and shrubs (7')
Fort Tilden Interior/Forest	Nov. 13-15, 2005	90	Suburban	Forest	Shrub/maritime forest
Marshlands Cons. Forest	Sept. 29-Oct 1, 2005	69	Suburban	Forest	Old (~100 yr) secondary forest
Marshlands Cons. Meadow	Sept. 29-Oct 3, 2005	69	Suburban	Grassland	Mix of vines, shrubs, grass (5')
Sandy Hook High Marsh	Nov. 3-5, 2005	1	Suburban	Shrubland	Shrub/maritime forest
Sandy Hook Low Marsh	Nov. 3-5, 2005	3.5	Suburban	Marsh	*Spartina Alterniflora*
Black Rock Forest (2004 site)	Oct. 17-19, 2004	5625	Rural	Forest	Old (~100 yr) secondary forest
Black Rock Forest High Slope	Aug. 5-9, 2005	5625	Rural	Forest	Old (~100 yr) secondary forest
Black Rock Forest Low Slope	July 24-27, 2005	5625	Rural	Forest	Old (~100 yr) secondary forest

trapping arrays were surveyed: one located in low marsh (e.g., dominated by *Spartina alterniflora*) and one in adjacent upland vegetation. The two grids were placed relatively close to one another (<30m apart) to increase the likelihood of recapturing animals from the neighboring grid, which could potentially detect animal movement between low and high marsh habitats. Because of the similarities between these trapping arrays, we considered adjacent grids as paired samples. Because all target species are nocturnal, their activity in salt marsh habitat is likely to be highest when low tide occurs during the night. We therefore trapped in salt marshes during nights when low tide occurred between 12am and 4am. Since salt marshes were flooded during the hours surrounding high tide, Sherman traps could not be placed overnight; instead, during prebaiting, bait was scattered at trap locations without actual traps present, and on subsequent trapping nights baited traps were placed in the grid approximately three hours before low tide and checked and removed approximately six hours later.

Captured animals were removed from traps, sexed, weighed, aged, individually marked with numbered ear tags, and promptly released at the capture site. Most captured animals were also photographed before release. Ear-tagging was the preferred method for marking animals in this study because it is a relatively painless form of permanent marking, and neither restricts the normal activity nor adversely affects the well-being of the animal. In most cases, properly applied metal ear tags do not burden small mammals or increase their vulnerability to injury or predation, and are appropriate for the habits and body form of the target species (American Society of Mammalogists ACUC 1998). Additionally, other marking techniques (such as bleaches, paints, fur-clipping, etc.) generally require longer handling time and are not detectable from year to year, and are therefore much less suitable for multi-year research. However, alternate techniques were used in some sites and for some species. According to the preferences of the New York Botanical Garden (NYBG) administration, all animals captured in the NYBG Forest were marked either by fur-clipping or permanent nontoxic markers (Avery Marks-A-Lot). Meadow voles (*Microtus pennsylvanicus*) and Norway rats (*Rattus norvegicus*) were also marked with non toxic permanent markers due to smaller ear size and handling difficulty.

Data Analysis
We used an α value of 0.05 for all statistical tests of significance. All statistical tests are two-tailed unless otherwise indicated and were computed using the StatsDirect program (StatsDirect Ltd 2005).

We computed an estimate of the total population of each species for each trapping survey. When a survey contained 7 or more recaptures of a single species, we used the CAPTURE program (Otis et al. 1978; White et al. 1982) to compute population size; when at least one individual of a species was recaptured, we used the Schnabel population estimate (Schnabel 1938); and failing either of these conditions, we used the minimum number of animals captured as an estimate of the total population. CAPTURE is widely regarded as a powerful and accurate estimator of true population sizes from capture-mark-recapture data (Rexstad and Burnham 1991). The Schnabel population estimate is not as powerful as the CAPTURE model, but it is a more robust estimator of population when a substantial number of new individuals are still being captured on the final day of trapping. To account for uncertainty in these tests, the population estimate reported here and used in statistical calculations was an average of the two most powerful estimators of total population size.

To calculate small mammal density for each site, we used the final population estimate for each species, added the populations for all species from one trapping survey, and divided by the area surveyed. To calculate the total area surveyed, we estimated that each trap caught animals from a 15x15m square centered on the trap.

We also calculated the diversity of the small mammal community using the Shannon-Weiner Diversity index $[H' = -\sum pi*ln(pi)]$. We used one-way ANOVAs to assess overall differences between the four different habitat types (forest, salt marsh, grassland, and shrubland) and we used Tukey's post-hoc test to determine differences between individual habitat types. Trapping surveys from the same location were treated as paired samples, as were surveys in salt marshes and adjacent vegetation.

Deer mice (*Peromyscus maniculatus*) are generally not present in the New York Metropolitan region, and we therefore assumed that all our mice captures represented *P. leucopus* and not *P. maniculatus*, as the two species are extremely difficult to differentiate in the field (Burt and Grossenheider 1976, Rich et al. 1996, Whitaker 1996, Tessier et al. 2004).

Results

CORRELATES OF HABITAT TYPE

Our 24 surveys showed considerable variation in density and diversity of the small mammal communities at different sites. Trapping surveys were not all conducted at the same time of year, and it is possible that seasonality influenced our results. At certain sites, we observed some differences in the small mammal community that could be attributed to seasonality; however as surveys took place during different years it is unclear whether these differences were due to yearly fluctuations, seasonal fluctuations, or random chance.

Table 2. Small mammal density and community diversity for each of the 24 surveys.

Site	Survey date	Habitat type	Total small mammals / ha	Shannon-Weiner Diversity	Trap-nights
New York Botanical Garden	May 13-19, 2004	Forest	109	0.0	280
New York Botanical Garden	Oct. 2-4, 2004	Forest	105	0.18	180
New York Botanical Garden	July 16-19, 2005	Forest	44	0.0	147
New York Botanical Garden	Sept. 12-17, 2005	Forest	130	0.30	147
Marshlands Cons. Forest	Sept. 29-Oct 1, 2005	Forest	1	0.0	147
Black Rock Forest (2004 site)	Oct. 17-19, 2004	Forest	17	0.82	147
Black Rock Forest Low Slope	July 24-27, 2005	Forest	7	0.0	147
Black Rock Forest High Slope	Aug. 5-9, 2005	Forest	8	0.50	147
Pelham Bay Old Oak	June 9-13, 2004	Forest	17	0.42	176
Hunter's Island (Plot 207)	Oct. 23-26, 2004	Forest	38	0.0	196
Hunter's Island (Plot 204)	July 9-11, 2004	Forest	29	0.40	196
Van Cortlandt Park (Plot 310)	July 15-16, 2004 (incomplete)	Forest	15	0.21	196
Fort Tilden Interior/Forest	Nov. 13-15, 2005	Forest	59	0.0	147
Marshlands Cons. Meadow	Sept. 29-Oct. 3, 2005	Grassland	19	0.33	147
Floyd Bennett Field Area D	Oct. 27-29, 2005	Grassland	0	0.0	147
Floyd Bennett Field Area G	Oct. 27-29, 2005	Grassland	0	0.0	147
Fort Tilden Edge/Grassland	Nov. 13-15, 2005	Grassland	93	0.0	147
Spring Creek Low Marsh	Oct. 16-17, 2005 (incomplete)	Salt marsh	7	0.64	76
Marshlands Cons. Salt Marsh	Sept. 29-Oct 1, 2005	Salt marsh	4	0.35	151
Big Egg Low Marsh	Oct. 16-20, 2005	Salt marsh	9	0.50	147
Sandy Hook Low Marsh	Nov. 3-5, 2005	Salt marsh	20	0.96	135
Spring Creek High Marsh	Oct. 10, 2005 (incomplete)	Shrubland	31	0.22	49
Big Egg High Marsh	Oct. 10, 19, 21, 2005	Shrubland	117	0.0	145
Sandy Hook High Marsh	Nov. 3-5, 2005	Shrubland	89	0.13	147

There were no significant differences in small mammal densities between different habitat types (One-way ANOVA, p>0.10; Figure 1). Differences in diversity, were, however, significant between the four sampled habitat types (One-way ANOVA, p<0.01; Figure 2). This finding was almost entirely driven by differences between small mammal communities at salt marshes compared to other habitats: small mammal communities in salt marshes were significantly more diverse than in forests, grasslands, and shrublands (Tukey's post hoc test, salt marsh vs. grassland p<0.01, salt marsh vs. forest p<0.01, salt marsh vs. shrubland p<0.05), while there were no significant differences in diversity between forest, grassland, and shrubland sites (Tukey's post hoc test, forest vs. grassland p>0.10, forest vs. shrubland p>0.10, grassland vs. shrubland p>0.10). Several species were restricted to a subset of habitat types: Norway rats (*Rattus norvegicus*) were entirely restricted to salt marshes, while meadow voles (*Microtus pennsylvanicus*) were entirely absent from forests, and short-tailed shrews (*Blarina brevicauda*) were restricted to forests. Salt marshes had higher diversity scores largely because small mammal species were more evenly distributed than in other habitat types, where *P. leucopus* were typically most abundant.

At salt marsh sites there were significant differences in the small mammal community between the paired salt marsh and adjacent vegetation: salt marsh grids reported significantly higher diversity than adjacent shrubland or forest grids (Paired t-test, N=8, p<0.05). There was, however, no

Figure 1. Small mammal density (# animals per ha ± SE) in each of the sampled habitat types.

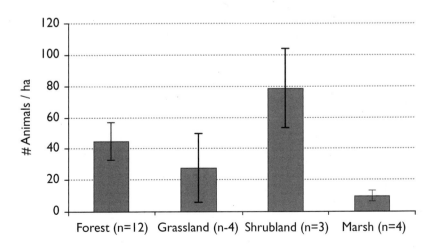

Forest (n=12)   Grassland (n-4)   Shrubland (n=3)   Marsh (n=4)

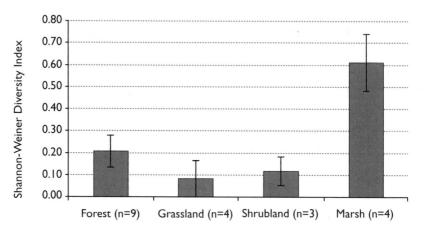

Figure 2. Small mammal diversity (Shannon-Weiner diversity index ±SE) in each of the sampled habitat types.

corresponding significant difference in overall small mammal density between grids in salt marsh and adjacent vegetation (paired t-test, N=8, p>0.10). Salt marshes also contained different small mammal species than adjacent vegetation. We captured *R. norvegicus* in 3 of the 4 low marsh sites, and density was significantly different between low marsh and adjacent sites (Fisher's exact test, N=8, p<0.01), and the species was only observed in low marshes. Salt marshes also appeared to contain lower densities of *P. leucopus* compared to adjacent vegetation, but the difference was not significant (paired t-test, N=3, p>0.05, mean_shrubland = 77.8 mice/ha, mean_salt marsh = 1.7 mice/ha). However, we sampled only three paired sites, including one incomplete survey artificially reduced in density, suggesting that, with more data, this effect may be significant.

There were also differences apparent between the small mammal communities at the four salt marsh sites. Although Shannon-Weiner diversity indices were similar across all four sites, species present at each one varied: *M. pennsylvanicus* was found in higher densities at Sandy Hook than in other salt marshes (Fisher's exact test, N=4, p<0.05; Table 3); *R. norvegicus* was observed in low densities in Spring Creek, Big Egg, and Sandy Hook salt marshes, and not at all in Marshlands Conservancy, though differences in rat capture rates between sites were not statistically significant (Fisher's exact test, N=4, p>0.10).

We found some evidence that individual animals move between low

Table 3. Shannon-Weiner diversity index and number of animals captured for all four
salt marsh sites

Site	Shannon-Weiner diversity index	Peromyscus leucopus captured	Rattus norvegicus captured	Microtus pensylvanicus captured
Marshlands Cons. Salt Marsh†	0.69	2	0	2
Spring Creek Low Marsh	0.64	0	2	1
Big Egg Low Marsh	0.50	1	4	0
Sandy Hook Low Marsh	0.96	2	3	7

†All animals were captured in Phragmites above the tidal zone

salt marsh and adjacent vegetation at low rates. In 997 trap-nights, an animal
was captured both in salt marsh and in adjacent vegetation only once, though
all salt marsh sites had grids in adjacent vegetation with no apparent dispersal
barriers between them.

CORRELATES OF PATCH SIZE, DEER DENSITY, AND
URBANIZATION IN FORESTS

As we surveyed small mammals in only four grassland, four salt marsh, and
three shrubland sites, we were unable to statistically analyze the effects of
patch size, deer density, and urbanization within these three habitat types.

At forest sites, patch size and deer density, when analyzed together
in a multiple linear regression, significantly correlated with small mammal
density—though neither individual correlation was significant in the same
analysis (Multiple linear regression with patch size transformed to log patch
size, N=13, overall $p<0.05$, $R^2=0.47$, adjusted $R^2=0.36$, log patch size $p<0.10$,
deer density $p>0.10$).

Analyzed individually, the relationships between deer density and
small mammal density, and patch size and small mammal density, are clearer;
the relationship between urbanization and small mammal density is less so.
Deer density had a strong negative correlation with small mammal density
at forested sites (Single linear regression, N=12, exponential model, $p<0.001$,
$R^2=0.73$, Figure 3), and patch size was also negatively correlated with small
mammal density (Single linear regression, N=12, $p<0.05$, $R^2=0.62$, Figure
4). Though we had too few data points to conduct an ANOVA between
urban, suburban, and rural sites, there appears to be a positive relationship

between increased urbanization and increased small mammal densities in forests (Figure 5). As more urbanized sites were generally smaller and never contained deer, it is unclear whether 1) smaller patch size, 2) reduced deer density, or 3) a third (as yet unidentified) factor associated with urbanization may have caused the higher small mammal densities generally found in urban forests.

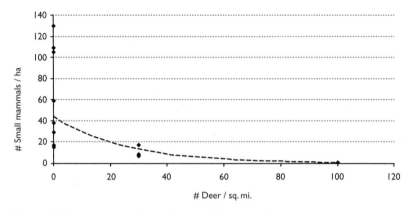

Figure 3. Deer density and small mammal density at forest sites.

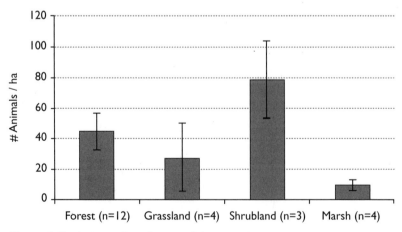

Figure 4. Patch size and small mammal density at forest sites.

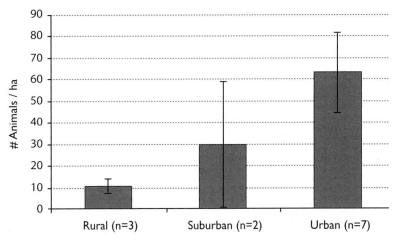

Figure 5. Urbanization and small mammal density at forest sites.

In contrast to these results, patch size and deer density were not significantly correlated with small mammal diversity in forest sites (multiple linear regression with patch size transformed to log patch size, $N=12$, overall $p>0.10$, $R^2=0.30$, adjusted $R^2=0.15$, log patch size $p<0.10$, deer density $p>0.10$). There was no relationship between patch size and diversity ($N=12$, $p>0.10$, $R^2=0.19$, Figure 6) and no relationship between deer density and diversity

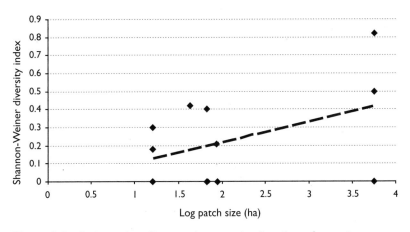

Figure 6. Patch size and small mammal community diversity at forest sites.

(N=12, p>0.10, R²=0.00, Figure 7). Again, we had too few data points to conduct an ANOVA on the effects of urbanization on small mammal diversity though the data suggest that no relationship appears to exist (Figure 8).

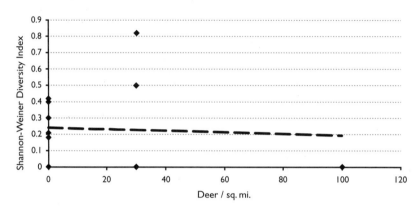

Figure 7. Deer density and small mammal community diversity at forest sites.

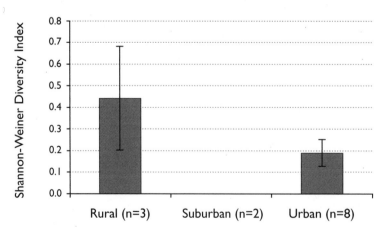

Figure 8. Urbanization and small mammal community diversity at forest sites.

MICROHABITAT CORRELATES OF *P. LEUCOPUS* DENSITY IN A GRASSLAND-SHRUBLAND MOSAIC SITE

The Fort Tilden grassland survey was taken on a mosaic of beach grass, shrubs, and scrub vegetation that offered an opportunity to evaluate capture rates in different habitat types. Of 144 trap nights, 45 took place in beach grass, 54 in shrubs (vegetation <5ft tall, ground cover >50% woody vegetation), and 45 in scrub (vegetation >5ft tall, ground cover >25% trees). White-footed mice were found at significantly higher densities in shrub and scrub vegetation than in beach grass (2x3 Chi square test, N=55 captures, p<0.05).

Discussion

EFFECTS OF HABITAT TYPE ON SMALL MAMMAL DIVERSITY AND DENSITY

Results from our study indicate that habitat type has a strong influence on small mammal community diversity across the New York Metropolitan Region, even at vastly different spatial scales. On a regional scale, small mammal communities in salt marsh, forest, and shrubland macrohabitats shared clear similarities within themselves and distinct differences from each other. All survey sites of the same habitat type contained similar species, and all of the species we trapped—with the exception of *P. leucopus*—were present in only a subset of the habitat types. For instance, we trapped *B. brevicauda* only in forests, *R. norvegicus* only in salt marshes, and *M. pennsylvanicus* in all habitat types except forests. Habitat type also had a clear influence on small mammal communities on a microhabitat scale. Shrubland and salt marsh habitats consistently contained distinct small mammal communities, even when they were separated by only a few meters. Similarly, at Fort Tilden, small patches of shrubs showed statistically significant differences in *P. leucopus* density from the surrounding beach grass matrix. These findings are consistent with previous studies suggesting that microhabitat structure is a major determinant of which small mammal species are present at a particular site (Dueser and Shurgart 1978).

Habitat type did not have nearly the same influence on overall small mammal density, as we did not find any significant differences in density between the four habitat types. These data, together with the absences of certain species from entire habitat types, lend support to the hypothesis that habitat type influences the density of individual species. That small mammal density remained regionally consistent despite these individual species variations implies that as one species declines in abundance from one habitat to the next, one or several others replace it at roughly similar densities.

Such habitat selection by small mammal species is a well-documented phenomenon that may explain the coexistence of multiple small mammal species across macrohabitats (Rosenzweig 1973; M'Closkey 1976). Previous research has implicated predation risk (Thompson 1982a, b), interspecific competition (Bowers et al. 1987) and temporal partitioning (Brown et al. 1989) as underlying mechanisms for the macro- and microhabitat selection of individual small mammal species.

EFFECTS OF MICROHABITAT ON SMALL MAMMAL DENSITY AND DIVERSITY

Our results suggest that the microhabitat feature most influential to *P. leucopus* densities, and perhaps for other small mammal species, is the structure and density of understory cover. Previous studies on *P. leucopus* microhabitat affinities have reached similar conclusions (Dueser and Shurgart 1978; Kaufman et al. 1983; Anderson et al. 2003). Kaufman et al. (1983) found that *P. leucopus* individuals were captured more frequently near trees with large and small shrubs, large shrubs alone, and at the bases of rocks, logs, and stumps; they also avoided grassy areas. These findings suggest that *P. leucopus* strongly selects for microhabitats with a complex vertical structure, and subsequent studies have refined this hypothesis to state that *P. leucopus* selects for dense understory cover (Kaufman et al. 1983; Barnum et al. 1992; Flowerdew and Ellwood 2001). In our study, sites with denser understory cover tended to have higher *P. leucopus* densities. For example, the New York Botanical Garden forest had a much thicker understory and a much higher *P. leucopus* density than either Black Rock Forest or the Marshlands Conservancy forest. Similarly, the Marshlands Conservancy meadow, with its tall (3-5 ft) and profuse herbaceous growth had a much higher density of *P. leucopus* than the adjoining forest habitat. Sites with extremely low *P. leucopus* densities—outside of regularly-flooded salt marshes—also shared the common feature of sparse understory cover. At the time of our survey, grasses at Floyd Bennett Field (where we captured no animals in 294 trap-nights) were roughly 6 inches tall, and the forest at Marshlands Conservancy (where we captured one animal in 147 trap-nights) was notably lacking in understory cover.

It should be noted that several other factors could potentially explain the absence of small mammals from Floyd Bennett Field. Small mammals may not be able to cross the asphalt runways to colonize the site's grasslands, since previous studies have indicated that roads may serve as dispersal barriers for many small mammals (Oxley et al. 1974; Merriam et al. 1989). Other studies have shown that mowed grass can also act as a dispersal barrier for some small mammals, suggesting that the grasslands at Floyd Bennett Field may simply not be suitable habitat for many small mammal species (Krohne and Hoch 1999; Mahan and O'Connell 2005).

EFFECTS OF DEER DENSITY ON FOREST COMMUNITIES OF SMALL MAMMALS

In our study, deer density had a significant negative correlation with small mammal density in forests, and there is some reason to believe that this relationship was causally related. Studies from a variety of different habitats have indicated an inverse relationship between ungulate and small mammal densities. Flowerdew and Ellwood (2001) found that increased densities of deer in wooded areas of England decreased small mammal densities. They suggested 2 potential pathways for ungulates to reduce small mammal densities: by the modification or removal of habitat (which can remove nesting materials, shelter from predators, and alter the balance of competition between species), and/or through competition for food resources (Flowerdew and Ellwood 2001). Browsing activity of Reeves' muntjac, roe deer, and fallow deer caused reductions in the ground cover of the study site, resulting in a significant decline in bank vole populations (Flowerdew and Ellwood 2001). Keesing (1998), working in a savannah in Kenya, found that small mammal populations inside ungulate exclosures increased significantly over a 2-year period. Keesing concluded that, because of the similarities in diets of small mammal and ungulate species, removing ungulates caused an increase in the quantity or quality of food available to small mammals. Rooney and Waller (2003) found that increased white-tailed deer (*Odocoileus virginianus*) browsing lead to profound habitat alterations including reductions in vegetative cover, particularly of shrubs and saplings, and decreased the diversity of the understory herb, effectively reducing the habitat's vertical complexity (Rooney and Waller 2003; Giuliano and Homyack 2004). Given this typical removal of understory cover by deer at high densities and the preference of *P. leucopus* for habitats with high levels of vertical complexity (Kaufman et al. 1983; Barnum et al. 1992; Flowerdew and Ellwood 2001; Brannon 2005); the tendency of some small mammal species to avoid unsheltered habitat due to predation risk (Kotler et al. 1991; Vasquez 1994; Morris and Davidson 2000; Orrock et al. 2000); and the confirmed presence of small mammal predators in several sites (Brady 1994; Gompper et al. 2003; A. Beall, pers. comm.), it is plausible that increased

O. virginianus density is causally linked to the reduced small mammal densities in forests we observed in the New York Metropolitan region.

Our data are not conclusive, however, as the apparent relationship between deer density and small mammals may be driven by a third factor such as predator densities. Notably, coyotes were present in all sites where deer density was high and small mammal density low, and they were absent from all sites where small mammal populations were high. Snake densities are also likely to be suppressed in urban areas, where deer are absent. Since we do not have data on predator densities at different sites, we cannot at this stage evaluate their influence on small mammal communities.

SMALL MAMMAL COMMUNITIES IN SALT MARSHES

This study was the first to evaluate how effective restoration efforts at Big Egg Marsh have been at re-establishing a small mammal community representative of those found in other salt marshes in the region. Overall, the restoration appears to have been successful, as *P. leucopus* and *R. norvegicus* utilized the site and both were found at other salt marshes in the region. *M. pennsylvanicus* was either absent from Big Egg or present at a sufficiently low density to avoid capture in 147 trap-nights. Since few *M. pennsylvanicus* were captured in Spring Creek and none at the Marshlands Conservancy salt marsh, the apparent absence of the species in the restored marsh may simply reflect the low capture probability for a species at low densities—not the absolute absence of the species (there were no significant differences in *M. pennsylvanicus* capture rates between the Big Egg, Spring Creek, and Marshlands Conservancy salt marshes: 2x3 Chi Square; $p>0.10$). That we captured only juvenile rats at Big Egg suggests that the restoration area may not yet be able to support as diverse and numerous a small mammal community as other salt marshes in the region; that we captured any animals, however, indicates that the site is capable of supporting, at least temporarily, some small mammal populations.

Our data provide partial support for the hypothesis that some small mammals species are permanent salt marsh residents. We captured *M. pennsylvanicus* at significantly higher densities in the Sandy Hook low marsh than in the adjacent upland vegetation, where we captured none (Fisher's exact test, $p<0.05$). As traps in the upland vegetation remained open from evening high tide through the morning, we had ample opportunity to trap animals moving into the low marsh at low tide and retreating to upland vegetation during high tide. That we did not, suggests that *M. pennsylvanicus* is a permanent resident of the Sandy Hook low salt marsh, and not just a transient visitor nesting above the tide line. Data from other sites are less clear: at Marshlands Conservancy *M. pennsylvanicus* was found in Phragmites reeds bordering the low marsh, but not in the low marsh itself, and at Spring Creek we captured *M. pennsylvanicus* in both low marsh and adjacent Phragmites. We also captured *R. norvegicus* solely in low marsh habitat. These results suggest that individuals of these species may not leave low marshes, at least not in favor of upland vegetation. *P. leucopus* individuals in salt marshes, however, may act as transients, as we captured one individual in both Sandy Hook low marsh and in the adjacent shrubland. Although we could not determine the frequency of such movement events, our data suggest that these events are fairly rare (1 capture in adjacent low marsh/upland sites in 997 trap-nights). Overall these results do not conclusively determine that small mammals are permanent residents in salt marshes, but they suggest that *M. pennsylvanicus* and *R. norvegicus* can be.

EFFECTS OF URBANIZATIONI AND PATCH SIZE ON FOREST COMMUNITIES OF SMALL MAMMALS

Remarkably, our data suggest that urbanization and patch size have no direct influence on small mammal diversity. These findings are decidedly contrary to the recognized consequences of habitat fragmentation, which typically include an overall reduction in species diversity (Saunders et al. 1991; Iida and Nakashizuka 1995; Laurance et al. 2002; Fahrig 2003). One possible explanation for the persistence of small mammals is that competitors and predators are more likely to be lost through the fragmentation process (Nupp and Swihart 1996; Rosenblatt et al. 1999). Many urbanized patches may also contain sufficiently large and heterogeneous habitats to support a diverse small mammal community (Johnson et al. 1979; Clark et al. 1998). Furthermore, the survival of *P. leucopus* populations in fragmented landscapes may be due to an apparent flexibility in territorial behavior: in habitat patches with very high densities, home ranges decrease in size and have a much higher amount of overlap (Nadeau et al.1981; Wolff 1985). Adler and Wilson (1987) also suggested that *P. leucopus* exhibits a flexible demographic structure that may enable individuals to survive in poor quality habitat. If other small mammal species exhibit similar traits (and *M. pennsylvanicus* does; Ostfeld and Canham 1995), then small mammals may be more resilient to urbanization and fragmentation than other taxa.

As with deer density and understory cover, patch size had a significant influence on overall small mammal density. Urbanization often fragments habitat and decreases patch size, and with more data we may expect to find significantly higher densities in urban patches than in rural, likely larger, patches. Such findings are mostly in accordance with previous studies on small mammal responses to urbanization, which have found increased densities in smaller and more isolated patches (Yahner 1992; Nupp and Swihart 1996; Nupp and Swihart 1998, 2000). *P. leucopus* in forest patches exhibits an inverse correlation with patch size, with a peak density occurring in patches less than 2 ha (Nupp and Swihart 1996). In addition, Barko et al. (2003) found higher small mammal capture rates in sites surrounded by a higher percentage of urban habitat, with most captures occurring in small patches directly adjacent to urban development. Higher small mammal densities in urban areas may be caused by the presence of barriers like roads, sidewalks, and landscaping. In a constricted urban landscape, small mammals may have minimal opportunities for emigration, creating patches with high abundances (Adler and Levins 1994; Barko et al. 2003).

Elevated small mammal densities have been thought to indicate high quality habitat (Ostfeld et al. 1985; Krohne and Hoch 1999; Carey and Harrington 2001), and they may also support higher densities of predators (such as raptors, snakes, and mammalian carnivores) that are often targeted in conservation efforts. In our study, small mammal densities in some small urban forest patches were as much as 19 times higher than those in large, intact, rural forests. Such high densities in more restricted urban sites can potentially lead to a variety of non-desirable effects. High small mammal densities may reduce (or even prevent) regeneration of masting tree species (Ostfeld et al. 1996), and they can also lead to detrimental crowding effects or reduction in genetic variation (Krebs et al. 1973; Gaines et al. 1997; Krohne and Hoch 1999; Mossman and Waser 2001; Barko et al. 2003). Without a more comprehensive understanding of urban ecosystems, it is unclear whether the high densities of small mammals we observed in small, urban natural areas lead to conservation benefits or unfavorable ecological effects.

Conclusion

Our results largely concur with recent studies emphasizing the ecological value of urban natural areas, but drawing any definite conclusions from our data about the effects of urbanization and patch size on small mammal communities is not yet fully warranted. First of all, these effects are limited to forests, as we did not have sufficient data to perform similar analyses in other habitats. Second, and perhaps more importantly, our survey methods may not have been conducive to determining true species richness. Our traps were baited for species that feed on seeds and nuts, and our captures therefore

likely under-represented insectivores and other species not attracted to seeds
and nuts. This problem might have been exacerbated by the number of trap-
nights that we used to complete a survey (147 trap-nights), which may not
have been sufficient to fully sample insectivorous species at low densities.
Such species may in fact be negatively influenced by urbanization and reduced
patch size, but these effects would not have been detectable in our data. Since
species that live at low density are often of greater conservation concern than
more commonly found species, these shortcomings are not insubstantial. As
we did not find higher abundances of low density or rare small mammal
species in rural study sites than in urban and suburban sites, our results
suggest that natural areas across all levels of urbanization have similar
conservation value. This is surely not the case. Though we did not capture
rare species during our surveys in rural areas, island biogeography and
conservation theory suggest that such species are almost certainly more
prevalent in large, rural forests as opposed to fragmented, urban forests.
Nonetheless, our results are compelling because they indicate that small,
urban forests can support mostly intact small mammal communities. Non-
native small mammal species, such as *R. norvegicus* or the house mouse *Mus
musculus*, were no more prevalent in urban forests (with low levels of garbage)
than in more intact forests. Some rare species may be missing, and generalist
species may be found at atypically high densities, but species that are common
in more intact natural areas remain common in small urban patches.

References

Adler, G. H., and R. Levins. 1994. The island syndrome in rodent populations.
  Quarterly Review of Biology. 69: 473-490.
Adler, G.H. and M.L. Wilson. 1987. Demography of a habitat generalist, the White-
  Footed Mouse, in a heterogeneous environment. *Ecology*. 68(6): 1785-
  1796.
Allan, B.F., Keesing, F., and R.S. Ostfield. 2003. Effect of Forest Fragmentation on
  Lyme Disease Risk. *Conservation Biology*. 17 (1): 267-272.
American Society of Mammalogists Animal Care and Use Committee (ACUC).
  1998. Guidelines for the capture, handling, and care of mammals as approved
  by the American Society of Mammalogists. *Journal of Mammalogy* 79(4):
  1416-1431.
Anderson, C.S., Cady, A.B., and D.B. Meikle. 2003. Effects of vegetation structure
  and edge habitat on the density and distribution of white-footed mice
  (*Peromyscus leucopus*) in small and large forest patches. *Canadian Journal of
  Zoology*. 81(5): 897-904.
Barko, V.A., Feldhamer, G.A., Nicholson, M.C., and D.D. Kevin. 2003. Urban

Habitat: a determinant of white-footed mouse (*Peromyscus leucopus*) abundance in southern Illinois. *Southeastern Naturalist.* 2(3): 369-376.

Barnum, S.A., Manvile, C.J., Tester, J.R., and W.J. Carmen. 1992. Path Selection by *Peromyscus leucopus* in the presence and absence of vegetative cover. *Journal of Mammalogy.* 73(4): 797-801.

Bengston, D., Fletcher, J., and Nelson, K. 2004. Public policies for managing urban growth and protecting open space: policy instruments and lessons learned in the United States. *Landscape and Urban Planning.* 69: 271-286.

Bowers, M.A., Thompson, D.B., and J.H. Brown. 1987. Spatial organization of a desert rodent community: food addition and species removal. *Oecologia.* 72 (1): 77-82.

Brady, J.F. 1994. *Black Rock Forest deer population management report (1984-1994).* Unpublished report, Black Rock Forest. Cornwall, N.Y.

Brannon, M.P. 2005. Distribution and Microhabitat of the Woodland Jumping Mouse, *Napaeozapus insignis*, and the White-footed Mouse, *Peromyscus leucopus*, in the Southern Appalachians. *Southeastern Naturalist.* 4(3): 479-486.

Brown, J. S. 1989. Desert rodent community structure: a test of four mechanisms of coexistence. *Ecological Monographs.* 59: 1-20.

Burns, C.E. 2005. Behavioral ecology of disturbed landscapes: The response of territorial animals to relocation. *Behavioral Ecology.* 16(5): 898-905.

Burns, C. E., B. J. Goodwin, and R. S. Ostfeld. 2005. A prescription for longer life? Bot fly parasitism of the white-footed mouse. *Ecology.* 86: 753-761.

Burt, W.H., and Grossenheider, R.P. 1976. *Peterson Field Guides Mammals.* Houghton Mifflin Company: New York, NY.

Carey, A. and C. Harrington. 2001. Small mammals in young forests: implications for management for sustainability. *Forest Ecology Management.* 154: 289-309.

Clark, B.K., Clark, B.S., Homerding, T.R., and W.E. Munsterman. 1998. Communities of small mammals in six grass-dominated habitats of Southeastern Oklahoma. *American Midland Naturalist.* 139(2): 262-268.

Cook, R.P. 1989. *Mammals of Gateway National Recreation Area.* USDI, National Park Service, Gateway National Recreation Area. 8 pp booklet.

Cousins, S. 1982. Species size distributions of birds and snails in an urban area. Pp. 99-109 in: R. Bornkamm, J. Lee, and M. Seward (eds), *Urban Ecology.* Oxford: Blackwell Scientific Publications.

Dickman, C.R., and C.P. Doncaster. 1987. The Ecology of Small Mammals in Urban Habitats. I. Populations in a Patchy Environment. *Journal of Animal Ecology.* 56(2): 629-640.

Donahue, J.G., J. Piesman, and A. Spielman. 1987. Reservoir competence of white-footed mice for Lyme disease spirochetes. *Journal of Tropical Medicine and Hygiene.* 36: 92-96.

Dueser, R.D. and H.H. Shugart Jr. 1978. Microhabitats in a forest-floor small mammal fauna. *Ecology.* 59(1): 89-98.

Fahrig, L. 2003. Effects of Habitat Fragmentation on Biodiversity. Annual Review of Ecology, Evolution and Systematics. 34: 487-515.

Flowerdew, J.R. and S.A. Ellwood. 2001. Impacts of woodland deer on small mammal ecology. *Forestry.* 74(3): 277-287.

Francl, K., Castelberry, S., and Ford, W. 2004. Small mammal communities of high elevation central Appalachian wetlands. *American Midland Naturalist* 151: 388-398.

Gaines, M.S., Diffendorfer, J.E., R.D., Tamarin, R.H., and T.S. Whittam. 1997. The effects of habitat fragmentation on the genetic structure of small mammal population. *Journal of Heredity.* 88(4): 294-304.

Getz, L.L. 1961. Factors Influencing the Local Distribution of Shrews. *American Midland Naturalist.* 65(1): 67-88.

Giuliano, W.M., and J.D. Homyack. 2004. Short-term grazing exclusion effects on riparian small mammal communities. *Rangeland Ecology and Management.* 57(4): 346-350.

Goldstein-Golding, E. 1991. The ecology and structure of urban greenspaces. Pp. 392-411 in: S. Bell and H. Mushinsky (eds), *Habitat Structure.* London: Chapman and Hall.

Gompper, M.E., Goodman, R.M., Kays, R.W., Ray, J.C., Fiorello, C.V., and S.E. Wade. 2003. A Survey of the Parasites of Coyotes (Canis latrans) in New York based on Fecal Analysis. *Journal of Wildlife Diseases.* 39(3): 712-717.

Google. 2005. Google Maps. http://www.maps.google.com. Last accessed 12/15/2005.

Hollander, J. and Vander Wall S. 2004. Effectiveness of six species of rodents as dispersers of single leaf pinon pine (*Pinus monophylla*). *Oecologia* 138: 57-65.

Howell, P.T. 1984. Use of Salt Marshes by Meadow Voles. *Estuaries.* 7(2): 165-170.

Iida, S. and Nakashizuka, T. 1995. Forest fragmentation and its effect on species diversity in sub-urban coppice forests in Japan. *Forest Ecology and Management.* 73(1-3): 197-210.

Johnson, W.C., Schreiber, R.K., and R.L. Burgess. 1979. Diversity of small mammals in a powerline right-of-way and adjacent forest in East Tennessee. *American Midland Naturalist.* 101 (1): 231-235.

Kaufman, D.W., Peterson, S.K., Fristik, R., and G.A. Kaufman. 1983. Effect of Microhabitat Features on Habitat Use by *Peromyscus leucopus*. *The American Midland Naturalist.* 110(1): 177-185.

Keeling, M.J., and Gilligan, C.A. 2000. Metapopulation dynamics of bubonic plague. *Nature.* 407: 903-906.

Keesing, F. 1998. Impacts of ungulates on the demography and diversity of small mammals in central Kenya. *Oecologia.* 116: 381-389.

Kitchings, J.T., and D.J. Levy. 1981. Habitat patterns in a small mammal community. *Journal of Mammalogy.* 62(4): 814-820.

Klee, R. V., Mahoney, A. C., Christopher, C. C., and G. W. Barett. 2004. Riverine Peninsulas: An Experimental Approach to Homing in White-footed Mice (*Peromyscus leucopus*). *The American Midland Naturalist* 151(2): 408-413.

Kotler, B. P., Brown, J.S., and O. Hasson. 1991. Factors affecting gerbil foraging behavior and rates of owl predation. *Ecology.* 72: 2249-2260.

Krebs, C.J., Gaines, M.S., Keller, B.L., Meyers, J.H., and R. H. Tamarin. 1973. Population cycles in small rodents. *Science.* 179, 35-41.

Krohne, D. T., and G. A. Hoch. 1999. Demography of Peromyscus leucopus populations on habitat patches: the role of dispersal. *Canadian Journal of Zoology.* 77:1247-1253.

Kunick, W. 1982. Comparison of the flora of some cities of central European lowlands. Pp. 255-275 in: R. Bornkamm, J. Lee and M. Seward (eds), *Urban Ecology.* Oxford: Blackwell Scientific Publications.

Laurance W.F., Lovejoy T.E., Vasconcelos H.L., Bruna E.M., Didham R.K., Stouffer P.C., Gascon C., Bierregaard R.O., Laurance S.G., and Sampaio E. 2002. Ecosystem decay of Amazonian forest fragments: a 22-year investigation. *Conservation Biology.* 16(3): 605-618.

M'Closkey, R.T. 1976. Community structure in sympatric rodents. *Ecology.* 57(4): 728-739.

McDonnell, M.J., Pickett, S.T.A., Groffman, P., Bohlen, P., Pouyat, R.V., Zipperer, W.C., Parmelee, R.W., Carreiro, M.M., and Medley, K. 1997. Ecosystem processes along an urban-to-rural gradient. *Urban Ecosystems.* 1:21-36.

Mahan, C.G., and T.J. O'Connell. 2005. Small mammal use of suburban and urban parks in central Pennsylvania. *Northeastern Naturalist.* 12(3): 307-314.

Marzluff, J. M., R. Bowman, and R. Donnelly. 2001. A historical perspective on urban bird research: trends, terms, and approaches. Pp.1-18 in: J. M. Marzluff, R. Bowman, and R. Donnelly, editors. *Avian ecology in an urbanizing world.* Kluwer Academic: Norwell, Massachusetts, USA.

Merriam, G., Kozakiewicz, M., Tsuchiya, E., and K. Hawley. 1989. Barriers as boundaries for metapopulations and demes of *Peromyscus leucopus* in farm landscapes. *Landscape Ecology.* 2(4): 227-235.

Mills, J.N. and J. E. Childs.1998. Ecologic studies of rodent reservoirs: their relevance for human health. *Emerging Infectious Diseases.* 4(4): 529-553.

Morin, P. 1999. *Community Ecology.* Malden, MA: Blackwell Science Publications, 424pp.

Morris, D. W., and D. L. Davidson. 2000. Optimally foraging mice match patch use with habitat differences in fitness. *Ecology.* 8(1): 2061-2066.

Mossman, C.A. and P.M. Waser. 2001. Effects of habitat fragmentation on population genetic structure in the white-footed mouse (*Peromyscus leucopus*). *Canadian Journal of Zoology.* 79: 285-295.

Nadeau, J., R. Lombardi, and R. H. Tamarin. 1981. Population structure and dispersal of *Peromyscus leucopus* on Muskeget Island. *Canadian Journal of Zoology.* 59:793-799.

Nupp, T. E., and R. K. Swihart. 1996. Effect of forest patch area on population attributes of white-footed mice (*Peromyscus leucopus*) in fragmented landscapes. *Canadian Journal of Zoology.* 74:467-472.

Nupp, T.E., and R.K. Swihart. 1998. Effects of forest fragmentation on population attributes of white-footed mice and eastern chipmunks. *Journal of Mammology.* 79: 1234-1243.

Nupp, T.E., and R.K. Swihart. 2000. Landscape-level correlates of small-mammal assemblages in forest fragments of farmland. *Journal of Mammalogy.* 81: 512-526.

Orrock, J. L., J. F. Pagels, W. J. McShea, and E. K. Harper. 2000. Predicting presence and abundance of a small mammal species: the effect of scale and resolution. *Ecological Applications.* 10: 1356-1366.

Ostfeld, R.S., W.Z. Lidicker, and E.J. Heske. 1985. The relationship between habitat heterogeneity, space use, and demography in a population of California voles. *Oikos.* 45: 433-442.

Ostfeld, R.S., and C.D. Canham. 1995. Density-dependent processes in meadow voles: an environmental approach. *Ecology.* 76(2): 521-532.

Ostfeld, R. S., Jones, C. G. and J.O. Wolff. 1996. Of mice and mast: ecological connections in eastern deciduous forests. *BioScience.* 46: 323-330.

Ostfeld, R. S., and F. Keesing. 2000. Biodiversity and disease risk: the case of Lyme disease. *Conservation Biology.* 14: 722-728.

Otis, D.L., Burnham, K.P., White, G.C., and D.R. Anderson. 1978. Statistical inference from capture data on closed animal populations. *Wildlife Monographs.* 62: 1-135.

Oxley, D.J., Fenton, M.B. and Carmody, G.R. 1974. The effects of roads on populations of small mammals. *J. Appl. Ecol.* 11: 51-59.

Pickett, S.T.A., Cadenasso, M.L, Grove, J.M., Nilon, C.H., Pouyat, R.V., Zipperer, W.C., and R. Costanza. 2001. Urban ecological systems: linking terrestrial ecological, physical, and socioeconomic components of metropolitan areas. *Annual Review of Ecological Systematics.* 32: 127-157.

Pusenius, J., Ostfeld, R. and Keesing, F. 2000. Patch selection and tree-seedling predation by resident versus immigrant meadow voles. *Ecology.* 8: 2951-2956.

Rexstad, E. A., and K. P. Burnham. 1991. User's guide for interactive program CAPTURE. Colorado Cooperative Wildlife Research Unit, Colorado State University, Fort Collins, CO. 29 pp.

Rich, S.M., Kilpatrick, C.W., Shippee, J.L., and Crowell, K.L. 1996. Morphological differentiation and identification of *Peromyscus leucopus* and *P. maniculatus* in Northeastern North America. *Journal of Mammalogy.* 77(4): 985-991.

Rooney, T.P., and D.M. Waller. 2003. Direct and indirect effects of white-tailed deer in forest ecosystems. *Forest Ecology and Management.* 181: 165-173.

Rosenblatt, D. L., E. J. Heske, S. L. Nelson, D. M. Barber, M. A. Miller, and B. MacAllister. 1999. Forest fragments in east-central Illinois: islands or habitat patches for mammals? *American Midland Naturalist.* 141:115-123.

Rosenzweig, M. L. 1973. Habitat selection experiments with a pair of coexisting heteromyid species. *Ecology.* 54:111-117.

Saunders, D.A., Hobbs, R.J., and Margules, C.R. 1991. Biological consequences of ecosystem fragmentation: A review. *Conservation Biology.* 5(1): 18-32.

Sauvajot, R., Buechner, M., Kamradt, D., and Schonewald, C. 1998. Patterns of human disturbance and response by small mammals and birds in chaparral near urban development. *Urban Ecosystems.* 2: 279-297.

Shanholtzer, G.F. 1974. Relationships of vertebrates to salt marsh plants. pp. 463-474. In R.J. Reimold and W.H. Queen (eds.). *Ecology of Halophytes.* Academic Press, New York.

Schnabel, Z.E. 1938. The estimation of the total fish population of a lake; *American Mathematics Monthly.* 45: 348-352.

Shure, D.J. 1971. Tidal Flooding Dynamics: Its influence on Small Mammals in Barrier Beach Marshes. *American Midland Naturalist.* 85(1): 36-44.

StatsDirect Ltd. 2005. StatsDirect statistical software. http://www.statsdirect.com. England: StatsDirect Ltd.

Tessier, N., Noël, S., and Lapointe, F.J. 2004. A new method to discriminate the deer mouse (*Peromyscus maniculatus*) jfrom the white-footed mouse (*Peromyscus leucopus*) using species-specific primers in multiplex PCR. *Canadian Journal of Zoology.* 82(11): 1832-1835.

Thompson, S. D. 1982a. Microhabitat utilization and foraging behavior of bipedal and quadrupedal heteromyid rodents. *Ecology.* 63: 1303-1312.

Thompson, S. D. 1982b. Structure and species composition of desert heteromyid rodent species assemblages: effects of a simple habitat manipulation. *Ecology.* 63:1313 – 1321.

Vasquez, R.A. 1994. Assessment of predation risk via illumination level—facultative central place foraging in the cricetid rodent *Phyllotis darwini. Behavioral Ecology and Sociobiology.* 34: 375-381.

Whitaker, J.O., Jr. 1996. *National Audubon Society Field Guide to North American Mammals.* Chanticleer Press Inc.: New York, NY.

White, G.C., Anderson, D.R., Burnham, K.P., and D.L. Otis. 1982. Capture-recapture and removal methods for sampling closed populations. Los Alamos National Laboratory, Los Alamos, New Mexico.

Wolff, J.O. 1985. The effects of density, food, and interspecific interference on home range size in *Peromyscus leucopus* and *Peromyscus maniculatus. Canadian Journal of Zoology.* 63(11): 2657-2662.

Yahner, R.H. 1992. Dynamics of a small mammal community in a fragmented forest. *American Midland Naturalist.* 127: 381-391.

Great Gull Island: 1963-2006

Helen Hays
Great Gull Island Project
American Museum of Natural History
Central Park West at 79th Street
New York NY 10024
hays@amnh.org

History

GREAT GULL ISLAND LIES AT THE EASTERN END of Long Island Sound. The island is capped by the remains of Fort Michie, begun in 1897 as one of a series of forts in our U.S. coastal defense system. Today its 6.9 hectares (17 acres) of terminal moraine are home to this hemisphere's largest nesting concentrations of Common Terns (*Sterna hirundo*) and Roseate Terns (*Sterna dougallii*). Terns have held the island for centuries with a short break between 1897 and 1949 during construction of Fort Michie, the army's occupation of the fort and for five years after the army left. Great Gull Island was named for the terns that nested there. In the 19th century, terns were called mackerel gulls, because each spring they came in with the mackerel. No gulls nested on Long island until the mid-1940s.

By 1949 Fort Michie was considered obsolete and the government put the island up for sale. Through the efforts of Richard Pough, chairman of the American Museum of Natural History's Conservation Department at the time, the Museum took title to Great Gull Island that year and assigned the Linnaean Society of New York the task of making the island attractive to terns. Work began immediately. Linnaean members went to the island, dumped sand, took down buildings and then left the island undisturbed in the hope terns would come back.

In 1955, six years after the army departed, the terns reclaimed the island. That year Irwin Alperin, a Linnaean Society member, flew over Great Gull Island and spotted 25 pairs of Common Terns nesting at its far eastern tip. Subsequently, as the colony grew in size, terns took over the beaches and gun emplacements of the island's eastern half and after 1966 also began nesting on the paths at the western end of the island. The birds adapted well to the change in their habitat imposed by the structures of the fort. In fact, these structures have ensured birds nesting space for a much longer period than would be possible in their usual beach habitat, which often becomes overgrown after about twenty years. Common Terns on Great Gull Island, in addition to nesting on beaches, paths and upland sections of the island, nest on the exfoliating concrete of the fort's gun emplacements. These structures remain open islands in the thick vegetation, which inevitably toward the end of every summer, covers the meadows and parts of the beaches. In the mid 1960s many Roseate Terns nested in American Beach Grass (*Ammophila breviligulata*) which grew inside the retaining wall at the eastern end of the island. Over time these grasses were replaced by other vegetation and the area was no longer used intensively by Roseate Terns. Today a few Roseate Terns find protected nesting sites on the retaining walls of the fort. Most members of the species, however, nest under the boulders dumped, during construction of the fort, along the edge of the island to stabilize the shoreline. Habitat under many of these boulders remains mostly free of vegetation, perhaps because these areas not only lack soil and direct light, but are washed over periodically by winter storm tides.

On my first visit in 1963, I was immediately excited by the possibilities of doing research on Great Gull Island. The adaptation to, and use of the fort structures by both species suggested that as long as these structures lasted there would be open areas where birds could nest. If we could reduce the vegetation in the island's meadow sections, there would be room for more nesting terns and the numbers of both species might increase. The terns' vigorous defense of the island suggested they were not put off by human presence and it would be possible for a group of researchers to live in the remains of the fort buildings and work in the colony without putting undue stress on the birds.

In the beginning, if anyone suffered undue stress, it was probably the researchers and volunteers when they landed and viewed where they would be living and working for the next six weeks! At the center of the island, three hollow-eyed buildings stood silent and empty, their copper gutters torn off by enterprising "treasure" hunters. Rooms had been stripped of doors, windows and anything else that could be removed. The roofs of all buildings leaked, causing floor boards to rot. The bottom of an old pot-bellied stove, two coal-burning cook stoves and a few radiators were the only furnishings left in buildings which had once been offices and officers' quarters. We brought drinking water and food from the mainland, stored milk in the cooler tunnels of the fort, set up a 25-meter-square grid and, in 1969, began the study as we do it today.

Researchers

Each year field assistants help with the work in the colony, marking nests, banding chicks and trapping adults. Many are students who come from colleges in the northeastern U.S., some assistants have come from the far west (California) and some from other countries. In 2006 Dick Young, from Naperville, Illinois, marked his 25th season as field assistant on Great Gull Island. Students stay from one to six weeks. We try to have a crew of 20 to 30 working on the island during the peak hatching period, usually the last two weeks in June.

During the season students divide into two teams for the daily check of the western and eastern ends of the island to mark nests and band young Common Terns. Joseph DiCostanzo, Loretta Stillman, Richard Young and I lead teams for the daily checks and for morning and evening trapping. Grace Cormons organizes and leads a third team that checks Roseate Terns. In the past Kathy Brittingham from the Nature Conservancy sent students from Long Island to help with the check. From 2000-2002, Alexander Brash, then chief of the Urban Park Rangers, sent us volunteers from Americorps with one or two of his rangers to help for a week during the peak nesting period. Since 2000 Esteban Bremer has brought students and rangers from Argentina to help for two weeks during the peak hatch. This cooperative effort between Argentinian and U.S. teams on Great Gull Island was funded by the Sounds Conservancy Grant program administered by the Quebec-Labrador Foundation. All Bremer's volunteers had netted with him at Punta Rasa, Argentina, where they worked with Common Terns during the nonbreeding season and so were eager to see the terns in their nesting colony.

The daily checks of the island take a good part of the day, with breaks for meals. Cooking is done by the students, and there is a major clean up each week on Friday before the boat comes from Connecticut bringing supplies, field assistants and mail.

Ternwatch

In 1972 a friend of mine, Joan Black, came to Great Gull Island to perfect her photography skills, and offered us any of the pictures that we would like. Her wonderful pictures were later shown in exhibits at the American Museum of Natural History, the Cornell Laboratory of Ornithology and the Cape Cod Museum of Natural History. One of her pictures, a Roseate Tern, was used in 1973 on the cover of the last issue of, *On The Sound*, a magazine for boaters and people interested in Long Island Sound. Michael Male, then a sophomore in college, saw the issue and came to Great Gull Island as a student in 1974. Michael wanted to do a movie of the work on Great Gull Island. We had been given a grant by Mrs. George C. White and I had saved it for something that we might want to do as a special project. After some discussion Dr. Nicholson, the director of the museum, approved the film project and Michael completed the movie for his senior course in film in 1976. *Ternwatch* was a great success, giving the project good publicity. Between 1976 and 1978 fees received for showing the film were contributed to the Linnaean Society Centennial Fund. Michael Male and his wife Judy Feith formed the Blue Earth Film Company and today produce beautiful wildlife movies from their home in Virginia.

Common Tern and Roseate Tern: Numbers and Management

Between 1969 and 1984 1500-2000 pairs of Common Terns nested on Great Gull Island. Predation by Black-crowned Night-Herons (*Nycticorax nycticorax*) limited success in the colony from 1978 to 1984. In addition, thick vegetation covered many of the areas once used by nesting terns. Throughout the period we tried different methods of clearing: fire, flooding with sea water, shoveling. In 1980 David Allen of Chesterfield Associates offered us a bulldozer with a man to run it if we could use it by July 31, the day he would finish his work closing the lighthouse on Little Gull Island. The bulldozer cleared in half a day what would have taken us over two months to do by hand. Later his son Alex did a second bulldozing, but the vegetation returned quickly. In 1981, at the suggestion of Karl Koopman in the Mammalogy Department at the Museum, we reintroduced a grass-eating rodent, the Meadow Vole (*Microtus pennsylvanicus*). Robert W. Dickerman trapped 35 voles in Westchester, N.Y. and he and Karl released them on Great Gull Island. The voles underwent a population explosion. At the end of 1982 there wasn't a blade of grass visible anywhere. By spring of 1984, the voles had girdled all the bayberry at the western end of the island. When we took out this bayberry, the space available for nesting terns more than doubled and over 6,000 pairs of Common Terns nested.

Many different plants came in to fill the areas the *Microtus* had cleared, but the voles preferred grass and did not make noticeable inroads in these plants. In the early 1990s, we received a grant from the Norcross Foundation to purchase a tractor equipped with a disk harrow, rake, and brush-hog. Matthew Male, a former student on Great Gull Island, using the tractor each spring, has enlarged areas available for nesting Common Terns and by 1997 a little over 11,000 pairs nested. Matthew returns to the island each April to keep Common Tern nesting areas open.

A number of areas on the gun emplacements have not exfoliated and, if provided with suitable substrate, the terns will nest on the concrete. In 1972 Alan Poole and Roger Pasquier, students at the time, put four metal grate doors from the fort on top of the eastern end gun emplacement and covered them with dirt and gravel. Terns nested on them and still do. In 2000 we received a grant from Deutsche Bank for lumber to build rectangles to be placed on top of the gun emplacement at the center of the island and filled with dirt and gravel. These "sand boxes" increased the number of areas on the gun emplacement where Common Terns could nest successfully. During the peak nesting period there are nests in every suitable spot on the island. However there always seem to be birds ready to occupy sites if any become available. Each season, while checking the island, we weed areas next to solid concrete throwing the vegetation on the concrete and often these "weed sites" are used by nesting Common Terns.

Between 1988 and 1991 we built three sets of terraces on the sides of the eastern end gun emplacement to provide additional places for Roseate Terns to nest. The New York State Department of Environmental Conservation contributed lumber for the nest shelters we built and placed on two of the terraces and the Bernice Barbour Foundation funded a third set. Roseate Terns used these sites, but we would have to build many more to have any hope of realizing a notable increase in the nesting population.

Grace Cormons organizes the work on Roseate Terns and leads the field team. She has worked with the Roseate Tern census on Great Gull Island since the project began in 1969, when the team checking the island marked nests of both Common and Roseate Terns. Grace took a break from 1975 through 1987 to rear a family and with the increase in numbers of Common Terns during this period we could not continue marking nests of Roseate Terns. Grace returned in 1988 with her two sons and undertook the Roseate check which she continues today. She reports Roseate nest numbers decreased initially from about 1500 to 1200-1300 pairs in the late 1980's and early 1990's. Numbers increased slightly to 1400-1600 between 1993 and 1996, and then increased to about 1800 pairs between 1997-1999. Peak nest numbers estimated for 2000 were 1952 pairs. The number dropped to 1700 pairs in 2001-2003.

In 2004 and 2005 the numbers of both Common and Roseate Terns nesting decreased. Common Tern nests marked dropped to about 9500 in both years. Cormons estimated that 1466 pairs of Roseate Terns nested in 2004 and 1273 in 2005. Coincident with these decreases we found dead adults and young of both species in the colony with a hole in the back of the skull and most of the brain gone, evidently the victims of a predator. Numbers of birds found in this condition are as follows: in 2004, Common Tern adults 58, young 9, Roseate Tern adults 72, young 20; in 2005, Common Tern adults 10, young 4, Roseate Tern adults 14, no young Roseate Terns found dead with marks of predation.

In August, 2004 we found tracks in the Great Gull Island colony identified as raccoon (*Procyon lotor*) but we never saw the animal. The Department of Agriculture sent two men to Great Gull Island in 2004 and 2005 to try to trap the predator, but they were unsuccessful. The traps were set, however, during the time the terns were nesting, a period when the predator would have had plenty of food and no incentive to go into a trap. In mid-April of 2006 The Department of Agriculture sent two men to Great Gull Island to trap the predator. They were successful in removing two raccoons from the island. In 2006 we had no raccoon predation—a definite relief.

In 2004 Matthew Male reported increases in both Roseate Terns (240 pairs) and Common Terns (1,000 pairs) nesting on Cartwright Island 16 km. southwest of Great Gull Island. Adding the numbers of both species nesting on Cartwright to those nesting on Great Gull, the totals for both species nesting at the eastern end of Long Island Sound in 2004 remain about the same as in previous years. No counts of nesting birds were made on Cartwright in 2005. It is possible that some of the Common Terns as well as a number of Roseate Terns changed their nest sites from Great Gull Island to Cartwright Island during the period the raccoons were on the island.

Discoveries

Our daily checks of the island, together with observations from the blinds enable us to closely monitor the Great Gull Island colony. During the course of these annual checks we have discovered a number of previously undescribed phenomena for both species.

Abnormal Chicks and PCBs

In 1970, 35 or 1% of the young terns we found in the colony were abnormal. This was an unusually high number and included one with four legs. Analysis of these abnormal young terns showed higher levels of PCBs than of DDT or mercury. This was the first demonstration that PCBs had accumulated in a wild population and were adversely affecting it. The terns and sport fish were feeding on bait fish containing high levels of this industrial chemical. The abnormal terns served as an early warning. As humans were eating the sport fish, there was a chance that, like the terns, we could be affected by the PCBs. These discoveries led to bans on PCB use in open systems.

Common x Roseate Hybrids

In 1972 we found five Common x Roseate hybrids in the colony. In two pairs both members were hybrids and in a third pair a hybrid was backcrossed to what looked like a Common Tern. All three pairs had healthy, viable offspring. We continue to find hybrids in the colony today. Although hybrids between the two species had been mentioned in the popular literature, the paper on the Great Gull Island hybrids was the first to document their occurrence and included pictures of adults and young.

Roseate Bringing In Multiple Fish

We were used to seeing Common and Roseate Terns bringing in fish to their chicks. They would come in calling and carrying a fish which would then be taken by the chick and swallowed immediately. We were quite surprised in 1972 to see Roseate Terns bringing in multiple fish in their bills and feeding their young. Roseates do this regularly, but infrequently and can carry as many as five fish in their bills at once. If their young are not too hungry they will take one fish from the parent's bill at a time, but if the young are very hungry they may rush out, hit the parents bill with their bill and the fish scatter, usually on the rock where the parent stands. They are then picked up by the chick.

Common Terns With Multiple Nests

In 1979 and 1980 we found several nests on which a female was incubating a second clutch while a chick from the first brood stood nearby and was still being fed. In 1980 we found a 16-year-old female incubating two new eggs nine days after her first two eggs hatched. Her male fed the first two young, raising one. The female hatched the second clutch of eggs and the male raised one in that brood as well!

Multiple Roseates On One Nest

In 1991 while marking Roseate nests on a retaining wall at the eastern end of the island, I asked one of the students to check for a nest at a spot where

I'd been watching the behavior of the birds the night before. The student marked an egg at the site where there had been none the preceding evening. The following day a second egg was found in this nest. Eggs are never laid on successive days, there is always a day between eggs. We set up a watch at the nest the day we found the second egg. One male and two females attended the nest, all incubating the eggs and later feeding the young. Usually all chicks in a clutch have similar down color, but these chicks had different down colors: the first and third had dark down, while the second was blond. The females were quite lackadaisical about feeding, bringing in 13% and 11% of the fish fed the young compared to 76% brought in by the male. All three young fledged. The eggs laid on successive days and the difference in down color of the chicks suggested both females contributed to the clutch. This was the first record of multiple Roseates on a nest, in this instance a male and two females.

Common Tern and Roseate Tern Age Records

The oldest Common Terns found nesting on Great Gull Island have been 26 years old, and we have trapped a number of 25 year olds. We have worked on the island long enough now that we are beginning to be able to sample the large age classes that fledged from 1984 to the present. By trapping these birds we will learn the contribution birds 20 to 26 years old make to the colony compared with younger birds. We know Common Tern pairs may stay together for 12 years. We also know if members of a pair do not get back to the island at the same time, neither waits for the other to return before pairing. However, in the following year, if both arrive at the same time they will nest together.

On 8 February 1997, while netting in South America with Pedro Lima at Mangue Seco, Bahia, Brazil, we captured a 25.6 year old Roseate Tern. The bird had been originally banded as a chick 20 July 1971 on Bird Island, Massachusetts, USA by Ian Nisbet under William C. Drury's permit. This bird also set an age record for the species. Age records for both Common and Roseate Terns are set to be broken. It seems probable that banders in the northeastern U.S. and/or Canada will soon have records of older birds for both species.

Intercolony Exchanges

Some of the terns we trapped when we first began working on Great Gull Island were already banded. We were curious about the amount of exchange there might be between terns nesting on Great Gull Island and those nesting in nearby colonies. Between 1972 and 1976 David Duffy, working with Alan Poole and Bill Webb, all Great Gull Island students, banded whenever possible at Falkner's Island, Southold, Gardiners Island, and Hicks Island to create a database of banded birds to follow in future. During the 1970s and early 1980's a number of different cooperators worked with us in the larger colonies at Falkner's and Southold as well as some of the colonies on Long Island, staying near the colony site and visiting the colony to mark nests, trap adults, and band chicks.

Falkner's: 1970 Noble Proctor, 1971 Kirk and Harriet Bryan, 1972, 1975, 1976 David Duffy, 1977 Jamie Canfield, 1978-1980 Fred Sibley, assisted by Jeff Spendelow, 1981-2003 Jeff Spendelow. The Great Gull Island Project supported work on Falkner's Island through 1983 after which Spendelow produced funding for the project.

Southold: 1977 Matthew and Grace Cormons, 1979-1980 Matthew Male made trips to the island, 1981 Cameron Faustman and an assistant, 1982 Katie Ray and Jim Sime.

Long Island: Eaton's Neck, 1981 Mary Windels, Hick's Island 1973 Ron Frank, 1985-1986 Jill Hamilton, South Shore 1979 Jill Hamilton and David Wilcox, 1980 Anne MacFarlane and Peter Houde, 1981 Brooke Lauro and Andy Feinson.

Between 1979 and 1984 Matthew Male headed an off-island trapping program from Great Gull Island in which he took volunteers to trap in other colonies. They trapped birds from Great Gull Island and from colonies nearby in all colonies they visited. This data combined with trapping data from Great Gull Island shows some exchange not only of birds from colonies at the eastern end of Long Island Sound but of birds from colonies along the east coast from Maine to Maryland as well as an inland colony on Lake Ontario.

Roseate and Common Tern Roosting Concentrations in the Southern Hemisphere

Roseate Terns have been intensively studied in their northeastern U.S. breeding colonies both before and after they were listed by the Federal Government in 1987 as endangered. However, no one knew where the species spent the non-breeding season. I obtained funding to look for Roseate Terns along the east coast of South America and began a search of the coast in January 1995, with Grace Cormons, Peter Cormons, Joseph DiCostanzo and our driver/translator Mauricio Calvo. We were very lucky and found Roseate Terns off the coast of southern Bahia, Brazil that year. We had almost given up hope, but on our last check along the coast we headed for the Abrolhos Islands. Eleven kilometers from shore we found a small mixed flock of Roseate and Common Terns.

The following year we found a sand spit in southern Bahia where Roseate Terns roosted in small numbers. Even more exciting, I received band recoveries of seven Great Gull Island Roseate Terns from Pedro Lima, a Brazilian bander who had netted them north of Salvador at Mangue Seco in northern Bahia. Pedro had become curious about the birds roosting at Mangue Seco in 1995. That year he and his 12-year-old son walked the beach between Salvador and the northern border of Bahia, surveying the coast for oiled birds. The night they reached the border at Mangue Seco they were exhausted and lay down on the sand and went to sleep. During the night birds came in, settling near them on the sand. It was too dark to see the birds, which left in the morning before first light. The following year Pedro returned to Mangue Seco to net at night so that he could identify the birds. Included in those he netted were seven Great Gull Island Roseate Terns. When the U.S. Bird Banding Laboratory notified me of his catch, I wrote to Pedro immediately and asked him if we could net with him in 1997. He agreed, and we have been working together each year since.

Between 1995 and 1999 we found five locations where Roseate and Common Terns roost together on the coast of Bahia. Roosts with the largest concentrations of birds are near Salvador, with smaller roosting concentrations of terns along the coast in southern Bahia. We conducted our checks of the coast of Bahia mainly from boats, but drove along sections of the coast where possible.

In 1995 we checked the beaches at Punta Rasa, Argentina, where we found twenty to thirty thousand Common Terns coming in to roost at night. There were also a few Common Terns on the beaches there during the day and some of them were wearing bands from Great Gull Island. On this first visit to Punta Rasa we met Esteban Bremer from the Fundacion Vida Silvestre Argentina. He began banding there in 1993 and found one in ten Common Terns he netted at Punta Rasa was from Great Gull Island. We continue to work with Esteban, both in Argentina and on Great Gull Island, on a number of cooperative projects.

In Brazil and Argentina netting was done at night roosts. In Brazil Common and Roseate Terns were not present at the roosting sites during the day. In Argentina relatively few Common Terns were present at the roost site during the day where thousands came in at night. To determine where the terns from the large roosts went during the day we radio-tagged terns in the night roosts in Brazil from 1998 through 2003, while Esteban Bremer and his group, radio-tagged Common Terns at Punta Rasa, Argentina from 2001 through 2003. Tom Cormons, who had worked with us in South America since 1997, tracked the radio-tagged birds in Brazil and Argentina. In Brazil in 1998-2000 tracking was done from a boat. Only a few birds were followed during the pilot studies in 1998 and 1999. In 2000 Tom and Grace with Pedro, Rita and their son Tateu Lima, working from a boat, demonstrated that the birds that come in to the large roosts in northern Bahia use the roosts interchangeably.

From 2001 through 2003 in Brazil and Argentina teams worked on the ground netting birds and attaching the transmitters, while Tom Cormons, working from a plane with a pilot and an assistant, tracked radio-tagged birds, following them when they left the roosts in the early morning to where they fed offshore during the day. In Brazil he found them feeding about 50 kilometers from shore. In 2003 he followed a Common Tern off the coast of Argentina for more than 100 kilometers. At that point the pilot signaled they must return to the mainland because fuel was low. They headed back while the tern continued out to sea.

At Mangue Seco in 1996 Pedro Lima netted several Common Terns originally banded in the Azores Islands. We wondered if Roseate Terns from the Azores might also be found in the nonbreeding season on the coast of Bahia. Between 1999 and 2002, Matt Cormons, assisted in different years by Talvi Ansel, Grace Cormons and Peter Cormons worked with Veronica Neves from the Azores and her assistants, trapping nesting Roseate Terns on a number of islands in the Azores archipelago. To date the Azores team has recovered two Roseate Terns; originally banded at Mangue Seco, Bahia, on nests in the Azores. They also trapped one Roseate Tern on a nest in the Azores wearing a Darvic band, but no numbered government band. Darvic color bands had been used on Roseate Terns trapped on nests in Massachusetts, Connecticut and New York as part of a metapopulation study begun in 1988 and continuing today. No other banders used Darvic bands on Roseates in the U.S. or in Europe. This suggests the Roseate Tern, banded with the Darvic band, was originally banded on a nest in a western Atlantic colony. Between 1999 and 2002 the Brazilian/American team netted two Roseate Terns at Mangue Seco which were originally banded on nests in the Azores. The records of four of these five birds show that at least some Roseate Terns nesting in the Azores spend time during the non-breeding season on the coast of Bahia. The bird trapped on a nest in the Azores wearing only a Darvic band raises the possibility there may be gene exchange between colonies on the western Atlantic coast and the Azores.

Banded birds netted in the large roosts on the coast of Bahia provide the first evidence that Common and Roseate Terns from northeastern U.S. and European nesting colonies as well as Roseate Terns from the Caribbean and Common Terns from Bermuda spend the non-breeding season roosting together on the coast of Bahia. The recoveries on the coast of Bahia of both Common and Roseate Terns originally banded on nests in the Azores as well as Roseate Terns banded on nests in Ireland suggests a regular and previously undetected trans-Atlantic movement of both species.

From the time we first started working on the island we have had very capable and hard working crews, mainly from Connecticut, who helped us set up in the spring and pack up in the fall. Jim Sorensen and his wife let us store some of our gear each year in their barn which has been a tremendous help. As our program progressed and expanded the volunteers responded to the challenges it presented. In 1981 we reintroduced the Meadow Vole, (*Microtus pennsylvanicus*) to remove vegetation. The voles devoured the grass and girdled the bayberry. Nesting space for Common Terns on the island more than doubled and nesting pairs more than tripled. With the increase in colony size we needed more students, more housing for students and more observation blinds. Mathew Male, a student at the time, built 30 blinds mainly for observing Common Terns. Later Bob Kane with help from Kathy Dolan added 17 blinds from which students could read bands of Roseate Terns. Don Paight headed a crew to renovate a second building for students, which upon completion gave us a total of 20 rooms for field assistants. Over time the buildings needed new roofs. Bob Shailor and his son Gregg with help from Taylor Brugman and Liz Staples gave the two student buildings new roofs and Kathy Dolan headed a crew to put a roof on the headquarters building. Parker Cane, from New York renewed the grid in the mid eighties on a rainy weekend with four others. Since 1990 Melissa McClure, also from New York, has rented a truck and driven our gear to Niantic and back each year. Melissa also planted a vegetable garden on the island giving us fresh vegetables during the summer and recently adding flowers and fruit trees!

In 2006 the island presented us with one of the most challenging problems since we began working there. In mid-April I received an email from Captain Matt Poitras informing me that, while most of the dock pilings were still there, there was only one stringer left of the dock platform. He warned that there could not be a season unless the dock was repaired. Matthew Male undertook the job going to the island for three days before we planned to arrive with all the gear for the summer. Cliff Bentsen and Greg

Decker helped Matthew on his first trip and Bob Kane and Lisa Neild helped between 10:00 a.m. and 12:00 noon of the morning we were to arrive. As the boat approached the dock Matthew, walked from the shore to meet us. The dock was finished and in plenty of time!

In early September 2006 strong winds over Labor Day weekend washed away the dock planking. Nancy Stevens and I were the only ones on the island. We took down the blinds and packed during the week. Captain Matt, Captain John Wadsworth and Jon his mate came to pick us up with the scow on Friday. We had not been able to put shutters on the windows, take down the radio antenna, solar panels or bring in the generators.

During October Jim Sorensen called Captain Matt at least twice a week to see if they could go out and finish closing the island. Finally Jim called on October 31 to ask about going November 1. Captain Matt said, "Well it looks good for tomorrow, let's get it over with. We'll leave at six." Jim Sorensen, Cliff Bentsen, Dave Foltz and Bob Kane were ready the following morning. With Captain Matt at the helm they arrived at Great Gull Island a little before 7:00 a.m. Captain Bob Wadsworth took them to the island in the scow and they scattered to begin work. Unfortunately the scow's motor stopped and would not start so it could not be used to pick people up and drop them at the boat to return to the mainland. Fortunately, there was quite a lot of wood from the dock washed up on the shore. Captain Matt and Captain Bob dragged the wood with a rope to the boat. Then, sharing a hammer from the boat, they nailed the wood in place with help from the shore crew. By noon there was a plank path on the dock. Those on the island walked on it to the boat carrying gear from the island—a most successful finish, by an intrepid crew of an excellent season!

Acknowledgments

I am indebted to and thank the American Museum of Natural History for its backing of the Great Gull Island Project and for giving us office space in the Department of Ornithology. Throughout the study I have been most grateful for support contributed by members of the Linnaean Society of New York, first in answer to an annual appeal and later by participants and their backers in the Great Gull Island Birdathon.

I would like to thank the following individuals who have made generous contributions to the project; contributions which often were critical in helping us meet our expenses and/or have made it possible do a special project: Mr. Edward Barnard, Mr. Nicholas Gordon, Mr. and Mrs. Jay V. Grimm, Mr. and Mrs. Henry Guthrie, Mrs. Douglas Hays, Mr. Leo

Hollein, Dr. Ann M. Lacy, Mrs. David F. Lapham, Ms. Mary K. LeCroy, Mrs. John D. Macomber, Mrs. Hayward Manice, Ms. Pamela Manice, Dr. Alan Poole, Mr. and Mrs. Ralph Poole, Ms. Katie Ray, Ms. Mary Gordon Roberts, Mrs. Constantine Sidamon-Eristoff, Ms. Mary Ann Tilney, Mrs. George C. White.

Food and mail are two critically important things brought by the Friday boat. In 1986 meal preparation rocketed into the 20th Century with Robert G. Goelet's contribution of a propane refrigerator and later a propane freezer.

Between 1988 and 2006 generous and substantial grants from Albert H. Gordon enabled us to computerize the Great Gull Island data and begin its statistical analysis. There are over half a million records of adult Common Terns in our files and more than 200,000 nest records. We could not have completed this gigantic task without Albert H. Gordon's substantial contributions and challenging encouragement.

Grants from the Norcross Fund have provided equipment and appointments that have improved life on Great Gull Island for both students and terns: telescopes to enable students to read bands, a dinghy for off-island work, a tractor, disc harrow, rake and Brush Hog for clearing nesting areas in the spring and new roofs for two buildings. Grants from the Norcross Foundation enabled us to purchase transmitters to track the terns in the Southern Hemisphere. I am grateful to the Chairman of the Norcross Foundation, Richard Reagan, and to its Board of Directors for giving these critical pieces of equipment which facilitated behavioral work, both on and off the island.

Supported by generous contributions from the Goelet Fund, and the Gordon Fund we discovered sites along the South American coast where Roseate Terns concentrate during the non-breeding season, information previously unknown. Between 1995 and 1999 their support enabled us to check the coast of Bahia where we found five sites where non-breeding Roseate Terns roost, their support between 2000 and 2003 gave us time to track both Common and Roseate Terns to their feeding grounds off the coasts of Bahia, Brazil and Punta Rasa, Argentina. The composition of banded birds netted during the study demonstrated a previously undetected trans-Atlantic migration between Europe and the coast of Bahia. I thank Robert G. Goelet and Albert H. Gordon for taking a chance on our expeditions and continuing their support of our work in South America.

I thank Dr. Ralph Morris for lending us tracking equipment for a pilot study in 1998.

Recent surveys of Chile in 2004 and the north coast of Brazil in 2005 and 2006 were supported by the Goelet Fund.

Contributions from the following funds have supported field work on Great Gull Island during the period we have worked there. These grants have helped us meet our transportation costs, food expenses, reimbursements for field assistants and purchase of equipment, all critical elements of a successful field season. Thanks to this support we have been able to protect, monitor and manage the nesting Common and Roseate Terns on Great Gull Island. Increases in our populations bode well for their continued presence in Long Island Sound.

American Museum of Natural History
Bernice Barbour Foundation
BioDiversity Fund (American Museum of Natural History)
The Carlson Family Foundation
Deutsche Bank
The Drumcliff Foundation
The Estsate of Francis Goelet
Robert G. Goelet Fund
Albert H. Gordon Fund
John Hay Fund
Charles W. Kitchings Fund of the Quebec
Labrador Foundation (formerly of the Sounds Conservancy Fund)
Chester W. Kitchings Foundation
Members: Linnaean Society of New York
Norcross Fund
Ann S. Richardson Fund
Mae P. Smith Fund
Quebec Labrador Foundation
New York State DEC and Federal contracts have supported work on
    Roseate Terns.

Great Gull Island:
An Annotated Bibliography

Joseph DiCostanzo
Great Gull Island Project
American Museum of Natural History
Central Park West at 79th Street
New York NY 10024
jdicost@nyc.rr.com

GREAT GULL ISLAND, NEW YORK HAS BEEN A SITE OF RESEARCH and conservation efforts since the 19th century. In the 1880s, following the groundings of a couple of steamships in the area, the island was the site of research on the audibility of foghorns. However, the 1880s and 1890s were dominated by efforts to protect the tern colony on the island. In the 1890s, the Linnaean Society of New York joined with other local natural history organizations to hire a warden to protect the terns from plume hunters. The 1890s also saw the discovery of the endemic "Gull Island Mouse" (*Microtus pennsylvanicus nesophilus*). Not long after its discovery the "Gull Island Mouse" was pushed to extinction by the construction of Fort Michie on the island in the late 1890s.

For most of the first half of the 20th century the United States Army occupied the island. Some of this military history, as well as other aspects of the island's history, were traced by Michael Harwood in his 1976 book about Great Gull. The island's military history continues to be studied by members of the Coastal Defense Study Group. With the deactivation of Fort Michie after World War II, Great Gull Island again became a focus of conservation and research efforts.

The Linnaean Society and its members were deeply involved in the efforts to transfer the island from the federal government to the American Museum of Natural History. Once the Museum took control of the island Society members worked to attract nesting terns to the island. In 1955 these efforts succeeded when terns nested on the island for the first time since the 1890s.

Though the "Gull Island Mouse" has been extinct since before the turn of the 20th century, Great Gull Island's connection with mice did not end there. A legacy of the army's occupation was a feral population of the House Mouse (*Mus musculus*). These mice became the focus in the 1950s and 1960s of genetic studies by researchers from the Nevis Biological Station of Columbia University.

Since the creation of the Great Gull Island Project in 1969, research activity has focused on the nesting terns, but many other aspects of the island's natural history have also been the subjects of publications, as the following bibliography will show. The bibliography contains all the publications I have found that include data derived from work on Great Gull Island. The bibliography does not include the many bird reports from Great Gull Island that have appeared in the seasonal reports in *The Kingbird* and in *North American Birds* (and its predecessor publications), though I have included publications that cite some unusual bird records and band recoveries from the island. Student authors are indicated in the bibliography, by an asterisk (*).

Bibliography

1889

Dutcher, B. H. Bird notes from Little Gull Island, Suffolk Co., N.Y. *Auk* 6(2):124-131. [Reports birds seen at Great Gull and Little Gull islands in August 1888.]

1890

Dutcher, W. Birds of Gull Island, N. Y. *Forest and Stream* 34:246-247. [Reports on a July 1889 trip to Great Gull and Little Gull islands by Chapman and Dutcher. The report was presented at a Linnaean Society meeting on 21 March 1890. This is Part 1, in the 17 April 1890 issue. Chapman also wrote of this visit in his Handbook published in 1895. (below.)]

Dutcher, W. Birds of Gull Island, N. Y. *Forest and Stream* 34:267-268. [Part 2 of above, in the 24 April 1890 issue.]

1894

Johnson, A. B. The cruise of the Clover—further remarks on the aberrations of audibility of fog signals—the methods used. *Science* 23(570):3-6. [Reports on experiments done on Great Gull Island on the audibility of foghorns,]

White, C. A. The relation of the sounds of fog signals to other sounds. *Science* 23(574):59-62. [Reports on observations on Great Gull Island of the confusing echoes of the Little Gull foghorn produced off the sails of nearby ships.]

1895

Chapman, F. M. *Handbook of Birds of Eastern North America, 6th ed.* Appleton, New York. [Much of the Common Tern account concerns Chapman's visit to Great Gull Island in 1889, his first experience of a Common Tern colony.]

1896

Dutcher, W. Report of the Committee on Protection of North American Birds. *Auk* 13(1):98. [Reports on the protection of the Common Tern colony on Great Gull Island in 1895; estimate 3500 terns on island.]

1897

Dutcher, W. Report of the A. O. U. committee on protection of North American birds. *Auk* 14(1):21-32. [Reports on the protection of the Great Gull colony by a warden partially paid for by the Linnaean Society of New York.]

1898

Bailey, V. Description of eleven new species and subspecies of voles. *Proc. Biological Soc. Washington* 12:85-90. [Describes the Gull Island Mouse as a new species of vole, *Microtus insularis*; later authorities consider it a subspecies of the widespread Meadow Vole *Microtus pennsylvanicus.*]

Bailey, V. A new name for *Microtus insularis* Bailey. *Science* 8(285):783-784. [Because the scientific name *Microtus insularis* was previously used for another species, the Gull Island Mouse was renamed *Microtus nesophilus.*]

Dutcher, W. Report of the A. O. U. committee on protection of North American birds. *Auk* 15(1):81-114. [Reports the abandonment of the Great Gull Island colony by Common Terns because of the construction of Fort Michie.]

Reed, J. H. The terns of Great Gull Island, N. Y., during 1897. *Auk* 15(1):40-43. [Reports on the beginning of the construction of Fort Michie and the depredation on the terns of the island by the construction workers and others. Excerpts from this paper appeared in "100 Years Ago in *The Auk*" in 1998.]

1900

Dutcher, W. Notes and news: report of the Committee on Protection of North American Birds. *Auk* 17(2):198-200. [Reports the Great Gull Island colony of Common Terns has moved to Gardiner's Island.]

1901

Dutcher, W. Results of special protection to gulls and terns obtained through the Thayer Fund. *Auk* 18(1):76-104. [Reports a few Common Terns attempted to nest on Great Gull Island but were driven off by the harassment of the soldiers at the fort.]

1902

Helme, A. H. Notes on mammals of Long Island, New York. *Proc. Linnaean Soc. New York* Nos. 13-14:19-30. [Reports the Gull Island Mouse is apparently extinct. The native Gull Island Mouse was later replaced on the island by a feral population of the House Mouse *Mus musculus*, undoubtedly a legacy of the Army's residence on the island.]

1948

Unsigned. U. S. puts islands up for sale. *Linnaean News-Letter* 2(5). [Announces the Federal government has put Great Gull Island up for sale after the deactivation of Fort Michie.]

1949

Arbib, R. S., Jr. Museum Acquires Great Gull Island. *Natural History* 58(6):242.
Unsigned. Gull Island Fund – a rare plea. *Linnaean News-Letter* 3(4).
Unsigned. Gull Island Fund. *Linnaean News-Letter* 3(5).
Unsigned. Museum of Natural History acquires Great Gull Island. *Linnaean News-Letter* 3(2).
Unsigned. Progress of Great Gull Island. *Linnaean News-Letter* 3(3). [Announces the formation of the Great Gull Island Committee.]

1950

McKeever, C. K. Gull Island. *Linnaean News-Letter* 4(3).
Unsigned. Progress report on Gull Island. *Linnaean News-Letter* 4(5).

1951

Hussey, L. J., and C. M. Pessino. An island venture. *Natural History* 60(4):182-189.

McKeever, C. K. Further report on Great Gull Island. *Linnaean News-Letter* 5(1).

Unsigned. Linnaean field trip to Great Gull Island. *Linnaean News-Letter* 5(4).

1952

McKeever, C. K. Gull Island clearing under way. *Linnaean News-Letter* 5(9).

1955

Alperin, I. M. Common Terns re-establish colony on Great Gull Island. *Linnaean News-Letter* 9(5).

1960

Dunn, L. C., A. B. Beasley, and H. Tinker. Polymorphisms in populations of wild house mice. *Journal Mammalogy* 41(2):220-229. [This and subsequent papers on the House Mouse were based on work done by researchers from the Nevis Biological Station of Columbia University on the feral House Mouse population then on Great Gull Island.]

1961

Hussey, L. Report on trip to Great Gull Island: July 31, 1961. *Linnaean News-Letter* 15(5).

1964

Anderson, P. K., L. C. Dunn, and A. B. Beasley. Introduction of a lethal allele into a feral house mouse population. *American Naturalist* 98(898):57-64.

1965

Pessino, C. Great Gull Island, 1964. *Linnaean News-Letter* 18(9).

1967

Bennett, D., R. Bruck, L. C. Dunn, B. Klyde, F. Shutsky, and L. J. Smith. Persistence of an introduced lethal in a feral House Mouse population. *American Naturalist* 101(922):538-539.

Schaeffer, F. The Barn Swallows of Great Gull Island. *Eastern Bird-Banding Association News* 30(5):221-223.

Schaeffer, F. Some Gull Island field work. *Linnaean News-Letter* 21(1).

1968

Donaldson, G. Bill color changes in adult Roseate Terns. *Auk* 85(4):662-668.

Pessino, C. Red-winged Blackbird destroys eggs of Common and Roseate Terns. *Auk* 85(3):513.

1969

Donaldson, G., and H. Hays. Roseate Tern in unusual plumage. *Bird-Banding* 40(3):255.

Hays, H. Differential survival among nestling Red-winged Blackbirds after a storm. *Auk* 86(3):563-564.

1970

Collins, C. T. The Black-crowned Night Heron as a predator of tern chicks. *Auk* 87(3):584-586.

Cooper, D., H. Hays, and C. Pessino. Breeding of the Common and Roseate Terns on Great Gull Island. *Proc. Linnaean Soc.* New York 71:83-104.

Duffy, D. C.* Observations on Great Gull Island—summer 1969. *Kingbird* 20(4):169-170.

Hays, H. Common Terns pirating fish on Great Gull Island. *Wilson Bulletin* 82(1):99-100.

Hays, H. Great Gull Island report on nesting species, 1967-1968. *Proc. Linnaean Soc.* New York 71:105-119.

Hays, H., and G. Donaldson. Sand-kicking camouflages young Black Skimmers. *Wilson Bulletin* 82(1):100.

Heilbrun, L. H. Great Gull Island, its history and biology. *Proc. Linnaean Soc.* New York 71:55-79. [L. H. Heilbrun was formerly L. Hussey.]

Pessino, C. Great Gull Island visits:1962-1966. *Proc. Linnaean Soc.* New York 71:80-82.

Pessino, C. An island for the birds. *Nature and Science* 7(16):4-6.

Jenner, J. In Camille's wake a Wide-a-wake. *Kingbird* 20(1):13.

1971

Duffy, D. C.* Report on Great Gull Island: summer, 1970. *Kingbird* 21(2):60-61.

Donaldson, G. Roseate Tern breeds during its second year. *Bird-Banding* 42(4):300.

Harlow, R. A., Jr. Roseate Tern breeds during its third year. *Bird-Banding* 42(1):50.

Hays, H. Roseate Tern, *Sterna dougallii*, banded on Atlantic coast recovered on Pacific. *Bird-Banding* 42(4):295.

Hays, H., and M. LeCroy. Field criteria for determining incubation stages in eggs of the Common Tern. *Wilson Bulletin* 83(4):425-429.

Hays, H., and R. W. Risebrough. The early warning of the terns. *Natural History* 80(9):38-47. [Reports on developmental abnormalities in the terns on Great Gull Island apparently caused by concentrations of pollutants, particularly PCBs. This article and Hays and Risebrough (1972) were the first reports of problems caused by PCBs in a wild population.]

Parkes, K. C., A. Poole, and H. Lapham. The Ruddy Turnstone as an egg predator. *Wilson Bulletin* 83(3):306-308.

1972

Collins, C. T., and M. LeCroy. Analysis of measurements, weights, and composition of Common and Roseate Tern eggs. *Wilson Bulletin* 84(2):187-192.

Duffy, D. C.* Records from Great Gull Island, 1972. *Kingbird* 22(4):163-164.

Hays, H. Polyandry in the Spotted Sandpiper. *Living Bird* 11:43-57. [The first report of polyandry in the Spotted Sandpiper (*Actitis macularius*).]

Hays, H., and R. W. Risebrough. Pollutant concentrations in abnormal young terns from Long Island Sound. *Auk* 89(1):19-35.

LeCroy, L.* Monarch Banding on Great Gull Island. *Linnaean News-Letter* 26(4). [Reports on a summer season of marking Monarch (*Danaus plexippus*) butterflies and their recovery in Connecticut, New Jersey, and New York.]

LeCroy, M. Young Common and Roseate Terns learning to fish. *Wilson Bulletin* 84(2):201-202.

LeCroy, M., and C. T. Collins. Growth and survival of Roseate and Common Tern chicks. *Auk* 89(3):595-611.

Pasquier, R. F., and A. Poole. Visitants to Great Gull Island during the summer of 1971. *Kingbird* 22(2):75-76.

1973

Duffin, K.* Barn Swallows use freshwater and marine algae in nest construction. *Wilson Bulletin* 85(2):237-238.

Duffy, D. C.*, and C. LaFarge. *The Birds of Great Gull Island*. The Linnaean Society of New York, 44 pp.

Duffy, D. C.*, and A. Poole. The status of the Least Tern on eastern Long Island in 1972. *Linnaean News-Letter* 27(1).

Hays, H., and G. D. Cormons. Plastic particles found in tern pellets, on coastal beaches and at factory sites. *Linnaean News-Letter* 27(5). [This article was reprinted in 1974 in the *Marine Pollution Bulletin*; G. D. Cormons was formerly G. Donaldson.]

Hays, H., E. Dunn, and A. Poole. Common, Arctic, Roseate and Sandwich Terns carrying multiple fish. *Wilson Bulletin* 85(2):233-234.

Josephson, B. Counting your terns before they hatch. *On The Sound* 3(5):28-31. [An account of a weekend spent on Great Gull Island assisting with the tern research.]

Pasquier, R. F. Parasitic Jaegers seen from Great Gull Island, N.Y. *Kingbird* 23(2):75-78.

1974

Allen, T. B. Warning to an endangered species. In *Vanishing Wildlife of North America*. Pp 177-202. National Geographic Society, Washington, DC. [Chapter highlights the tern research on Great Gull Island.]

Hays, H., and G. D. Cormons. Plastic particles found in tern pellets, on coastal beaches and at factory sites. *Marine Pollution Bulletin* 5:44-46 [Reprinted from 1973 *Linnaean News-Letter* article above.]

LeCroy, M., and S. LeCroy*. Growth and fledging in the Common Tern (*Sterna hirundo*). *Bird-Banding* 45(4):326-340.

Van't Hof, T.* Spring migration on Great Gull Island, 1974. *Kingbird* 24(4):170-172.

1975

Connors, P. G., V. C. Anderlini, R. W. Risebrough, M. Gilbertson, and H. Hays. Investigations of heavy metals in Common Tern populations. *Canadian Field-Naturalist* 89:157-162.

Hays, H. Probable Common X Roseate Tern hybrids. *Auk* 92(2):219-234.

1976

Cormons, G. D. Roseate Tern bill color change in relation to nesting status and food supply. *Wilson Bulletin* 88(3):377-389.

Harwood, M. *The View From Great Gull*. E. P. Dutton & Co., Inc., New

York. [Book about Great Gull Island, its history, and the tern research on the island.]

Male, M. *Ternwatch.* [A thirty-five minute film by Michael Male about the tern research on Great Gull Island.]

1977

Duffy, D. C.* Breeding populations of terns and skimmers on Long Island Sound and eastern Long Island: 1972-1975. *Proc. Linnaean Soc. New York* 73:1-48.

Duffy, D. C.* Incidence of oil contamination on breeding Common Terns, *Bird-Banding* 48(4):370-371.

Grimm, C. T.* Hoary Bat in Niantic, Connecticut, in January. *Proc. Linnaean Soc. New York* 73:85-86.

Houde, P.* Gull-tern interactions on Hicks Island, 1975. *Proc. Linnaean Soc. New York* 73:58-64.

Houde, P.* Low productivity of terns on Hicks Island, 1975. *Proc. Linnaean Soc. New York* 73:49-57.

MacFarlane, A. E.* Roof-nesting by Common Terns. *Wilson Bulletin* 89(3):475-476.

Pasquier, R. F. Herring Gull eating bayberry. *Wilson Bulletin* 89(2):338.

1978

DiCostanzo, J. Great Gull Island: migrants banded in 1977. *Linnaean News-Letter* 31(8).

DiCostanzo, J. Great Gull Island: migrants banded in 1978. *Linnaean News-Letter* 32(6).

DiCostanzo, J. Occurrences of the Common Tern in the interior of South America. *Bird-Banding* 49(3):248-251.

DiCostanzo, J., R. E. Harrison, and J. O. Biderman. Photographs of New York State rarities. 28. Townsend's Warbler. *Kingbird* 28(3):150-151. [A male Townsend's Warbler (*Dendroica townsendi*) netted and photographed on Great Gull Island was the first confirmed record of the species for New York State.]

Hays, H. Timing and breeding success in three-to seven-year-old Common Terns, *Ibis* 120(1):127-128.

Talbot, C. J. *The Great Rat Island Adventure.* Atheneum, New York. [Book for young adults set on a fictionalized version of Great Gull Island.]

1979

Ricklefs, R. E. Patterns of growth in birds. V. A comparative study of development in the Starling, Common Tern, and Japanese Quail. *Auk* 96(1):10-30.

1980

Coulter, M. Stones: an important incubation stimulus for gulls and terns. *Auk* 97(4):898-899.

DeBenedictis, P., K. P. Able, R. F. Andrle, T. H. Davis, Jr., and R. O. Paxton. Report of the New York State Avian Records Committee. *Kingbird* 30(4):201-205. [Includes report of a Magnificent Frigatebird (*Fregata magnificens*) from Great Gull Island.]

DiCostanzo, J. Population dynamics of a Common Tern Colony. *Journal Field Ornithology* 51(3):229-243.

Harwood, M. Great Gull Island. *Smithsonian* 11(5):28-37.

Hays, H. Great Gull Island—past and present. *Linnaean News-Letter* 34(2).

Hays, H. The liberated spotted. *Anima* 5(86):26-30. [Published in Japanese translation.]

1981

Coulter, M. The flora of Great Gull Island, Long Island, New York. *Bulletin Torrey Botanical Club* 108(2):272-277.

Coulter, M. A source of variation in avian growth studies: undigested food. *Journal Field Ornithology* 52(1):62.

Hamilton, J. Recoveries of wintering Roseate Terns. *Journal Field Ornithology* 52(1):36-42.

Ricklefs, R. E., and S. C. White. Growth and energetics of chicks of the Sooty Tern (*Sterna fuscata*) and Common Tern (*S. hirundo*). *Auk* 98(2):361-378

Windels, M.* Observations on a Snowy Owl at Great Gull Island. *Kingbird* 31(2):65-66.

1982

Coulter, M. Development of runt Common Tern chick. *Journal Field Ornithology* 53(3):276-278.

1983

Custer, T. W., I. C. T. Nisbet, and A. J. Krynitsky. Organochlorine residues and shell characteristics of Roseate Tern eggs, 1981. *Journal Field Ornithology* 54(4):394-400. [Includes data on eggs collected on Great Gull Island.]

Hatch, J. J., and I. C. T. Nisbet. Band wear and band loss in Common Terns. *Journal Field Ornithology* 54(1):1-16. [Bands from Great Gull Island Common Terns form a significant part of the study.]

Nisbet, I. C. T., and J. J. Hatch. Band wear and band loss in Roseate Terns. *Journal Field Ornithology* 54(1):90. [Bands from Great Gull Island Roseate Terns form a significant part of the study.]

1984

Hays, H. Common Terns raise young from successive broods. *Auk* 101(2):274-280.

Hays, H. The vole that soared. *Natural History* 93(5):7-16. [Reports on the reintroduction of Meadow Voles to Great Gull Island. The feral House Mouse population on the island since the army's occupation was apparently not able to compete with the voles and disappeared a few years after the voles' reintroduction.]

Nisbet, I. C. T. Migration and winter quarters of North American Roseate Terns as shown by banding recoveries. *Journal Field Ornithology* 55(1):1-17. [Recoveries of birds banded on Great Gull Island form a significant part of the study; these recoveries had previously been analyzed in Hamilton (1981) above.]

1985

Hays, H. 1985 Great Gull Island Report. *Linnaean News-Letter* 39(6).

Parkes, K. C. Several "adult" Common Terns attempt to feed juveniles. *British Birds* 78:147-148.

Parkes, K. C. Yellow-rumped warbler in flight feather molt on Great Gull Island. *Kingbird* 35(2):114-115.

1986

Coulter, M. Assortative mating and sexual dimorphism in the Common Tern. *Wilson Bulletin* 98(1):93-100.

Dancis, D. The terns return. *Urban Audubon* August - September.

Duffy, D. C. Foraging at patches: interactions between Common and Roseate Terns. *Ornis Scand.* 17:47-52.

1987

Hays, H. Great Gull Island Project report for 1986. *Linnaean News-Letter* 40(7).

1988

Duffy, D. C. Predator-prey interactions between Common Terns and Butterfish. *Ornis Scand.* 19:160-162.

Hays, H. Great Gull Island annual report: 1987. *Linnaean News-Letter* 41(8).

Parkes, K. C. A brown-eyed adult Red-eyed Vireo specimen. *Journal Field Ornithology* 59(1):60-62.

1989

Hays, H. Great Gull Island report-1988 (part 1). *Linnaean News-Letter* 42(8,9).

Hays, H. Great Gull Island report-1988 (part 2). *Linnaean News-Letter* 43(1).

1990

Hays, H. Great Gull Island report: 1989. *Linnaean News-Letter* 44(2).

1991

Hays, H. Great Gull Island Project report-1990. *Linnaean News-Letter* 44(9).

Hays, H. Great Gull Island Project report-1991. *Linnaean News-Letter* 45(7).

1992

DiCostanzo, J. Hurricane Bob on Great Gull Island. *Linnaean News-Letter* 46(7).

Ellison, Walter G. Blue-gray Gnatcatcher. In *The Birds of North America,* No. 23 (A. Poole, P. Stettenheim, and F. Gill, Eds.). The Academy of Natural Sciences, Philadelphia; The American Ornithologists' Union, Washington, DC. [Includes a previously unpublished report of a Blue-gray Gnatcatcher (*Polioptila caerulea*) banded on Great Gull Island and recovered in western Mexico nine months later.]

Hays, H. Great Gull Island report: 1992. *Linnaean News-Letter* 46(5).

Morris, A. One good tern: Helen Hays and the Great Gull Island Project. *Birder's World* 6(3):22-26.

1993

Cane, W. P. The ontogeny of post-cranial integration in the Common Tern, *Sterna hirundo. Evolution* 47(4):1138-1151.

Dancis, D. My 1992 Great Gull Island birdathon. *Linnaean News-Letter* 47(2).

Hays, H. Roseate Tern trio fledges three young. *Auk* 110(3)653-658. [First published report of multiple female Roseate Terns nesting with a single male.]

Hays, H. Great Gull Island report: 1993. *Linnaean News-Letter* 47(7).

Hays, H., and K. C. Parkes. Erythrystic eggs in the Common Tern. *Journal Field Ornithology* 64(3):341-345.

Parkes, K. C. Erythrystic Northern Orioles. *Kingbird* 43(1):13-17.

1994

Burg, N.* A Great Gull Island weekend. *Linnaean News-Letter* 47(9).

Cane, W. P. Ontogenetic evidence for relationships within the Laridae. *Auk* 111(4):873-880

Shealer, D. A., and S. W. Kress. Post-breeding movements and prey selection of Roseate Terns at Stratton Island, Maine. *Journal Field Ornithology* 65(3):349-362. [Includes reports of color-banded Roseate Terns from Great Gull Island.]

Spendelow, J. A., J. Burger, I. C. T. Nisbet, J. D. Nichols, J. E. Hines, H. Hays, G. D. Cormons, and M. Gochfeld. Sources of variation in loss rates of color bands applied to adult Roseate Terns (*Sterna dougallii*) in the western North Atlantic. *Auk* 111(4):881-887.

1995

Able, K. P., R. F. Andrle, T. J. Burke, R. O. Paxton, and B. J. Spencer. Report of the New York State Avian Records Committee 1993. *Kingbird* 45(2):71-78. [Includes report of a Mississippi Kite (*Ictinia mississippiensis*) from Great Gull Island.]

Hays, H. Great Gull Island report: 1994. *Linnaean News-Letter* 48(8).

Spendelow, J. A., J. D. Nichols, I. C. T. Nisbet, H. Hays, G. D. Cormons, J. Burger, C. Safina, J. E. Hines, and M. Gochfeld. Estimating annual survival and movement rates within a metapopulation of Roseate Terns. *Ecology* 76(8):2415-2428.

1996

Blokpoel, H., J. Neuman, and G. D. Tessier. Winter sightings of Common Terns banded in eastern North America. *North American Bird Bander* 21(1):1-3. [Reports sightings of color-banded Common Terns from Great Gull Island in Peru.]

Kornhauser, E. Great Gull Island. *Linnaean News-Letter* 50(7).

1997

Hays, H., J. DiCostanzo, G. Cormons, P. de Tarso Zuquim Antas, J. L. Xavier do Nascimento, I. de Lima Serrano do Nascimento, and R. E. Bremer. Recoveries of Common and Roseate Terns in South America. *Journal Field Ornithology* 68(1):79-90. [First paper resulting from the Great Gull Island Project's South American tern surveys. Includes report of a large wintering concentration of terns in Argentina.]

1998

Hays, H. Common Tern. In *Bull's Birds of New York State* edited by E. Levine. Pp. 299-302. Cornell University Press, Ithaca.

Hays, H. Roseate Tern. In *Bull's Birds of New York State* edited by E. Levine. Pp. 297-299. Cornell University Press, Ithaca.

Reed, J. H. From "The terns of Great Gull Island, N.Y., during 1897". *Auk* 115(1):276-277. [An extensive reprint of Reed's 1898 note presented as "100 years ago in The *Auk*".]

1999

DiCostanzo, J. The butterflies of Great Gull Island: a preliminary checklist. *Linnaean News-Letter* 53(2).

DiCostanzo, J., and H. Hays. First record of Swainson's Hawk for Long Island. *Kingbird* 49(4):309-312.

Hays, H., P. Lima, L. Monteiro, J. DiCostanzo, G. Cormons, I. C. T. Nisbet, J. E. Saliva, J. A. Spendelow, J. Burger, J. Pierce, and M. Gochfeld. A nonbreeding concentration of Roseate and Common Terns in Bahia, Brazil. *Journal Field Ornithology* 70(4):455-464. [Includes report of the first indication of a regular transatlantic migration of Common Terns from the Azores to Brazil.]

2000

Hays, H., S. Newton, P. Lima, and O. Crowe. Rockabill Roseate Tern recaptured in Brazil. *Irish Birds* 6(4):585-586. [Reports the recovery in Brazil of a Roseate Tern banded in the largest Roseate Tern colony in Europe, on Rockabill Island, Ireland.]

Smith, B. Buried Mistakes. *Coast Defense Journal* 14(3):90-92. [Reports on some of the antiaircraft gun mounts at Fort Michie.]

2001

Richardson, J. T. E. A physician with the Coast Artillery Corps: the military career of Dr. Howard Andrew Knox, pioneer of psychological testing. *Coast Defense Journal* 15(4):88-93. [Traces the career of one of Fort Michie's` military doctors.]

2002

Cooper, H. S. F., Jr. Tern, Tern, Tern. *Natural History* 111(8):12-15

Hays, H., V. Neves, and P. Lima. Banded Roseate Terns from different continents trapped in the Azores. *Journal Field Ornithology* 73(2):180-184. [First report of a possible regular transatlantic migration of Roseate Terns from the Azores to Brazil.]

Hays, H., S. F. Newton, and G. Cormons. Rockabill Roseate Terns *Sterna dougallii* sighted in west Atlantic colony. *Irish Birds* 7(1):133-134. [Reports sighting on Great Gull Island of a Roseate Tern banded in Ireland.]

Neves, V. C., R. E. Bremer, and H. Hays. Recovery in Punta Rasa, Argentina of Common Terns banded in the Azores Archipelago, North Atlantic. *Waterbirds* 25(4):459-461.

2003

Hays, H. Great Gull Island: a short report. *Linnaean News-Letter* Oct/Nov 2003

Prostak, J. Fort Michie beyond the batteries: the non-tactical structures. *Coast Defense Journal* 17(1):26-48.

2004

Hollein, L. Banding terns at Great Gull Island. *New Jersey Audubon* 30(2):18-21.

Sime, S. Camera shy. *Birder's World* 18(3):90. [Presents what is possibly the first photograph taken in the wild of a Dot-winged Crake (*Porzana spiloptera*). The picture was taken at Punta Rasa, Argentina during Great Gull Island Project fieldwork.]

Lima, P. C., H. Hays, R. Lima, T. Cormons, G. Cormons, J. DiCostanzo, and S. Sampaio dos Santos. Recuperações de *Sterna dougallii* (Montagu, 1813) na Bahia, Brasil, entre 1995 e 2004. *Ararajuba* 12(2):51-53. [Reports recoveries of banded Roseate Terns from North America, the Azores, and Ireland in Bahia, Brazil.]

2005

Bugoni, L., T. D. Cormons, A. Boyne, and H. Hays. Feeding grounds, daily foraging activities, and movements of Common Terns in southern Brazil determined by radio-telemetry. *Waterbirds* 28(4):468-477.

Clark, J. S., G. Ferraz, N. Oguge, H. Hays, and J. DiCostanzo. Hierarchical bayes for structured and variable populations: from capture-recapture data to life-history prediction. *Ecology* 86(8):2232-2244.

Hays. H. Catherine Pessino, 1925-2005. FOGGI: *Friends of Great Gull Island* 1(1).

Lima, P. C., H. Hays, R. Lima, T. Cormons, G. Cormons, J. DiCostanzo, and S. Sampaio dos Santos. Recuperações de *Sterna hirundo* (Linnaeus, 1758) na Bahia, Brasil, entre 1995 e 2004. *Revista Brasileira de Ornitologia* 13(2):41-43. [Reports recoveries of banded Common Terns from North America in Bahia, Brazil.]

2006

Girão, W. *Projeto Gaivotas aliança com o Ceará.* Aquasis, Caucaia, Brazil. [A picture booklet in Portuguese aimed at promoting knowledge and conservation of terns on the coast of the Brazilian state of Ceará. A joint project of Aquasis, the Great Gull Island Project and the Quebec Labrador Foundation.]

Girão, W., J. DiCostanzo, A. Campos, and C. Albano. First record of Bar-tailed Godwit *Limosa lapponica* (Linnaeus, 1758) for the Brazilian mainland. *Revista Brasileira de Ornitologia* 14(4):468-469.

Hays, H., J. Hudon, G. Cormons, J. DiCostanzo, and P. Lima. The Pink Feather Blush of the Roseate Tern. *Waterbirds* 29(3):296-301.

Leahy, M. K. and A. E. Camp. Making way for terns: restoration at Great Gull Island. *Ecological Restoration* 24(1):36-40.

2007

Barnard, E. S. All About Animals: Birds. Reader's Digest, Pleasantville. [A book for young people in the "Reader's Digest Young Families" series. The first chapter is about the tern colony on Great Gull Island. Note: the copyright page says 2006, but the book was printed and published in April 2007.]

DiCostanzo, J. Mississippi Kite on Great Gull I. Linnaean News-Letter 60(9):4.

DiCostanzo, J. Great Gull Island: an annotated bibliography. *Transactions Linnaean Society New York* 10.

Hays, H. Great Gull Island: 1963-2006. *Transactions Linnaean Society New York* 10.

Publications of the
Linnaean Society of New York

Transactions

Volume I, 1882, Royal Octavo, 168 pp. Frontispiece—Portrait of Linnaeus.
  The Vertebrates of the Adirondack Region, Northeastern New York.
  First Installment.
      C. Hart Merriam.
  Is Not the Fish Crow (*Corvus ossifragus* Wilson) a Winter as Well as
  a Summer Resident of the Northern Limit of Its Range?
      William Dutcher.
  A Review of the Summer Birds of a Part of the Catskill Mountains,
  with Prefatory Remarks on the Faunal and Floral Features of the
  Region.
      Eugene P. Bicknell.

Volume II, 1884, Royal Octavo, 233 pp. Frontispiece—Plate of Bendire's
Shrew.
  The Vertebrates of the Adirondack Region, Northeastern New York.
  Second Installment, concluding the Mammalia.
      C. Hart Merriam.
  A New Genus and Species of the Soricidae (*Atophyrax bendirii*
  Merriam).
      C. Hart Merriam.

Volume III, 1933, Royal Octavo, 184 pp., 3 plates.
> The Birds of Dutchess County, New York. From records compiled by
> Maunsel S. Crosby.
> Ludlow Griscom.

Volume IV, 1937, 247 pp., 3 plates, 33 tables, 18 charts, 14 maps.
> Studies in the Life History of the Song Sparrow, I. A Population Study
> of the Song Sparrow.
> Margaret M. Nice.

Volume V, 1939, 94 pp., 2 plates, 20 text figures.
> The Behavior of the Snow Bunting in Spring.
> Nikko Tinbergen.

Volume VI, 1943, 328 pp., 6 text figures, 26 tables.
> Studies in the Life History of the Song Sparrow, II. The Behavior of
> the Song Sparrow and Other Passerines.
> Margaret M. Nice.

Volume VII, 1955, 128 pp.
> The Species of Middle American Birds.
> Eugene Eisenmann.

Volume VIII, 1962, 212 pp.
> Development of Behavior in Precocial Birds.
> Margaret M. Nice.

Volume IX, 1980, 158 pp.
> The Habitats, Distribution, and Numbers of Northern Seabirds.
> W. R. P. Bourne.
> The Pelagic Ecology of Seabirds.
> R. G. B. Brown.
> Population and Colony-Site Trends of Long Island Waterbirds for five
> years in the Mid 1970s.
> Paul A. Buckley and Francine G. Buckley.
> Coastal Surveys—Northeast and Northwest.
> William H. Drury.
> Censussing Waterbird Colonies: Some Sampling Experiments.
> R. Michael Erwin.

The Effects of Timing of Breeding, Dispersion of Nests, and Habitat Selection on Nesting Success of Colonial Waterbirds.
    Donald A. McCrimmon, Jr.
Effects of Toxic Pollutants on Productivity in Colonial Waterbirds.
    Ian C.T. Nisbet.
The Influence of Annual Variation in Rainfall and Water Levels on Nesting by Florida Populations of Wading Birds.
    John C. Ogden, Herbert W. Kale, II, and Stephen A. Nesbitt.
Census Methods for Gulf Coast Waterbirds.
    John W. Portnoy.
Why Are There Different Kinds of Herons?
    Harry F. Recher and Judy A. Recher.

Proceedings

Number 1, for the year ending March 1, 1889, 9 pp.
    An Account of the Former Abundance of Some Species of Birds on New York Island at the Time of Their Migration to the South.
    George N. Lawrence.

Number 2, for the year ending March 7, 1890, 10 pp.
    Notes on the Carolina Paroquet in Florida.
    Frank M. Chapman.

Number 3, for the year ending March 6, 1891, 11 pp.

Number 4, for the year ending March 2, 1892, 8 pp.

Number 5, for the year ending March 1, 1893, 41 pp.
    Milicete Indian Natural History: A List of Bird Names, Together with a Supplementary List of Names of Other Animals.
    Tappan Adney.

Number 6, for the year ending March 27, 1894, 103 pp.
    Recent Progress In the Study of North American Mammals.
    J. A. Allen.
    A Consideration of Some Ornithological Literature with Extracts from Current Criticism: 1876-1883.
    L. S. Foster.

Number 7, for the year ending March 26, 1895, 41 pp.
    Notes on Cuban Mammals.
        Juan Gundlach.
    Salamanders Found in the Vicinity of New York City, with Notes
    upon Extra-Limital or Allied Species.
        William L. Sherwood.

Number 8, for the year ending March 24, 1896, 27 pp.
    The Snakes Found within Fifty Miles of New York City.
        Raymond L. Ditmars.

Number 9, for the year ending March 9, 1897, 56 pp.
    The Fishes of the Fresh and Brackish Waters in the Vicinity of New
    York City.
        Eugene Smith.

Number 10, for the year ending March 8, 1898, 27 pp.
    The Frogs and Toads Found in the Vicinity of New York City.
        William L. Sherwood.

Number 11, for the year ending March 14, 1899, 32 pp.
    The Turtles and Lizards in the Vicinity of New York City.
        Eugene Smith.

Number 12, for the year ending March 13, 1900, 9 pp.

Numbers 13-14, for the two years ending March 11, 1902, 70 pp.
    Notes on the Mammals of Long Island, N. Y.
        Arthur H. Helme.
    The Mammals of Westchester County, N. Y.
        John Rowley.
    Some Food Birds of the Eskimos of Northwestern Greenland.
        J. D. Figgins.

Numbers 15-16, for the two years ending March 9, 1904, 70 pp. Date of
issue: Dec. 19, 1904.
    Field Notes on the Birds and Mammals of the Cook's Inlet Region of
    Alaska.
        J. D. Figgins.

Some Notes on the Psychology of Birds.
    C. William Beebe.
The Eggs and Breeding Habits of Some Comparatively Little Known
North American Birds.
    Louis B. Bishop.

Numbers 17-19, for the three years ending March 12, 1907, 136 pp. Date
of issue: Oct. 22, 1907.
    A List of the Birds of Long Island, N. Y.
    William C. Braislin.

Numbers 20-23, for the four years ending March 14, 1911, 122 pp. Date
of issue: Feb. 8, 1913.
    Bird's Nesting in the Magdalen Islands.
    P. B. Philipp.
    The Bird-Colonies of Pamlico Sound.
    P. B. Philipp.
    A List of the Fishes Known to Have Occurred within Fifty Miles of
    New York City.
    John T. Nichols.

Numbers 24-25, for the two years ending March 11, 1913, 156 pp. Date
of issue: April 15, 1914.
    The Red-Winged Blackbird; A Study in the Ecology of a Cat-tail Marsh.
    Arthur A. Allen.
    An Interesting Ornithological Winter around New York City.
    Ludlow Griscom.

Numbers 26-27, for the two years ending March 9, 1915, 49 pp. Date of
issue: Nov. 23, 1915.

Numbers 28-29, for the two years ending March 13, 1917, 114 pp. Date of
issue: Dec. 11, 1917.
    Natural History Observations from the Mexican Portion of the
    Colorado Desert.
    Robert C. Murphy.

Number 30, for the year ending March, 12, 1918, 38 pp. Date of issue:
Sept. 18, 1918.
>   Bird Notes from Florida.
>   John T. Nichols.
>   Bird Temperatures.
>   Jay A. Weber.

Number 31, for the year ending March 11, 1919, 67 pp. Date of issue:
Dec. 23, 1919.
>   Bird-Banding by Means of Systematic Trapping.
>   S. Prentiss Baldwin.

Number 32, for the year ending March 9, 1920, 39 pp. Date of issue:
Dec. 6, 1920.
>   A Revision of the Seaside Sparrows.
>   Ludlow Griscom and J. T. Nichols.

Numbers 33-36, for the four years ending March 11, 1924, 148 pp. Date of
issue: Nov. 1, 1924.
>   Notes on the Winter Bird Life of Southeastern Texas.
>   T. Gilbert Pearson.
>   A New *Ameiva* from Nevis Island, British West Indies.
>   Karl P. Schmidt.
>   Some New and Rare Amphibians and Reptiles from Cuba.
>   Karl P. Schmidt.
>   A New Cyclura from White Cay, Bahama Islands.
>   Karl P. Schmidt.

Numbers 37-38, for the two years ending March 9, 1926, 139 pp. Date of
issue: May 15, 1927.
>   The Observations of the late Eugene P. Bicknell at Riverdale, New
>   York City, Fifty Years Ago.
>   Ludlow Griscom.
>   A Detailed Report on the Bird Life of Greater Bronx Region.
>   John F. Kuerzi.
>   Birds of Prospect Park, Brooklyn.
>   Lester L. Walsh.

Numbers 39-40, for the two years ending March, 1928, 103 pp. Date of issue: Feb. 10, 1930.

The Ornithological Year 1926 in the New York City Region.
Ludlow Griscom.

The Ornithological Year 1927 in the New York City Region.
L. Griscom and W. F. Eaton.

Birds of Union County, N. J., and Its Immediate Vicinity—A Statistical Study.
C. A. Urner.

Numbers 41-42, for the two years ending March 1930, 68 pp. Date of issue: Oct. 15, 1931.

The Ornithological Year 1928 in the New York City Region.
John F. Kuerzi.

The Ornithological Year 1929 in the New York City Region.
John F. Kuerzi.

Notes on the Breeding Birds of Putnam County, New York.
John F. Kuerzi.

Gardiner's Island Spring Bird Records, 1794-1797.
L. N. Nichols.

Numbers 43-44, for the two years ending March, 1932, 86 pp. Date of issue: Nov. 15, 1934.

Notes on the Summer Birds of Western Litchfield County, Conn.
John Kuerzi and Richard Kuerzi.

Eighteen Years of Wyanokie (1916-1933).
Warren Eaton.

More's American Bird Lists of 1769 and 1793.
L. Nelson Nichols.

Rhode Island Bird Records from 1781 to 1804. Compiled from "Tom Hazard's Diary."
L. Nelson Nichols.

The Eel Grass Blight on the New Jersey Coast.
Charles A. Urner.

What Ditching and Diking Did to a Salt Marsh.
Charles A. Urner.

The Ornithological Year 1930 in the New York City Region.
T. Donald Carter.

The Ornithological Year 1931 in the New York City Region.
William Vogt.
General Notes:
Some Little Known Notes of the Blue-headed Vireo (*Vireo solitarius solitarius*).
John F. Kuerzi.
The Purple Martin—A Correction.
John F. Kuerzi.
A Bird-catching Insect.
James L. Edwards.
Young Wood Ducks Use Wings Under Water.
James L. Edwards.
Yellow-headed Blackbird (*Xanthocephalus xanthocephalus*) at the Jones Beach Bird Sanctuary.
Helene Lunt.
A Dovekie Return.
William Vogt.
An Observation of the Mating Habits of the Yellow-billed Cuckoo.
Allen M. Thomas.

Numbers 45-46, for the two years ending March, 1934, 119 pp. Date of issue: April 15, 1935.
Remarks on the Origins of the Ratites and Penguins. (with discussion by R. C. Murphy).
William Gregory.
How Many Birds Are Known?
Ernst Mayr.
Bernard Altum and the Territory Theory.
Ernst Mayr.
A Preliminary List of the Birds of Jones Beach, Long Island, New York.
William Vogt.
Some Mid-Nineteenth Century Records from Westbury, Long Island.
John Matuszewski, Jr.
The Ornithological Year 1932 in the New York City Region.
William Vogt.
The Ornithological Year 1933 in the New York City Region.
Ernst Mayr.

General Notes:
Female Tanager Eating Her Eggs.
William Gibson.
Occurrence of Lesser Black-backed Gull (*Larus fuscus graellsi*) in Bronx County, New York City.
John Kuerzi and Richard Kuerzi.
Notes from Beaverkill, Sullivan County, NY.
Ernst Mayr.
Two Rare Sight Records from Orient, Long Island.
Roy Latham.

Number 47, for the year ending March, 1935, 142 pp. Date of issue: March 31, 1936.
Warren Francis Eaton: 1900-1936.
Charles A. Urner.
A List of the Birds of Essex County and of Hudson County, New Jersey with Especial Reference to City Growth and Bird Populations.
Warren F. Eaton.
Shorebirds of the North and Central New Jersey Coast.
Charles A. Urner.
The Half-Hardy Birds That Wintered Through 1933-34 in the New York City Region.
Walter Sedwitz.
The Ornithological Year 1934 in the New York City Region.
Joseph J. Hickey.
General Notes:
A Surprising Encounter.
Charles A. Urner.
Bird Mental Capacity.
Charles A. Urner.

Number 48, for the year ending March, 1936, 112 pp. Date of issue: Oct. 31, 1937.
The Great Wisconsin Passenger Pigeon Nesting of 1871.
A. Schorger.
Notes on the Development of Two Young Blue Jays (*Cyanocitta cristata*).
A. L. Rand.

Recent Notes on Bermuda Birds.
   William Beebe.
The Ornithological Year 1935 in the New York City Region.
   Allan D. Cruickshank.
General Notes:
   Intimidation Display in the Eastern Meadowlark.
      William Vogt.
   Another Six Egg Clutch of the Song Sparrow.
      Howard Kraslow.
   The Black-backed Gull as a Predator.
      Richard G. Kuerzi
   Additional Notes from Litchfield County, Conn.
      Ernst Mayr, John Kuerzi, and Richard Kuerzi.
   On the Nesting of the Black Skimmer in New York State.
      J. J. Hickey and LeRoy Wilcox.
   Migrating Gannets.
      Allan D. Cruickshank.

Number 49, for the year ending March, 1937, 103 pp. Date of issue: Oct. 15, 1938.
   Charles Anderson Urner: 1882-1938.
      J. L. Edwards.
   Preliminary Notes on the Behavior and Ecology of the Eastern Willet.
      William Vogt.
   Black-crowned Night Heron Colonies on Long Island.
      Robert P. Allen.
General Notes:
   Birds on an Atlantic Crossing.
      Ernst Mayr.
   A Probable Eared Grebe on Long Island.
      E. R. P. Janvrin.
   A Flight of Red Phalaropes (*Phalaropus fulicarius*) on Long Island, N. Y.
      LeRoy Wilcox.
   Notes on a Captive Kumlien's Gull (*Larus kumlieni*).
      Joseph J. Hickey.
   Black Terns Sitting on Telegraph Wires.
      O. K. Stephenson, Jr.

Approximate Incubation Period of the Florida Gallinule.
   Robert G. Kramer.
Hoarding Behavior of the Red-headed Woodpecker.
   O. K. Stephenson, Jr.
A Long Island Bird Roost.
   Allan D. Cruickshank.
A Few Warbler Observations.
   Allan D. Cruickshank.
Colonial Birds on Long Island, 1938.
   LeRoy Wilcox.

Numbers 50-51, for the two years ending March, 1939, 93 pp. Date of issue:
Oct. 25, 1940.
   Studies of the Nesting Behavior of the Black-crowned Night Heron.
      Robert P. Allen and Frederick P. Mangels.
   The Ornithological Year 1936 in the New York City Region.
      Walter Sedwitz.
   The Ornithological Year 1937 in the New York City Region.
      Walter Sedwitz.
   The Ornithological Year 1938 in the New York City Region.
      Alfred E. Eynon.
General Notes:
   Faunal Records from Eastern New York State.
      Joseph Janiec.
   A Doubtful Occurrence of the Reddish Egret in New Jersey.
      Dean Amadon.
   A Nest of the Black Duck (*Anas rubripes*).
      Allen Frost.
   Albinism in Gulls.
      Allan D. Cruickshank.
   The Breeding of the Herring Gull (*Larus argentatus smithsonianus*) on
Long Island in 1939.
      Christopher K. McKeever.
   A Christmas Census of Banded Herring Gulls.
      Samuel C. Harriot and Joseph J. Hickey.
   Scandinavian Lesser Black-backed Gull on Long Island.
      John Elliott.
   A Note on the 'Begging' of Nestling Flickers.
      Daniel S. Lehrman and O. K. Stephenson, Jr.

The Roosting of Tree Swallows (*Iridoprocne bicolor*).
    Richard G. Kuerzi.
Nesting of the White-eyed Vireo in the Housatonic Valley.
    Richard G. Kuerzi.

Numbers 52-53, for the two years ending March, 1941, 164 pp. Date of issue: Dec. 29, 1941.
    Life History Studies of the Tree Swallow.
        Richard G. Kuerzi.
    Notes on the Distribution of Oceanic Birds in the North Atlantic, 1937-1941.
        Hilary B. Moore.
    The Ornithological Year 1939 in the New York City Region.
        Robert W. Storer.
    Notes on Bermuda Birds.
        Hilary B. Moore.
    Red-wing Observations of 1940.
        Ernst Mayr.
    Distribution and Habitat Selection of Some Local Birds.
        Christopher K. McKeever.
General Notes:
    Hawk Migration Routes in the New York City Region.
        Alfred E. Eynon.
    Local Roosting and Migration Routes near New York City.
        Joseph J. Hickey.
    A Local Migration Route of the Barn Swallow.
        Hustace H. Poor.
    Autumnal Migration Counts in Central Park.
        Geoffrey Carleton.
    Some By-products of Bird Banding.
        B. S. Bowdish.
    Report on the Wyanokie Bird Census 1934 to 1940 Inclusive.
        Julius M. Johnson.
    Additional Remarks on the Wyanokie Census.
        Laura W. Abbott.
    A Breeding-Bird Census on the Adirondack Forest.
        Geoffrey Carleton.
    Duck Hawk Killing American Egret.
        Walter Sedwitz.

Feeding Habits of Black-crowned Night Herons.
  Richard A. Herbert.
Golden-eyes Roosting in Spring.
  John L. Bull, Jr.
Aggressive Incidents Relative to Marsh Hawks.
  John J. Elliott.
Feeding Behavior of a Harassed Duck Hawk.
  Richard A. Herbert and Joseph J. Hickey.
The "Freezing" Reaction of a Ruffed Grouse.
            Dean Amadon.
On Piping Plover Feeding.
  J. T. Nichols.
Wilson's Plover Again Nesting in New Jersey.
  Gilbert Cant.
A Curious Plumage of the Solitary Sandpiper.
  Ruth L. Allyn, Richard Allyn, Geoffrey Carleton, and Walter Sedwitz.
Visits to Gull Colonies in New York State.
  Hustace H. Poor.
An Intoxicated Yellow-bellied Sapsucker.
  John L. Bull, Jr.
Roosting and House-wrecking Downy Woodpeckers.
  Marie V. Beals.
Purple Martin Notes at Rye, N. Y.
  Michael Oboiko.
On the Field Identification of the Immature Orange-crowned Warbler.
  Geoffrey Carleton.
Red Crossbills Nesting in New Jersey.
  David Fables.
A Peculiar Oven-bird Song.
  John L. Bull, Jr. and Addison Young.
Green-tailed Towhee in New Jersey.
  William J. Norse.
A Tree Sparrow that Dropped Dead.
  Richard B. Fischer.
The Henslow's Sparrow on Long Island.
  John J. Elliott.
Alder Flycatcher Breeding on Long Island.
  Richard B. Fischer.

Numbers 54-57, for the four years ending March, 1945, 85 pp. Date of issue:
Sept. 16, 1946.

Some Critical Phylogenetic Stages Leading to the Flight of Birds.
William K. Gregory.

The Chickadee Flight of 1941-1942.
Hustace H. Poor.

The Ornithological Year 1944 in the New York City Region.
John L. Bull, Jr.

Suggestions to the Field Worker and Bird Bander.
Gordon M. Meade and Hustace H. Poor.

Clinton Hart Merriam (1855-1942): First President of the Linnaean
Society of New York.
A. K. Fisher.

General Notes:

Rare Gulls at the Narrows, Brooklyn, In the Winter of 1943-44.
Jerome Soll.

Comments on Identifying Rare Gulls.
Hustace H. Poor.

Breeding of the Herring Gull in Connecticut.
Hustace H. Poor.

Data on Some of the Seabird Colonies of Eastern Long Island.
Christopher K. McKeever.

New York City Seabird Colonies.
Christopher K. McKeever.

Royal Terns on Long Island.
Richard B. Fischer.

A Feeding Incident of the Black-billed Cuckoo.
John J. Elliott.

Eastern Long Island Records of the Nighthawk.
Roy Latham.

Proximity of Occupied Kingfisher Nests.
R. L. Wood.

Further Spread of the Prairie Horned Lark on Long Island.
Christopher K. McKeever.

A Late Black-throated Green Warbler.
George Komorowski.

Interchange of Song Between Blue-winged and Golden-winged
Warblers.
Eugene Eisenmann.

Predation by Grackles.
    Hustace H. Poor.
Observations on Birds Relative to the Predatory New York Weasel.
    John J. Elliott.

Numbers 58-62, for the five years ending March, 1950, 109 pp. Date of issue: December, 1951.
    Territorial Behavior in the Eastern Robin.
        Howard Young.
    Food Habits of New Jersey Owls.
        William J. Rusling.
    Data on the Food Habits of Local Owls.
        Richard B. Fischer.
    A Numerical Study of Shorebirds on Long Island in 1947.
        Walter Sedwitz.
    Seven Years of Bird-Watching in Chelsea (Manhattan).
        Lawrence F. Hawkins.
    Notes on the Northward Movement of Certain Species of Birds into the Lower Hudson Valley.
        Robert F. Deed.
    Dr. Clyde Fisher.
    John Kieran.
    Samuel Harmsted Chubb.
        Edmund R. P. Janvrin.
General Notes:
    Notes on Early Least Bittern on Long Island.
        John J. Elliott.
    Gadwall Nest Found on South-Western Long Island.
        Walter Sedwitz, Irwin Alperin and Malcolm Jacobson.
    Occurrence of European Teal on Long Island.
        J. J. Hickey.
    Copulatory Behavior in the Least Tern.
        Eugene Eisenmann.
    The Prairie Warbler on Long Island.
        John J. Elliott.
    Warbler Dates for Central Park.
        Geoffrey Carleton.
    Brewer's Sparrow on Long Island.
        Irwin Alperin and Eugene Eisenmann.

Numbers 63-65, for the three years ending March, 1953, 96 pp. Date of issue: March, 1954.

Seventy-five Years of the Linnaean Society of New York.
Eugene Eisenmann.
Historical Developments of Sight Recognition.
Ludlow Griscom.
Life History of the Tropical Kingbird.
Alexander F. Skutch.
Do Birds Hear Their Songs as We Do?
Hudson Ansley.
The Behavior of Birds Attending Army Ant Raids on Barro Colorado Island, Panama Canal Zone.
R. A. Johnson.

General Notes:

Observations on the Screech Owl *(Otus asio)*.
Mary T. Arny.
Peculiar Behavior of Tree Swallows in Relation to Dead of Their Species.
Eugene Eisenmann and John L. Bull., Jr.
Common Tern Feeding from Tin Can.
Robert H. Grant.
A Possible Effect of Sewage Pollution on Duck Abundance.
Irwin M. Alperin.

Numbers 66-70, for the five years ending March, 1958, 122 pp. Date of issue: December, 1958.

The Birds of Central and Prospect Parks.
Geoffrey Carleton.
Six Years (1947-1952) Nesting of Gadwall *(Anas strepera)* on Jones Beach, Long Island, N.Y.
Walter Sedwitz.
Five Year Count of the Ring-billed Gull *(Larus delawarensis)*.
Walter Sedwitz.
The Birds of Baxter Creek, Fall and Winter of 1954.
Paul A. Buckley.

General Notes:

The 1955 Breeding Season in the Pelham-Baychester Area, Bronx County.
Charles F. Young.

Owls in Pelham Bay Park—Winter 1953-1954.
  Paul A. Buckley.
Spring Jaegers—1955.
  Irwin M Alperin.
Common Tern Attacking Greater Shearwater.
  Neal G. Smith.
Leg Color of the Blackpoll Warbler in Fall.
  Neal G. Smith.
The Calls of Warblers.
  Geoffrey Carleton.
Back-yard Migrants.
  Geoffrey Carleton.
A Big Owl Night.
  Paul A. Buckley, Geoffrey Carleton, Peter W. Post and Robert L. Scully.
"Seventy-five Years of the Linnaean Society of New York"—A
Correction.
  E. Eisenmann.

Number 71, for the twelve years ending March, 1970, 220 pp. Date of issue:
December, 1970.
  Supplement to Birds of the New York Area.
    John Bull.
  Great Gull Island, Its History and Biology.
    Lois H. Heilbrun.
  Great Gull Island Visits 1962-1966.
    Catherine Pessino.
  Breeding of the Common and Roseate Terns on Great Gull Island.
    D. Cooper, H. Hays and C. Pessino.
  Great Gull Island Report on Nesting Species.
    Helen Hays.
  Great Gull Island Committee Chairmen 1949-1970.
  Clapper Rail Investigations on the South Shore of Long Island.
    E. E. MacNamara and H. F. Udell.
  Supplement to the Birds of Central and Prospect Parks.
    Geoffrey Carleton.
General Notes:
  A New Jersey Specimen of *Branta canadensis parvipes*.
    John Bull.

Number 72, for the four years ending March 1974, 130 pp. Date of issue: December, 1974.
>   Breeding Biology of the California Least Tern.
>   Barbara W. Massey.
>   Experiments on the Nesting Behavior of the California Least Tern.
>   Milton E. Davis.
>   Reproductive Behavior of the Least Tern.
>   Robert G. Wolk.
>   Reproductive Success in Common Tern Colonies Near Jones Beach, Long Island, New York, in 1972: A Hurricane Year.
>   Michael Gochfeld and Darrell B. Ford.
>   General Notes:
>   First Long Island, New York, Nesting Record of the Kentucky Warbler.
>   David Ewert.
>   Recent Additions to the Birds of Central Park.
>   Roger F. Pasquier.

Number 73, for the three years ending March 1977, 108 pp. Date of issue: August, 1977.
>   Breeding Populations of Terns and Skimmers on Long Island Sound and Eastern Long Island, 1972-1975.
>   David Duffy.
>   Low Productivity of Terns on Hicks Island, 1975.
>   Peter Houde.
>   Gull-Tern Interactions on Hicks Island, 1975.
>   Peter Houde.
>   A Water Bird Study of a Limited Area: Jerome Park Reservoir.
>   Walter Sedwitz.
>   General Notes:
>   Incipient Distraction Displays of the Least Tern.
>   Michael Gochfeld.
>   Hoary Bat in Niantic, Connecticut, in January.
>   Cordelia T. Grimm.

Number 74, for the years 1977-1995, 152 pp. Date of issue: April, 1999.
>   Roger Tory Peterson: In Memoriam.
>   Julio de la Torre.
>   Hybridization in the Red-eyed Towhees of Mexico.
>   Charles G. Sibley.

A Field Study of the Golden-winged Warbler in the Pequannock Watershed, Sussex County, New Jersey.
  Robert L. Scully.
Albinism in the Sooty Shearwater.
  Paul R. Sweet.
Bibliography of Writings of Eugene Eisenmann, 1944-1984.
  compiled by Mary LeCroy and Sheila Walker.

Linnaean News-Letter

Vol. 1, Number 1, March 1947-present.

Compiled by **Joseph DiCostanzo.**

The Linnaean Society of New York

The Linnaean Society of New York, organized in 1878, is the second oldest American ornithological society. Members share an active interest in observing and learning about the birds and natural environment in and around New York City. Regular meetings of the Society are held on the second and fourth Tuesdays of each month from September to May, inclusive. Informal meetings are held once a month during June, July, and August. All meetings are open to the public and are usually held at the American Museum of Natural History.

Additional Information: *http://www.linnaeannewyork.org*

City of New York Parks & Recreation

Parks & Recreation (DPR) is the steward of almost 29,000 acres of land, 14 percent of New York City, including more than 4,000 individual properties ranging from Yankee Stadium and Central Park to community gardens and Greenstreets. DPR operates or manages more than 800 athletic fields, nearly 1,000 playgrounds, four major stadia, 550 tennis courts, 51 public pools, 34 recreation centers, 12 nature centers, 13 golf courses, and 14 miles of beaches, and cares for 1,200 monuments and 22 historic house museums. DPR also looks after 500,000 street trees, and two million more in parks. Not only is DPR the city's principal provider of athletic facilities, it is also the home to thousands of free concerts, world-class sports events, and cultural festivals.

Additional Information: *http://www.nycgovparks.org*

National Parks Conservation Association

The National Parks Conservation Association believes that America's National Parks and historical sites embody the American spirit. They are windows to our past, homes to some of our rarest plants and animal species, and places where every American can go to find inspiration, peace, and open space. But these living, breathing monuments to our nation's history, culture, and landscape need care and support to overcome the many dangers that threaten to destroy them forever. The National Parks Conservation Association works every day to ensure they get that vital care and support.

NPCA plays a crucial role in ensuring that these special places are protected in perpetuity:

- Monitoring the health and management of the parks through our regional field offices;
- Advocating for the national parks and the National Park Service;
- Educating Congress and the public about the importance of our national parks; and
- Fighting attempts to weaken laws or policies regarding our parks either in Congress or in the courts.

Additional Information: *http://www.npca.org*